WILL INDEXES AND OTHER PROBATE MATERIAL IN THE LIBRARY OF THE SOCIETY OF GENEALOGISTS

by Nicholas Newington-Irving

1996

Published by the
Society of Genealogists
14 Charterhouse Buildings
Goswell Road
London EC1M 7BA

First published 1996
(by Nicholas Newington-Irving)

ISBN 1 85951 030 2

CONTENTS

The two letter codes shown below are those used as part of the Shelf Mark on bound items in the Library; other code letters that appear are in the list of General Abbreviations

INTRODUCTION

Wills are one of the most reliable, important sources available to the genealogist. Unfortunately, few of our ancestors made wills that have survived and those which do exist are hard to find. Nevertheless a will found can do much to enhance family history - even when it is just a mention in the will of a neighbour, employer or landlord. Also, probate records can provide evidence of death or clues on burials and they can be useful in surname studies and for economic or social history surveys.

Wills are complex and their location can seem almost incomprehensible nowadays so their seeking requires careful preparation. The Society has collected many finding aids to wills as well as copies of actual documents. This Guide shows what is currently available in the Society's Library; it includes all books accessed up to early Summer 1996 and a digest of periodicals received up to late 1995. New items are always being added to the Society's collections: these are reported in the *Genealogists' Magazine*.

This Guide lists all indexes to, or collections of, wills and other testamentary material now available in the Library **except** where the number involved is less than about half a dozen or where the item is in a language other than English or Latin. No attempt has been made to include any item that relates to a single family: usually these can be found by reference to the Library's Family History Catalogue or to the Indexes for the Library's Document and Special Collections; such essential bibliographies (on the Textbooks shelves in the Middle Library) as G W Marshall's *The Genealogist's Guide*, J B Whitmore's *A Genealogical Guide*, G B Burrow's *The Genealogists' Guide* and Stuart Raymond's *Genealogical Bibliographies* can be useful here. Many periodicals include transcripts of individual wills; in particular *The New England Historical & Genealogical Register* has thousands of copies and summaries of wills proved in the British Isles and the Library has a complete run of this periodical, with cumulative nominal indexes, on the American periodicals shelves in the Upper Library. Although a wide range of testamentary material has been identified, **Inquisitiones Post Mortem** have not been included and many other borough, charitable, ecclesiastical, guild, legal and manorial records in the Library include isolated wills. However, because of its considerable probate business, Chancery Court actions have been included.

Much of the material lacks an adequate title or precise dating. To enhance the information given, many titles have been annotated by additions shown in *italics*. Wherever possible the date of probate, instead of the date of the will or a testator's death, is shown; many dates have been derived after a survey of the item's contents and this can result in the Guide indicating coverage (in the left-hand column) which differs from the title. If a title is vague, the work is shown under the most senior probate jurisdiction for that location (usually at diocesan level). Every attempt has been made to show the full title of each ancient court but the proper title of many has proved elusive and some may not even have been probate courts at all. There is no guarantee that any of these indexes or collections are complete, let alone the best version available. Some indexes are of better quality than others so the latest indexes in the record office concerned should be examined always before requesting probate material there. All items are described as found in the Library; copies in other libraries may not be identical.

Probate material in the Library falls into two groups:

A	Titles that indicate the existence of probate material somewhere else (although still useful for pointing to a date of death and sometimes the only surviving testamentary evidence) - these are termed *Calendar, Catalogue, Index* or *List*.
B	Titles that contain all or part of the contents of original probate documents - these are termed *Abstract, Copy, Extract, Facsimile, Summary* or *Transcript*.

Generally each author's terminology has been used in this Guide and this may not meet the definitions found in genealogical glossaries.

The preparation of this Guide has been greatly assisted by Library staff and volunteers who checked, type-set and edited it: their efforts are much appreciated. Comments and suggestions that can improve future editions of this Guide will be most welcome.

HOW TO USE THIS GUIDE

This Guide is divided into four parts:

* The NATIONAL section covers collections that cannot readily be allocated to a particular territory and collections that are special to religious, occupational or social groups. The coverage includes England beyond county level, the British Isles and world-wide; the county sections for the Channel Islands, Ireland, Isle of Man, Scotland & Wales each begin with their own national sub-section. If the Library holds information on a probate court or registry in the British Isles, details will be found in the COURTS section.

* The COUNTY section covers the British Isles county-by-county and island-by-island: see the Contents page. Pre-1974 administrative units are used in this Guide. Each county or territory includes items having a county-wide interest as well as local material and also has a list of all ancient probate jurisdictions together with known manorial & civil authorities having testamentary control within its boundaries. If the Library holds information on any of these probate courts or registries, details will be found in the COURTS section.

* The COURTS section covers all ancient or modern probate authorities in the British Isles for which the Library currently holds material. The section is in alphabetical order of the principal name (usually a place); where more than authority bears the same name, these are shown in descending order of seniority (Prerogative, Consistory, Archdeaconry, Peculiar, manorial, civil and so on).

* The OVERSEAS section covers the rest of the world and is arranged by countries: see the Contents page.

The best way to use this Guide is to prepare a search list of titles (including shelf marks) and this is done through the following steps:

Step 1 For probates outside the British Isles turn to the OVERSEAS section: this is organized by countries (and by states or provinces within those countries). The possibility of foreign wills being proved or re-sealed in the British Isles should be borne in mind and, for probates within the British Isles, proceed to **Step 2**.

Step 2 If the name of the court or registry is known, proceed to **Step 4**, otherwise proceed to **Step 3**.

Step 3 In the COUNTY section select the most likely county where the ancestor may have died; a genealogical atlas can be useful (see *Further Reading* below). From each selected county, note what county-wide or local material may be of interest. Then note the ancient probate jurisdictions applicable to the county; the major jurisdictions are shown in **BLOCK CAPITALS** and should be explored first. Now proceed to **Step 4**.

Step 4 In the COURTS section note what material is available for each court chosen (but remember that information is not available in the Library for every court or registry yet). Most entries in the COURTS section are cross-referred to other courts: **Superior Courts** being those to which testamentary work is most likely to have been referred on appeal or where the inferior court had only limited powers or during inhibitions, vacancies or visitations. Now proceed to **Step 5**.

Step 5 There is a list of probate jurisdictions having wider or national authority at the beginning of the COURTS section: suitable courts should be added to the search list. Now proceed to **Step 6**.

Step 6 Finally, the NATIONAL section should be searched for additional items.

If the selected county fails to produce results, try its neighbours. If the selected court and its superiors fail, try returning to **Step 3**. As a last hope, a **SUPPLEMENT** to the Library version of this Guide contains many articles illustrated by wills and as well as suggestions for other research avenues.

Tips

a It may be better to include all occurrences of a surname in the search plan rather than a particular ancestor as this widens the choice and saves research time. It may be advisable to limit each search to one or two generations (say, to fifty-year bands).

b Give priority to availability, listing microform items first, then books and journals and then items that are marked **"Apply to Staff"**.

c Items are listed in **starting date** order but the **finishing date** of an item may overlap subsequent titles, so search this Guide thoroughly.

d Unless otherwise stated, items consisting of more than one part or volume are split alphabetically.

FURTHER READING

It is highly recommended that some background reading be undertaken before commencing a search for wills. Most items mentioned in this Guide include significant introductions and it is always advisable to read these carefully. A digest of books and articles on probate records and practice has been collected during the preparation of this Guide and can be found in the **SUPPLEMENT** to the Library version of this Guide. The following reference works may be of assistance:-

General Finding Aids:

* Probate Jurisdiction - where to look for wills *In* "Gibson's Guides" [TB Quick Reference]

* Wills & their Whereabouts (Camp) [WILLS/GEN or TB Quick Reference]

* Wills & Where to Find Them (Gibson) [WILLS/GEN or TB Quick Reference]

Atlases:

* A New Genealogical Atlas of Ireland by Brian Mitchell [TB Quick Ref or IR/G 133]

* The Phillimore Atlas & Index of Parish Registers [TB Quick Reference]

* Pre-1858 English Probate Jurisdictions *including Wales* (LDS) [Apply to Staff]; Scotland - a Genealogical Research Guide (LDS) [SC/G 191]; A Genealogical Research Guide to Ireland (LDS) [IR/G 192]

* Researching British Probates 1354-1858: A Guide to the Microfilm Collection of the *LDS's* Family History Library - vol 1: Northern England & the Province of York [TB/RG]

Ancient English Probate Courts:

* An account of the different Registries of Wills in the several Ecclesiastical Dioceses with a list of peculiars within the same *In* "Notitia Historica" (*1824*) [TB/RG]

* A Handbook to the Ancient Courts of Probate & Depositories of Wills (Marshall) [Apply to Staff]

* Index of Courts of which the Records, Wills, Grants, Probates, Letters of Administration, Administrations Bonds, Processes, Acts, Proceedings, Writs, Documents and other instruments relating exclusively or principally to matters or causes testamentary and which have been transmitted to the Court of Probate, pursuant to Requisitions issued under Section 89 of 20 & 21 Vict. c.77, with a List of the several Registries of the Court of Probate, with the titles of the ecclesiastical Courts of which the Testamentary Records have been or are to be transmitted to the said Registries, pursuant to the Statute 20 & 21 Vict. c.77, Section 89 (includes list of all pre-1858 probate courts and the destination of their records) [Mf 912 or (*In* "Miscellaneous Reference material on Wills & other Probate Records") WILLS/GEN]

* Returns respecting the Jurisdiction, Records, Emoluments & Fees of Ecclesiastical Courts (*1830*) [SP/ECC]

GENERAL ABBREVIATIONS

The county or country abbreviations are shown on the Contents page. Some countries have prefixes to show the state or province and these are shown at the head of the country concerned. Other abbreviations used in this Guide are:-

Abst	= Abstract or Abstracts	G	= General section of the county or
Admon	= Administration		country shelves
ALM	= Almanacs shelves	GCI	= Great Card Index in the Library
Antqn	= Antiquarian		of the Society of Genealogists
appx	= Appendix or Appendices		[Lower Library]
Archl	= Archaeological	GEN	= General section **except** for
Assn	= Association		counties, countries or
BIOG	= Biography shelves		periodicals
BM	= British Museum (including the	Geneal	= Genealogical
	British Library)	GM	= The Gentleman's Magazine
BRS	= Index Library (British Record		shelves [Upper Library]
	Society) shelves [Upper Library]	Guardn	= Guardian; Guardnshp:
Bull	= Bulletin		Guardianship
C	= (as a shelf mark) Census section	Hist	= History or Historical; Hists,
	of the county or country shelves		Histories
	= (with a date or dates) Century or	HMC	= Royal Commission on Historical
	Centuries		Manuscripts
Cal	= Calendar	Hn	= Historian
CE	= Church of England section of	HS	= Harleian Society Publications
	the Religions shelves		shelves [Upper Library]
Co	= Company	HUG	= Huguenot section of the
Corp	= Corporation		Religions shelves
D	= Lists:Directories section of the	IMC	= Irish Manuscripts Commission
	county or country shelves	Info	= Information
Dept	= Department	Inst	= Institute
Div	= Division	Invents	= Inventories
Doc	= Document	IR/K	= Ireland:Public Record Office
Docs Coll	= Documents Collection in the		section of the Irish shelves - ie
	Library of the Society of		Reports of the Deputy Keepers
	Genealogists - in boxes in the		of Public Records (Northern
	Upper Library or in the		Ireland) and of Public Records
	Document Collection Drawer in		in Ireland (*now the National*
	the Lower Library if Mfc		*Archives Office, Dublin*)
E	= East	J	= Journal
ed	= Edition	JP	= Joint Publication
EDO	= Estate Duty Office or Stamp	JR	= Jewish section of the Religions
	Office		shelves
Extr	= Extract or Extracts	L	= Local section of the county or
Fam	= Family; Fams, Families; *see also*		country shelves
	FH	LDS	= Genealogical Society of the
FH	= Family History shelves		Church of Jesus Christ of
FHn	= Family Historian		Latter-Day Saints
FH/MISC	= Family History:Miscellaneous	Lib	= Library
	shelves	Loc	= Local
Folio	= Folio shelves for very large	M	= Monumental Inscriptions section
	books		of the county or country shelves

Mf	=	Microfilm reel number [Lower Library]	R	= Registers section of the county or country shelves
Mfc	=	Microfiche [fiche are in the Lower Library unless marked "Apply to Staff"]	RC	= Roman Catholic section of the Religions shelves
MI	=	Monumental Inscriptions	Rec	= Record
MIG	=	Migration section on the American shelves [Upper Library]	Reg	= Register
			Rep	= Report
			Res	= Research
Misc	=	Miscellaneous; Misc Gen et Her: Miscellanea Genealogica et Heraldica	S	= South; SE, South East; SW, South West
			ser	= Series
ms	=	Manuscript	Soc	= Society
MSS	=	Manuscripts (collection)	SP	= State Papers shelves [Upper Library - items have the first three letters of their class as a suffix]
N	=	North; NW, North West		
N&Q	=	Notes & Queries shelves [Upper Library]		
			St	= Saint
Nat	=	Natural	Supp	= Supplement or Supplemental or Supplementary
NEHGR	=	The New England Historical & Genealogical Register		
			TB/BIB	= Textbooks:Bibliographies shelves
N/L	=	Newsletter		
no	=	Number	TB/DIC	= Textbooks:Dictionaries shelves
P	=	Lists:Poll Books section of the county or country shelves	TB/HIS	= Textbooks:Histories shelves
			TB/MR	= Textbooks:Monetary Records shelves
Occ	=	Occasional		
Octo	=	Octavo	TB/RG	= Textbooks:Record Guides shelves
P/R	=	Peerage & Royalty shelves		
PCA	=	Prerogative Court of Armagh	Testmt	= Testament; Testmtry = testamentary
PCC	=	Prerogative Court of Canterbury		
PCY	=	Prerogative Court of York	Topo	= Topographical
PER	=	Periodicals section of the county or country shelves [items on the General Periodicals shelves in the Upper Library have the prefix PER and the first three letters of their titles as a suffix]	Tracts	= Tracts boxes for the county or country
			Trans	= Transactions
			Tuit	= Tuition
			ts	= typescript
			vol	= Volume
Pop	=	Population	UK	= United Kingdom (multi-county) - books other than directories are in the Middle Library *before* Bedfordshire
PR	=	Professions & Occupations shelves [Upper Library - items have the first three letters of their descriptions as a suffix]		
			W	= West; WI, West Indies
PRO	=	Public Record Office, London	WILLS	= Wills:General shelves in the Upper Library, suffixed by GEN or the name of the Court (PCC or PCY as appropriate); PCA records are on the Irish shelves
Prob	=	Probate		
Procs	=	Proceedings		
Prov	=	Provisional		
pt	=	Part		
Pub	=	Publication		
Qto	=	Quarto		

GLOSSARY

The introduction to "Wills and their Whereabouts" by Anthony J. Camp, London 1974 has a more detailed explanation of probate terminology; note that the following does not apply to Scotland

Accounts: the record of an estate's distribution kept by an **Executor** or **Administrator**; sometimes found in court or registry papers

Act: the decision of a court or registry, recorded in an **Act Book** and endorsed on or attached to a will

Administration: the distribution of the estate of an intestate, the right to do so being **granted** to an **Administrator** or **Administratrix** who has applied through an **Allegation** to a court or registry for **Letters of Administration**, often secured by an **Administration Bond**; if the estate is bankrupt, the grant can be to a **Creditor** to administer the debt first, irrespective of any will

Appeal: the resolving of **disputed estates** in the same or higher court or registry; the appeal being recorded in an **Assignation Book** with a warning, usually for three months, in a **Caveat Book** to show that a dispute is in progress; other records or **Cause Papers** include **Depositions**, **Exhibits**, etc; when settlement is reached a decision is recorded in the **Sentence Book**

Archdeaconry: (or Archidiaconal*) the territory under an Archdeacon, hence Archdeaconry Court

Calendar: a listing of records of a court or registry, generally in date order by name of the deceased (often by first letter only)

Cathedral: the principal church of the diocese governed by a Dean and Chapter

Chapter: the ruling body of a Cathedral or other **Collegiate** institution

Codicil: an amendment or addition to a will

Commissary: a deputy or agent acting under the commission of a church dignitary

Consistory Court: (or Consistorial*) the court of a Bishop

Deanery: (or Decanal*) the domain of a Dean, sometimes assisted by a **Sub Dean**;hence Decanal Court

Episcopal: pertaining to a Bishop (**Archiepiscopal:** pertaining to an Archbishop)

Inhibition: the period when an inferior church court is closed, often with its business undertaken by a superior court

Intestate: a person who dies without having made a wholly valid will

Inventory: a list of a deceased person's goods, often with values

Official: the lawyer or other officer of a court carrying out daily tasks in that court on behalf of a church dignitary; also called the **Registrar** or the **Surrogate**

Peculiar: a self-governing locality or a part of a district where ecclesiastical jurisdiction lies other than to that district; eg **extra-parochial** parishes may come directly under the Bishop rather than the Archdeacon; **Royal Peculiars** come directly under the Crown; **Prebends** (which provide the income of a canon or other member of a Chapter) are inferior to that Chapter; some deaneries are **Exempt** from the Archdeacon's authority too

Prerogative Court: the court of an Archbishop having jurisdiction over the whole province

Probate: the process of approving a will in a court or registry to enable lawful distribution of an estate in accordance with that will, the right to do so being **granted** to an **Executor** or **Executrix**; there is a **double probate** whenever a will has to be re-proved (eg when the original executor dies); if probate has to be re-proved in another country it is often **re-sealed** in the new country

Testament: the wishes of a testator as to the disposal of **personalty** (goods, chattels & money) on his death; *see also* **Will**

Testator or **Testatrix:** a person who makes a will or testament - which may be oral (**nuncupative**), written by the testator (**holographic**) or written by a third party

Tuition: the appointment of **Guardians** over **orphans** (traditionally over boys under 15 or girls under 13), often secured by a **Tuition Bond** (**Curation:** the appointment of **Curators** for **orphans** under 21); sometimes the court makes children **Wards** of court

Vacancy: the period when a church appointment is unfilled; the relevant court is often closed and its business transferred to a superior court; incidentally, *sede vacante* means 'empty seat'

Visitation: the period when a superior church dignitary visits an inferior; the relevant court is often closed with its business undertaken by that superior's court

Will: the wishes of a testator as to the distribution of his estate after his death; to be **valid** a will must comply with the law (eg be signed, dated & witnessed correctly), not superseded by a later will and not **voided** by illegality, subsequent marriage or incapacity (of the testator, witnesses or executors); depending on the prevailing law, an incomplete will might be **limited** (ie subject to restrictions determined by the court or registry), it might be **annexed** to an Administration grant (eg if the Executors declines (**renounces**) or is unable to administer an estate) or it can be **struck out** completely; a will in a court or registry can be **original** (or a copy of such) or **registered** (copied into a **Will Book**); it can be **proved** or **unproved** (see **Act**); *see also* **Testament**. Technically a will refers to the disposal of **realty** (landed property or real estate) only; hence "Last Will and Testament".

* some courts have the powers of a superior court

IMPORTANT NOTE .

Because of the size of this Guide, it was thought that a wider audience could be reached if a shorter version could be provided. This version has been reduced from the original work by some 20% - this has been achieved as follows:-

   a by abbreviating some of the longer or more widely-used words: details will be found in the table of General Abbreviations; because of their complexity, the names of courts and registries have NOT been reduced;

   b by adopting generally-accepted abbreviations for some English and Welsh counties;

   c American, Australian and Canadian states and provinces are indicated by the Library's shelf mark abbreviations;

   d by eliminating all page references;

   e by excluding leading definite and indefinite articles; and

   f by compacting notes, multi-volume and shared entries.

However NO factual element has been omitted from this version at all.

A copy of the full version[†], including page references, has been placed on the open shelves in the Upper Library [WILLS/GEN] should readers require further details on locating items. In most cases the page references can be found by using the index or contents pages to be found in the material.

It is hoped that these changes will not spoil the reader's use and enjoyment of this Guide.

The location of each item is given in **[square brackets]** after the title: the shelf marks can be identified from the codes listed in the Contents, General Abbreviations or, for Australia, Canada and the USA, the headings for those countries in the OVERSEAS section. **Apply to Staff** means that a Closed Access Application form should be completed and handed to staff at the Middle Library Enquiry Counter. Microfilms (**Mf** plus the reel number) are on open access in the Lower Library but most microfiche (**Mfc**) require an Closed Access Application form.

Many will indexes were published long ago and much of the original material is now **extremely fragile**: to preserve such items, please use microform copies where available. Any item is liable to withdrawal from open access without notice and some of the more fragile items are now in store and not readily available. If items cannot be found, check the Wills section of the Library's Subject Catalogue in the Upper Library before referring the matter to staff. In any event, Library staff will be happy to help locate items or to advise on alternatives.

     [†] photocopies of this version may be purchased from the Society: please ask for details

---

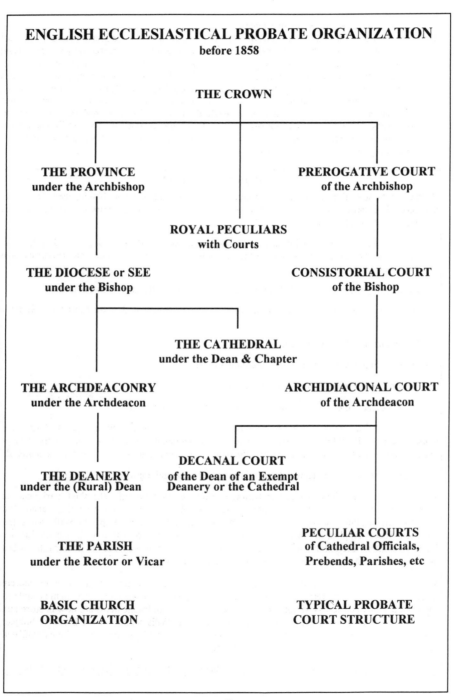

ENGLISH ECCLESIASTICAL PROBATE ORGANIZATION
before 1858

THE CROWN

THE PROVINCE
under the Archbishop

PREROGATIVE COURT
of the Archbishop

ROYAL PECULIARS
with Courts

THE DIOCESE or SEE
under the Bishop

CONSISTORIAL COURT
of the Bishop

THE CATHEDRAL
under the Dean & Chapter

THE ARCHDEACONRY
under the Archdeacon

ARCHIDIACONAL COURT
of the Archdeacon

DECANAL COURT
of the Dean of an Exempt
Deanery or the Cathedral

THE DEANERY
under the (Rural) Dean

PECULIAR COURTS
of Cathedral Officials,
Prebends, Parishes, etc

THE PARISH
under the Rector or Vicar

**BASIC CHURCH
ORGANIZATION**

**TYPICAL PROBATE
COURT STRUCTURE**

NATIONAL and INTERNATIONAL COLLECTIONS

for nation-wide courts and registries in the British Isles: see the checklist at the beginning of the COURTS section noting, in particular, the Estate Duty Office (from 1796) and the Principal Probate Registries (from 1858); see also the National sub-sections for IRELAND, SCOTLAND & WALES

SPECIAL GROUPS OF WILLS, INDEXES, ETC. CLASSIFIED BY RELIGION, OCCUPATION OR UNIVERSITY

Religions and Clergy
many church and parochial histories include references to wills, endowments and charitable bequests

Church of England: including the Pre-Reformation Church in England; the most of surviving medieval wills in the British Isles relate to clergymen or their families

List of Clerks' Wills 1440-1561 *In* appx to "Kentish Wills ..." [KE/G 66]

List of Vicars, Rectors & Testmtry Burials (*will abst for clergy buried in Bradford 1433-1612*) (Bradford Antiquary new ser vol 1) [YK/PER]

Some Ecclesiastical Wills (*absts for abbots & priors of suppressed Glos monasteries 1544-1545, 1577*) (Trans Bristol & Glos Rec Soc vols 49 & 52) [GL/PER]

Typical Invents of Clergymen c1600 (*Lichfield abst 1597-1614*) *In* "Clerical Invents" (appx 4 to Wm Salt/Staffs Rec Soc 3rd ser vol for 1915) [ST/PER]

Wills deposited at Lambeth (*Yorks wills index 1359-1589, mainly clergy*) (Yorks Arch & Topo J vol 24) [YK/PER]

Wills of Bishops & Capitular Members of Cathedral Churches (*Lambeth Palace & Somerset House lists 1384-1548*) (N&Q 5th ser vols 7 & 8) [N&Q]

Wills of Bucks Clergy in the 16th C (*Archdeaconry abst 1520-1528*) (Recs of Bucks vol 13 pt 3) [BU/PER]

Wills of Sussex Clergy (*wills & admons list 1520-1800*) (Sussex N&Q vol 8) [SX/PER]

Wills of Welsh Ecclesiastics holding appointments in England (*abst 1523-1540*) (Archaeologia Cambrenis vol 82 (1927) [WS/PER]

York Clergy Wills 1520-1600; vols 1: Minster Clergy & 2: City Clergy (Borthwick Texts & Cals nos 10 & 15) [*both* YK/PER]

Huguenots
List of certified extr from wills in the PCC or the Commissary of London relating to bequests to the French Protestant Church in London (*1723-1844*) (Huguenot Soc Pubs Qto ser vol 50) [HUG/PER]

Regs of the Baptisms in the Dutch Church at Colchester *with an index to "Dutch" registered wills proved 1565-1769, admons granted 1691-1769 in various Essex courts & unregistered wills 1619-1640* (Huguenot Soc Pubs Qto ser vol 12) [HUG/PER]

Regs of the Walloon or Strangers' Church in Canterbury (*will abst 1586-1704*) (Huguenot Soc Pubs Qto ser vol 5) [HUG/PER]

Some Huguenot Wills (*wills & admons list 1720, 1768-1807*) (Huguenot Soc Procs vols 11 & 17) [HUG/PER]

Walloons & their Church at Norwich; references to Strangers' wills (*Huguenot wills proved in Norwich list 1565-1852*) (Huguenot Soc Pubs Qto ser vol 1) [HUG/PER]

Jews
Anglo-Jewish Notabilities; Their Arms & Testmtry Dispositions (*cal of Jewish PCC wills & admons 1383-1848 with addenda*) (Trans Jewish Hist Soc Eng Spec Pub); Anglo-Jewish Wills & Letters of Admon 1384-1848 (reprint from "Anglo-Jewish Notabilities") [*both* JR/PER]

Abst of Jewish Wills for Bridgetown 1676-1739, Speightstown 1695-1735, etc *In* "Review of the Jewish Colonists in Barbados in the Year 1680" (Trans Jewish Hist Soc Eng vol 13) [WI/L 11 or JR/PER]

Quakers (Soc of Friends)
Abst of Wills 1665-1879 *In* "Guide to Irish Quaker Recs 1654-1860" (IMC *vol*) [IR/G 75]

Abst of Wills & *Invents* (*1684-1757*) *In* "Quaker Recs Dublin; Abst of Wills" (IMC *vol*) [IR/G 76]

List of Misc Quaker Wills in the Hist Lib, Eustace Street, *Dublin* (*1665-1869*) *In* appx 2 to "Quaker Recs Dublin; Abst of Wills"

(IMC *vol*) [IR/G 76]

Book of Quaker Wills (*extr 1697-1777*) (Trans Cumberland & Westmorland Antqn & Archl Soc new ser vol 29) [CU/PER]

Extr from Invents 1714-1726 *In* "Immigration of the Irish Quakers into PA, *USA* 1682-1750 with their Early Hist in Ireland" [Apply to Staff]

Invents of Five Dublin Quaker merchants in the late 17th C (*extr 1684-1695*) (Irish Ancestor vol 10) [IR/PER]

Irish Quaker Invents of the 17th & 18th C (Irish Ancestor vol 3) [IR/PER]

Some Westmorland Wills 1686-1738: *Extr from* Quaker Wills in the possession of the Soc of Friends at Kendal [WE/G 16]

Will Book of Ballyhagan Meeting of the Soc of Friends (*will & invent abst 1685-1740*) (Irish Genealogist vol 2) [IR/PER]; List of Quaker Wills preserved at Lisburn (*1685-1740*) *In* appx 1 to "Quaker Recs Dublin; Abst of Wills" (IMC *vol*) [IR/G 76]

Roman Catholics
see under Church of England for Pre-Reformation material

Abst of the original wills (unless otherwise specified) of various Priests of the Soc of Jesus (*1633-1805*) which are now deposited among the archives at Stonyhurst *In* "Supp HMC Rep upon the MSS at Stonyhurst College" [Apply to Staff]

Abst of Wills (*mainly of Roman Catholic priests in London & their fams 1617-1857*) (London Recusant vols 3-8 & new ser vol 1) [MX/PER]

Abst of Wills of Essex Catholic Interest (*1580-1843*) (Essex Recusant vols 15-17 & 19) [ES/PER]

Indexes to Enrolled Wills in the PRO; *pt 2: Close Rolls 1691-1799* & *pt 3: Recovery Rolls 1714-1768* (The Genealogist new ser vols 1-3) [*both* PER/GEN]; Roman Catholic Wills in the Close Rolls (1691-1799) & in the Recovery Rolls (1714-1768) *In* "List of Wills, Admons, etc in the PRO, London, England from 12-19th C" [WILLS/GEN]

Recs of the English Catholics of 1715 (*abst of some 400 wills & admons 1715-1769*) [RC/GEN]

Wills of Roman Catholics which were enrolled with the Clerk of the Peace *in 1717* (*index to Lancs enrolments*) (appx to Lancs & Cheshire Rec Soc Procs vol 105) [LA/PER]

Armed Forces

soldiers & sailors dying abroad or at sea usually had their wills proved in the PCC; see also Mariners

Cal of Naval Hospital Wills at Gibraltar 1809-1815 (*abst of* "An account of wills executed by patients of this hospital 17 Jul 1809-2 Nov 1815") (*PRO Class ADM 105/40*) [GIB/G 3]; *also listed In* "List of Wills, Admons, etc in the PRO, London, England from 12-19th C" [WILLS/GEN]

"Foreign" Wills proved at Carlisle (*wills & admon list for soldiers, marines & sailors 1764-1825*) (Genealogists' Mag vol 15) [PER/GEN]

Naval & Military Notes (*will & admon extr 1741-1802*) (Northern Genealogist vols 1 & 2) [PER/NOR]

Wills & Admons of the Nizam's Loc officers (*abst 1775, 1805-1887, 1926*) *In* "Anglo-Indian Colls vol 3" [IND/R 10]

Wills in Admiralty Papers (*cals for seamen 1860-1881 & for marines 1751-1768*) *In* "List of Wills, Admons, etc in the PRO, London, England from 12-19th C" [WILLS/GEN]

Wills of Officers & Soldiers who died at Fort Washington, Cincinnati, OH (*USA 1791-1809*) (Nat Geneal Soc Qtrly vol 57) [US/PER]

Occupations

Actors, Film Stars, etc
Wills of the Rich & Famous (*1929-1989*) [US/G 142]

Architects
Wills & Prob Recs *In* "English Medieval Architects; a biographical dictionary down to 1550" [PR/ARC]

Armourers, etc
Invents from Craftsmen's Wills *In* appx 1 to "Scottish Arms Makers" (*extr for Scottish armourers, bowyers, bucklermakers, gunners, gunmakers, lorimers, sheathmakers & sword stoppers 1571-1775*) [PR/ARM]

Artists
Wills of the Rich & Famous (*1970-1989*) [US/G 142]

Booksellers: see Printers

Cutlers

Cal of Cutlers' Wills *with some extr (1412-1685) In* "Hist of the Cutlers' Co of London ... vol 2: from 1500" [MX/CC 105]

Invents from Craftsmen's Wills *In* appx 1 to "Scottish Arms Makers" (*extr for Scottish cutlers 1571-1775*) [PR/ARM]

Drapers

Abst of Wills 1617-1727 In "Draper's Co; Hist of the Co's Property & Trusts vol 2" [MX/CC 29]

Gardeners

Some Wills of Early Nurserymen (*abst 1549-1799*) & Nurserymen's Invents of the 18th C (*extr from 1722*) *In* "Early Nurserymen" [PR/NUR]

Goldsmiths

Some Norwich Goldsmiths' Wills (*extr 1555-1715*) (Norfolk Archaeology vols 35 & 37) [NF/PER]

Grocers

Checklist of Invents of 17th C Suffolk Grocers *In* "Suffolk Grocers in the 17th C" (Suffolk Review new ser no 20) [SF/PER]

Mariners

sailors dying abroad or at sea usually had their wills proved in the PCC but some were ascribed to the parish of St Botolph Aldgate & their wills can be found in the records of the Archdeaconry of London (qv)

Channel Island Wills at the PRO (*index 1642-1762, mainly mariners*) (Channel Islands FHS J no 57) [CI/PER]

List of Wills, Admons & other Prob Recs of Anglesey Seamen, Allied Trades & Professions (*1684-1855*) (Gwynedd Roots no 1) [WS/PER]

"Foreign" Wills proved at Carlisle (*index to mariners' wills & admons 1736-1839*) (Genealogists' Mag vol 15) [PER/GEN]

Mariners & Shipowners *In* Elizabethan Life vol 5: Wills of Essex Gentry, *Merchants* & Yeomen preserved in the PCC (*list 1558-1603*) (Essex RO Pub no 75) [ES/G 35]

Summary of Royal National Lifeboat Institution Legacy Papers (*May 1850, Jun 1913-Jul 1918, pt 1921, Jul 1922-Dec 1923*) [WILLS/GEN]; (*Oct 1922-Mar 1923*) (Hants FHn vol 6 no 1) [HA/PER]

Wealth of 33 Captains who died in the Liverpool Slave Trade 1790-1800 (Trans Hist Soc Lancs & Cheshire vol 140)

[LA/PER]

A Yorks Town of the 18th C; the Prob Invents of Whitby, N Yorks 1700-1800 (*abst, many for mariners, 1701-1792*) [YK/L 159]

Medical Men

Some Physicians' Wills *proved at York* (*abst 1607-1768*) (Northern Genealogist vol 2) [PER/NOR]

Merchants: see Tradesmen

Musicians

Musicians' Wills vols 1-7 (*Bax Papers, 2 books of abst 1523-1799*) [PR/MUS]

Wills of the Rich & Famous (*1964-1985*) [US/G 142]

Pewterers

List of Pewterers' Invents (*1534-1747*) & List of Wills & Letters of Admon consulted (*1534-1822*) *In* "Provincial Pewterers: a Study of the Craft in the W Midlands & Wales" [PR/PEW]

Printers, etc

Booksellers & Stationers in Warrington 1630-1657: *Abst of* Wills, Invents & Notes (*In* "Lancs Tracts vol 1") [LA/G 1]

Coll of the Wills of Printers & Booksellers in Edinburgh 1557-1687 (*abst*) *In* "Bannantyne Miscellany vol 2" [SC/G 142]

Wills from English Printers & Stationers 1492-1630 [PR/PRI]

Scriveners

Writing to the Court; a Scrivener's Miscellany (*extr from scriveners' prob recs in the PCC (PRO Class PROB 24) 1658-1665*) [MX Tracts]

Stationers: see Printers

Tradesmen & Merchants

Abst of Wills & Invents (*1609-1668*) *In* "Merchants & Merchandise in 17th C Bristol" (Bristol Rec Soc Pubs vol 19) [GL/PER]

Elizabethan Life vol 4: Wills of Essex Gentry & Merchants proved in the PCC (*abst 1558-1603*) (Essex RO Pub no 71) [ES/G 34]

Elizabethan Life vol 5: Wills of Essex Gentry, *Merchants* & Yeomen preserved in the PCC (*abst 1558-1603*) (Essex RO Pub no 75) [ES/G 35]

Invents of Five Dublin Quaker merchants in the late 17th C (*extr 1684-1695*) (Irish Ancestor vol 10) [IR/PER]

Notes on London Aldermen (*Whitmore MSS, lists prob info 1604-1737*) (6 vols) [MX/G 8-13]

Petworth Town & Trades (*tradesmen's invent abst 1610-1760*) (Sussex Archl Colls vols 96, 98 & 99) [SX/PER]

Prob Invents of Worcs Tradesmen 1545-1614 *In* "Miscellany 2" (Worcs Hist Soc new ser vol 5) [WO/PER]

Rulers of London 1660-1685; a Biographical Rec of the Aldermen & Common Councilmen of the City of London *with prob info* (London & Middx Archl Soc *extra vol*) [MX/G 17]

Steyning Town & its Trades 1597-1787 (*with invent list*) (*1559-1787*) (Sussex Archl Colls vol 130) [SX/PER]

Testmtry Papers *In* "Guide to the Archives of the Co of Merchant Adventurers of York" (*extr 1285-1840*) (Borthwick Texts & Cals no 16) [YK/PER]

Academia
many college, school & university histories include references to wills & endowments

Schools

Abst of the original wills (unless otherwise specified) of various Priests of the Soc of Jesus (*1633-1805*) which are now deposited among the archives at Stonyhurst *In* "Supp HMC Rep upon the MSS at Stonyhurst College" [Apply to Staff]

Index of Wills & *Executors' Accounts* 1290-1761 *In* "Winchester College Muniments" (offprint from Archives vol 5 no 28) [HA Tracts]

HMC National Reg of Archives; Winchester College Archives Section: 'Pertinentia ad Alio' from descriptive list (*wills cal 1308-1541*) [Apply to Staff]

Universities

Index to Berks Wills proved in the Court of the Chancellor of Oxford University 1565-1734 (Berks N&Q vol 1) [BK/PER]

Court of the Vice Chancellor of the University of Cambridge: Cal of Wills 1501-1765 [CA/G 26]

Index to Wills proved in the Court of the Chancellor of the University of Oxford & to such of the recs & other instruments & papers of that court as relate to matters or causes testmtry (*wills 1436-1814, invents 1443-1740, accounts 1453-1719*) [OX/G 37]

Remarks on a recently published Selection from the Wills of Eminent Persons (*will &*

admon extr for the University of Cambridge 1495-1713*) (Cambridge Antqn Soc Rep no 14) [CA/PER]

Social Hist of Property & Possessions; pt 1: Invents & Wills including Renaissance Lib Catalogues from the Bodleian Lib, Oxford 1436-1814 consisting of an index to Wills proved in the Court of the Chancellor of the University of Oxford & to such of the recs of that Court as relate to matters or causes testmtry (with ms annotations); *abst of wills & admon bonds 1436-1814, invents 1443-1740, prob accounts 1413-1514, 1527-1661 & index to The Bodleian Lib Benefactors' Reg* [Mf 1756-1768]

WILLS OF THE FAMOUS
see also the Family History section of the Library Catalogue

Abst of Wills, Admons, Invents, Estate Settlements 1621-1727 relating to Mayflower Passengers & their Heirs *In* "Mayflower Reader (A Selection of Articles from Mayflower Descendant Excerpted from vols 1-8, 1899-1905)" [US/MA/G 6]

Ancient, Curious & Famous Wills (Harris) (*extr from 2550 BC to 1911*) [WILLS/GEN]

Handlist of Aristocratic Wills 1335-1530 (*Rosenthal's index to wills in English courts*) (Fam Hist vol 9 no 49) [PER/FAM]

Notes on London Aldermen (*Whitmore MSS, with prob info 1604-1737*) (6 vols) [MX/G 8-13]

Royal Wills sealed up by Order in Somerset House (*cal 1911-1974*) *In* "Wills, Invents & Death Duties; recs of the PCC & the EDO (Prov Guide)" [TB Quick Reference]

Rulers of London 1660-1685; a Biographical Rec of the Aldermen & Common Councilmen of the City of London *with prob info* (London & Middx Archl Soc *extra vol*) [MX/G 17]

Some Royal Wills (*list 1083-1901*) *In* "Wills, Invents & Death Duties; recs of the PCC & the EDO (Prov Guide)" [TB Quick Reference]

Testamenta Vetusta, being illustrations from wills, of manners, customs, &c as well as of the descents & possessions of many distinguished fams, from the reign of Henry II to the accession of Queen Elizabeth; vols 1 & 2 (*extr 1154-1558*) [WILLS/GEN]

Wills at the Court of Probate (*lists eminent persons' wills in print*) (N&Q 3rd ser vols 2 & 3) [N&Q]

Wills from Doctors' Commons; a selection from the wills of eminent persons, proved in the PCC 1495-1695 (Camden Soc old ser vol 83) [WILLS/PCC or PER/CS]; Remarks on a recently published Selection from the Wills of Eminent Persons (*will & admon extr for the University of Cambridge 1495-1713*) (Cambridge Antqn Soc Rep no 14) [CA/PER]

Wills of the Rich & Famous (*1799, 1826 & 1910-1989*) [US/G 142]

GENERAL COLLECTIONS OF WILLS, INDEXES, ETC

see also the National sections for Ireland, Scotland & Wales

Abst of Wills, Admons & Invents *In* "National Lib of Wales - Cal of Deeds & Docs; vols 1: Coleman Deeds" (*1622-1872*), 2: Crosswood Deeds" (*1546-1855*) & 3: Hawarden Deeds" (*1541-1828*) [WS/G 14-16]

Abst of Wills & Admons in the PCC & elsewhere with Extr from Testmts in Scottish Commissariots (*Hargreaves-Mawdsley*); vols 1 & 2: 1700-1893 [WILLS/GEN]

Abst of Ancient Wills *from the BM (Landsdowne MSS)* (*1300-1488*) (Coll Topo & Genealogica vol 3) [PER/COL]

Abst of Ancient Wills (*unindexed coll of UK wills 1518-1789*) (Geneal Mnthly vol 1) [PER/GEN]

Abst of Wills amongst Misc Deeds 1705-1858 *In* "Gleanings from Parish Chests" [CA/L 12]

Alphabetical hand-list to printed wills, admons, etc (*A-BAR 1374-1749*) *In* Sherwood's "Collectanea Genealogica" vol 3 [PER/COL]

Ancient, Curious & Famous Wills (*Harris's extr from 2550 BC to 1911*) [WILLS/GEN]

Baker's Transcripts & Abst of Wills (*1512-1600*) (Coll Topo & Genealogica vols 5-7) [PER/COL]

Bernau's Evidences; Misc London Will Abst *in 15 vols* (*13-19th C*) [WILLS/GEN]

Bloom's Index to Stray Wills not in Ecclesiastical Regs (*D missing*) [Apply to Staff]

Boddington's Abst of Wills & Admons (*1656-1799*) (Misc Gen et Her 3rd ser vol 4 & 4th ser vol 2) [PER/MIS]

Boddington's Unpublished Wills & Admons (*abst 1652-1856*) (Misc Gen et Her new ser vol 2 & 2nd ser vols 4 & 5) [PER/MIS]

Boyd's Inhabitants of London (*238 vols & 27 index vols include many probs 16-18th C*) [Middle Library]; Boyd's Units (*34 vols & index vols, in progress, include many probs 16-18th C*) [Upper Library]; Additional Card Index (*extra references*) [Lower Library:

Index drawers 111-112]

Crisp's Wills *in 7 vols plus index (13-19th C)* [WILLS/GEN]

Curiosities of the Search Room; a coll of serious & whimsical wills (*extr 1280-1880*) [WILLS/GEN]

Curious Wills (*extr 1439-1605*) (N&Q 5th ser vols 6 & 7) [N&Q]

English Adventurers & Colonial Settlers; abst of Legal Proceedings in 17th C English & Dutch Courts (*16-19th C*) [US/G 74]

English Adventurers & VA Settlers - the co-ordinated use of 17th C British American recs by Genealogists - vols 1 & 2: Abst of Wills 1484-1798; vol 3: Prob Cases 1641-1722 *In* "Abst of Legal Proceedings 1566-1700" [US/VA/G 6-8]

Extr from Wills & Deeds in Newfoundland Provincial Archives (*300 British & Irish will abst 1793-1859*) (NL Ancestor vols 8-11) [CAN/NL/PER]

Extr of some Wills *in the PCC, 1659-1795* (Misc Gen et Her new ser vol 3) [PER/MIS]

English Wills of Colonial Fams (*Currer-Briggs's abst 1461-1777*) [US/G 80]

Holworthy Coll - Boxes 1 & 2 (*will abst*) [Special Colls]

Index of Names 1411-1855 *In* "Researching British Probs 1354-1858: Guide to the Microfilm Coll of the FH Lib; vol 1: Northern England & the Province of York" [TB/RG]

Index of Wills; Soper's arbitrary coll of 15th & 16th C wills (*mostly PCC but some from York, Kent, Taunton & London*) [WILLS/GEN]

Index to Stray, Draft & other Wills & Admons in the Oxford RO (*1557-1937*); pts 1 & 2 (Oxon FHn vol 2) [OX/PER]

Indexes to a *large coll of modern* Wills, Admons & Will Books held by the Nantwich Group of the FHS of Cheshire; pt 1: Will Books & Admons (*1622-1938*); pt 2: Wills & Admons (*1659-1964*) [CH/G 41]

Last Will & Testmt: wills ancient & modern [WILLS/GEN]

Law Cases, Formulae & Opinions 1704-1757 (*will abst 1704-1757*) [Apply to Staff]; *copy of* Nominal Index [Topo Docs Coll: Subject, Wills]

Lea's Geneal Gleanings (*colls of will, admon & invent abst with notes 1464-1721*) (NEHGR vols 54-59) [US/NE/PER]

List of named Wills & Admons 1003-1833 *In* "Texts & Cals 2; an analytical guide to serial pubs" (Royal Hist Soc Guides & Handbooks no 12) [Apply to Staff]

List of 13th C English Wills (*Sheehan's*

English wills, temp Henry II to 1300)
(Genealogists' Mag vol 13) [PER/GEN]
List of Wills, Admons, etc in the PRO, London,
England from 12-19th C (*prob material in
court & departmental recs 1240-1885*)
[WILLS/GEN]
Misc Abst of Wills & Admons (*2 vols, 16-19th
C*) (*Glencross MSS*) [WILLS/GEN]
Notes on unpublished wills at Somerset
House (*will extr 16th & 17th C*) (The
Genealogist new ser vol 4) [PER/GEN]
Oldaker Coll of Wills
Note: *this very large coll of abst of prob recs
from the 16-19th C was made by "A.W.R."
during res on the Read(e) Fam & their
relations - particularly in the PCC, Leicester,
Lichfield, Lincoln & Northampton Probate
Courts: there are vols on the Family History
shelves [FH/REA & FH/MISC], on the Wills
shelves [WILLS/GEN & WILLS/PCC] & on
some county shelves; for Lichfield there is
also a vol of "Lichfield Probate Registry
Extracts" [ST/G 30], the original ms versions
of which are in store [Apply to Staff (vols 1-
3) or (vol 4) FH/MISC]; see also Abst of
Chancery Proceedings mainly in the
counties of Staffs, Derbys, Warwks, Worcs
& Glos together with some subsidy rolls &
Star Chamber Proceedings including prob
cases 1591-1712 (Oldaker MSS) [ST/G 5]*
References to Abst of Wills (*997-1293*)
(Genealogists' Ref J vol 1 pts 2-3)
[PER/GEN]
Some Wills in the PRO (*enrolled will indexes*);
pts *1: Miscellanea - Exchequer Rolls &
Treasury Rolls of Receipt from Henry III to
1679, 2: Close Rolls 1691-1799 & 3:
Recovery Rolls 1714-1768* (The Genealogist
new ser vols 1-3) [*all* PER/GEN]
Testamenta Vetusta, being illustrations from
wills, of manners, customs, &c as well as of
the descents & possessions of many
distinguished fams, from the reign of Henry
II to the accession of Queen Elizabeth; vols
1 & 2 (*1154-1558*) [WILLS/GEN]
Waters's Geneal Gleanings in England; vols 1
& 2 [US/G 83-84] (*will abst*); *Waters's*
Geneal Gleanings (NEHGR vols 37-52
indexed in vol 52) [US/NE/PER]
Wills, admons & invents of persons belonging
to places outside the Diocese of Chester
1568-1650 & now preserved at Chester
(Lancs & Cheshire Rec Soc Procs vol 4)
[LA/PER]
Wills from the Close Rolls (*extr 1420-1433*)
(N&Q 8th ser vol 1) [N&Q]
Wills in Anglo-Saxon & other Charters,

Cartularies, etc in the Earl of Ashburnham's
MSS (*list 874-1018*) *In* pt 2 of "8th HMC
Rep" [SP/HMC]
Wills in Cals of the Close Rolls preserved in
the PRO - Henry VI vol 4: 1441-1447;
Edward IV vols 1: 1461-1468 & 2: 1468-
1476 [*all* SP/CLO]
Wills, *Invents* & Admons deposited with the
Dept of Archives, Central Lib, Sheffield
(*1474-1920*) [Apply to Staff]
Withington's Abst of English Wills (*1569-1675*)
(NEHGR vols 51-54) [US/NE/PER]

NEXT OF KIN and OTHER MONETARY RECORDS
*see also High Court of Chancery & the
Treasury Solicitor in the COURTS section*
Bank of England Regs of Will Extr, etc for
various stock 1717-1845, 1852 & 1875
[Mf**]; Index to the Names to be found in the
Bank of England Reg called "GO" being for
3% Consolidated Annuities Stock, vol 16,
G-O: 16005-17124 (1805-1806)
[WILLS/GEN]; *Index to Bank of England
Wills Extr 1717-1807 in preparation***; Index
to the Bank of England Wills Extr 1807-1845
(also Mfc) [WILLS/GEN or Apply to Staff]
** *at present these 179 vols are in the Upper
Library but will be replaced by Mf when this
index has been published: check the Main
Catalogue for current availability*
British Wealth Holders 1809-1849:
alphabetical master listing of everyone
leaving £100,000 or more in Britain
[WILLS/GEN]
Dormant Funds in Court (supp to "London
Gazette" of 3 Mar 1911) [TB/MR]
Dramatis Personae (*Sherwood's prob abst
from Delegates' Examination Papers 1634-
1707 & other courts 1539-1841*) [FH/MISC]
General Index to Unclaimed Property &
Money & Heirs-at-Law, Next-of-Kin,
Legatees & others ... (Swan, *1886 ed*)
[TB/MR]
Index to Advertisements for Next-of-Kin,
Heirs-at-Law, Missing Heirs & Relatives,
Unclaimed Bank Deposits, Tax Refunds, etc
(Geneal Qtrly vols 23-26, 31-32 & 38-29)
[PER/GEN]
Index to Cornish Testators holding Stock in
the Public Funds: *wills in Bank of England
Regs 1807-1845* (Cornwall FH J no 73)
[CO/PER]
Index Reg to Next of Kin, Heirs at Law,
Legatees, etc who have been advertised for,
or are entitled to, vast sums of money &
property in Great Britain & the Colonies

since 1698 (Douglas) (*5th ed 1885*); (Douglas) (*8th ed 1888*) [*both* TB/MR]
"News of the World" Missing Heirs & Next-of-Kin *to 1911* [TB/MR]
Shrewsbury Canal Co - Copy Reg of Probs (*will & admon abst 1833-1847*) [SH/L 18]

Summary of National Lifeboat Institution Legacy Papers (*May 1850, Jun 1913-Jul 1918, pt 1921, Jul 1922-Dec 1923*) [WILLS/GEN]; (*Oct 1922-Mar 1923*) (Hants FHn vol 6 no 1) [HA/PER]

ENGLAND

BEDFORDSHIRE
Pre-1858 Probate Jurisdictions:-
Prerogative Court: Canterbury
Consistory Courts: Lincoln; Ely (from 1837); Peterborough
Archdeaconry Courts: BEDFORD; Huntingdon; Northampton
Peculiars, etc: Biggleswade; Leighton Buzzard; Lincoln (Dean & Chapter - until 1834)

1379-1607 *Abst of* Beds Wills & Admons proved at Lambeth Palace & in the Archdeaconry of Huntingdon 1379-1607 (Beds Hist Rec Soc Pubs vol 2) [BE/G 22 (*In* "Beds Tracts vol 1") or BE/PER]

1383-1548 *Abst of* Beds Wills proved in the PCC 1383-1548 (Beds Hist Rec Soc Pubs vol 58) [BE/PER]

1400-1780 Cal of Some Beds Wills collected from various sources relating chiefly to the Gentry & Clergy of the County of Bedford (*with many ms additions*) [BE/G 15]

1411-1712 Index of Early Beds Wills & Admons 1411-1712 [BE/G 18]

1486-1805 *Extr from* Early Bedford Wills *In* "Genealogia Bedfordiensis being a coll of evidences relating to the landed gentry of Beds" *with ms additions*; Lexicographical Cal of Abst of Beds Wills from Various Sources *as a* supp to "Genealogia Bedfordiensis" [BE/G 26-27]

1500-1701 *Abst of* Some Beds Wills in the Registry at Northampton (Beds N&Q vols 2 & 3) [BE/PER]

1562-1591 Elizabethan Invents *for Beds* (Beds Hist Rec Soc Pubs vol 32) [BE/PER]

1575-1710 *Abst of* Wills relating to Beds in "Crisp's Somerset Wills" (Beds N&Q vol 3) [BE/PER]

1653-1660 Cal of Invents 1653-1660 being lists of Invents exhibited in the

PCC for the Commonwealth period, for the following counties: ... Beds ... [WILLS/PCC]

Luton
1501-1812 *Index to* Wills & Admons of Luton People; vol 1: 1501-1752 *In* "Luton Parish Reg; vol 1" (Beds Parish Reg ser vol 53B); vol 2: 1753-1812 *In* "Luton Parish Reg vol 2" (Beds Parish Reg ser vol 54) [*both* BE/R 43]

Pertenhall
1505-1740 *Index to* Early Pertenhall Wills *In* "Pertenhall Parish Reg" (Beds Parish Reg ser vol 50) [BE/R 49]

Steppingley
1538-1810 *Index to* Steppingley Wills *In* "Steppingley Parish Reg" (Beds Parish Reg ser vol 51) [BE/R 50]

Turvey
1560-1608 Turvey Wills *being a list with some abst In* "Hist & Antiquities of the Hundred of Willey in the County of Bedford" [Apply to Staff]

Wilstead
1501-1656 *Index to* Wills of Wilstead People *In* "Wilstead Parish Reg" (Beds Parish Reg ser vol 49) [BE/R 42]

BERKSHIRE
Pre-1858 Probate Jurisdictions:-
Prerogative Court: Canterbury
Consistory Courts: Lincoln; Oxford (from 1836); Sarum
Archdeaconry Courts: BERKSHIRE; Oxford; Wiltshire
Peculiars, etc: Faringdon; Langford Ecclesia; Lincoln (Dean & Chapter - until 1834); Sarum (Dean); Wantage (Dean & Canons of Windsor); Windsor (Dean)

1391-1807 Snell's Geneal Coll: this consists of 48 ms vols mainly of will abst with a Berks connection [BK/G 1-48 or, *if not on shelves*, Apply to Staff]
Note: *there is a guide to this coll: "Catalogue of MSS bequeathed by Frederick Simon Snell (1862-1914) & Table of Abbreviations"* [BK/G 49]; *Snell's "Name Index to Abst of Berks Wills"* [BK/G 79]; *the ROC-RY, W-Z vol of the Index to Berks Wills is on Mf* [Mf 970]

1503-1557 *Abst of* Early Berks Wills from the PCC ante 1558 (*A-DAN*) ("Berks J" vols 2 & 3; new ser vols 1, 3-7 & 20) [BK/PER]

1520-1840 Consistory Court of Sarum: *Index to* Wills for Berks only c1520-c1840 *In* "Berks Wills from Various Sources" [BK/G 76]

1555-1730 *Index to* Misc Wills *for Berks* in the Wilts RO *In* "Berks Wills from Various Sources" [BK/G 76]

1555-1810 *Index to* Testmtry Papers at Salisbury; pt 1: Berks, Dorset & Uffculme Wills, Admons, Invents, etc preserved at Sarum (Genealogists' Mag vol 5) [PER/GEN or WL/G 52]

1565-1734 *Index to* Berks Wills proved in the Court of the Chancellor of Oxford University 1565-1734 (Berks N&Q vol 1) [BK/PER]

1653-1654 *Index to* Berks Admons in the PCC 1653-1654 (Berks N&Q vol 1) [BK/PER]

1801 *Index to* Berks & Oxon Wills & Admons in the PCC (Oxon FHn vol 1 no 8) [OX/PER]

Aldermaston
1508-1832 *Index of* Aldermaston Wills & Admons 1508-1710 & Aldermaston, Berks Wills & Admons at Sarum *1614-1832 In* "Aldermaston Regs pt 2" [BK/R 112]

Appleford
1531-1651 *Index of* Wills (*including Sutton Wick*) *In* "Parish of Appleford Baptisms, Marriages & Burials for the Years 1563-1835" [BK/R 73]

Arbourfield
1529-1690 *Index of* Arbourfield Wills 1508-1710 & Misc Wills in Wilts RO 1555-1730 *In* "Arbourfield Parish Regs" [BK/R 86]

Ashbury
1508-1804 *Index of* Ashbury Wills & *Admons* 1508-1710 & Wills in the Consistory Court of Sarum 1520-1840 (*including Ashdown Park, Idstone, Kingstone & Odstone*) *In* "Ashbury Parish Regs" [BK/R 102]

Ashdown Park *see Ashbury*

Avington
1523-1682 *Index of* Avington Wills 1523-1710 *In* "Regs of Avington" [BK/R 79]

Bagnor *see Speen & District*

Bagnor Shaw *see Shaw-cum-Donnington*

Beedon
1513-1707 *Index of* Beedon Wills & *Admons* 1508-1710 (*including Stanmore Wills & Admons 1698-1701*) *In* "Beedon Parish Regs" [BK/R 108]

Benham
(*including Benham Lovell, Benham Valence & March Benham*) *see Speen & District*

Binfield
1508-1835 *Index of* Binfield Wills & *Admons* 1508-1652 & *Binfield Wills & Admons in the* Consistory Court of Sarum (*1521-1835*) *In* "Parish Regs of Binfield pt 2" [BK/R 106]

Bracknell (*including New Bracknell*) *see Warfield*

Burchetts Green *see Hurley*

Cookham Parish
1512-1648 *Index of* Cookham Wills & Admons 1508-1652 *In* "Cookham Regs pt 1" [BK/R 94]

Culham *see Wargrave*

Donnington *see Shaw-cum-Donnington*

Faringdon
1737-1806   *Abst of* Deeds & Wills relating to 24 London Street, Faringdon, Oxon (previously in Berks) belonging to Mr Barker [BK/L 44]

Frilsham
1508-1710   *Index of* Frilsham Wills & *Admons* 1508-1710 & of E Garston Wills & *Admons* at Sarum (Wilts RO) [Topo Docs Coll: Berks]

Garston, East
1505-1710   *Index of* Frilsham Wills & *Admons* 1508-1710 & of E Garston Wills & *Admons* at Sarum (*1505-1710*) (Wilts RO) [Topo Docs Coll: Berks]
1531-1832   *Index of* Wills & *Admons* for E Garston 1531-1649, 1653-1710 (*1531-1832*) *In* "E Garston Regs pt 2" [BK/R 132]

Hare Hatch *see Wargrave*

Hawthorne *see Warfield*

Hendred, East
1417-1857   *List of* E Hendred Wills & *Admons* 1528-1857 & *Abst of* Wills 1417-1718 *In* "E Hendred: a Berks Parish" [BK/L 9]

Hurley
1545-1710   *Index of* Hurley Wills & *Admons* 1508-1710 (*including Burchetts Green & Knowl Hill*) *In* "Hurley Parish Regs pt 2" [BK/R 108]

Idstone *see Ashbury*

Inkpen
1508-1653   Index of Inkpen Wills 1508-1653 [Apply to Staff]

Kingstone *see Ashbury*

Kintbury
1543-1650   Index of PCC Wills from 1383: Kintbury, Berks [Topo Docs Coll: Berks]

Knowl Hill *see Hurley*

Maidenhead
1530-1648   Index of Maidenhead Wills & *Admons* 1508-1652 *In* "Cookham

Parish Regs pt 1" [BK/R 94]

Midgham
1508-1779   *Index of* Midgham Wills & *Admons* 1508-1710 & Consistory Court Sarum - *Midgham Wills* (*1530-1779*) *In* "Midgham Parish Regs" [BK/R 110]

Moulsford
1541-1706   *Index of* Moulsford Wills & *Admons* 1508-1710 *In* "Moulsford Parish Regs" [BK/R 109]

Nalder Hill *see Speen & District*

Odstone *see Ashbury*

Padworth
1522-1710   *Index of* Padworth Wills & *Admons* 1508-1710 [Topo Docs Coll: Berks]

Pusey
1491-1726   Abst of Some Wills & Invents *In* appx to "Pusey; a parish rec" [BK/L 16]

Reading
1493-1549   Abst of Wills *In* "Hist of the Municipal Church St Lawrence, Reading" [BK/L 17]
1541-1603   *Cal of* Prob Invents from Reading (Heritage vol 1 no 4) [BK/PER]

Shaw Bridge *see Speen & District*

Shaw cum Donnington
1540-1704   *Index of* Shaw-cum-Donnington Wills & *Admons* 1508-1710 (*including Bagnor Shaw, Donnington & Shawdene*) *In* "Shaw-cum-Donnington Parish Regs pt 2" [BK/R 114]

Shawdene *see Shaw-cum-Donnington*

Shefford, Great
1528-1710   *Index of* Great Shefford Wills & *Admons* 1508-1710 *In* "Great Shefford Reg pt 2" [BK/R 114]

Shottesbrook
1519-1697   *Index of* Shottesbrook Wills & *Admons* 1508-1710 *In* "Shottesbrook Parish Regs" [BK/R 80]

Sotwell
1546-1710 *Index of* Sotwell Wills 1508-1710
[Topo Docs Coll: Berks]
Note: *this is the wills section of*
"Sotwell Parish Regs & Bishop's
Transcripts" [BK/R 72] *& is*
included with Sotwell baptisms,
marriages & burials sections in
the cumulative index

Southridge *see Streatley*

Speen District
including Church Speen, Speenhamland &
Wood Speen
1653-1709 *Index of Speen Wills & Admons*
in the Archdeaconry of Berkshire
1508-1710 (*including Bagnor,*
Benham, Benham Lovell,
Benham Valence, Church Speen,
March Benham, Nalder Hill,
Shaw Bridge, Speenhamland &
Wood Speen) *In* "Speen Regs pt
2" [BK/R 87]

Stanmore *see Beedon*

Streatley
1507-1832 *Index of* Streatley Wills &
Admons 1507-1652 & Streatley
Wills *& Admons in the* Consistory
Court of Sarum (*1526-1832,*
including Southridge &
Westridge) *In* "Streatley Parish
Regs pt 3" [BK/R 85]

Sunninghill
1542-1709 *Index of* Sunninghill Wills &
Admons 1508-1710 *In*
"Sunninghill Regs pt 2" [BK/R
113]

Sutton Courtenay
1521-1710 *Index of* Sutton Courtenay Wills
& Admons 1508-1710 *In* "Sutton
Courtenay Parish Regs" [BK/R
110]

Sutton Wick *see Appleford*

Thatcham
1506-1835 *Index of* Thatcham Wills &
Admons 1506-1710 & of
Thatcham Wills at the Court of
Sarum (*1510-1835*) *In* "Thatcham
Burial Reg pt 2" [BK/R 127]

Ufton Nervet
1528-1710 *Index of* Wills & *Admons* 1508-
1710 [Topo Docs Coll: Berks]

Wantage
1568-1748 Ancient Wills (*abst from the*
Wantage area) ("Berks J" new
ser vol 5) [BK/PER]

Warfield
1508-1823 *Index of* Wills & *Admons* for
Warfield 1508-1710 & Warfield
Wills at Sarum (*1530-1823,*
including Bracknell, New
Bracknell & Hawthorne) *In*
"Warfield Parish Regs" [BK/R
109]

Wargrave
1508-1826 *Index of* Wargrave Wills &
Admons 1508-1710 & Consistory
Court Sarum Wills (*1529-1826,*
including Culham & Hare Hatch)
In "Wargrave Baptismal Reg pt 2"
[BK/R 123]

Wasing
1557-1708 *Index of* Wasing Wills & *Admons*
1508-1710 *In* "Wasing Parish
Regs pt 1" [BK/R 109]

Westridge *see Streatley*

Winkfield
1508-1851 *Index of* Winkfield Wills &
Admons 1508-1652 & Winkfield
Wills in the Consistory Court of
Sarum (*1530-1851*) *In* "Winkfield
Baptismal Reg" [BK/R 99]

Woolhampton
1556-1708 *Index of* Woolhampton Wills &
Admons 1508-1710 *In*
"Woolhampton Parish Regs"
[BK/R 89]

Wootton
1544-1704 *Index of* Wootton Wills &
Admons 1508-1710 *In* "Wootton
Parish Regs" [BK/R 132]

BUCKINGHAMSHIRE
Pre-1858 Probate Jurisdictions:-
Prerogative Court: Canterbury
Consistory Courts: Lincoln; London; Oxford
Archdeaconry Courts: BUCKINGHAM;
Oxford; St Albans
Peculiars, etc: Aylesbury; Bierton;
Buckingham; Eton; Lincoln (Dean & Chapter
- until 1834); Monks Risborough; Thame

14-20 C	List of Surnames *In* "Gurney Will Books" (*Gurney MSS will abst in Bucks RO*) (Origins vol 16) [BU/PER])
1354-1571	*Index of* Bucks Wills in Lambeth Palace [Topo Docs Coll: Bucks]
1406-1858	*Index of* Bucks Wills in the PCC [Topo Docs Coll: Bucks]
1520-1528	*Abst of* Wills of Bucks Clergy in the 16th C (Recs of Bucks vol 13 pt 3) [BU/PER]
1686-1693	Index to Bucks Wills in the PCC (*A-COX*) (Origins vol 7) [BU/PER]
1661-1714	*Abst of* Bucks Prob Invents in the PCC 1661-1714 (Bucks Rec Soc vol 24); Index of Testators in "Bucks Prob Invents in the PCC 1661-1714" (Origins vol 15) [*both* BU/PER]
1700-1800	Bucks Wills & Admons in the PCC 1700-1800 [BU/G 33]

Chesham
1483-1565	*Index of* Chesham Wills in the PCC from 1383 [Topo Docs Coll: Bucks]

Medmenham
1478-1808	Cal of Medmenham Wills 1478-1808 *In* "Manor & Parish Recs of Medmenham, Bucks" [BU/L 8]

Wooburn
1717-1824	Wills & *Admons listed In* "Original Docs relating to the Ownership & Hist of the Estate at Wooburn, Bucks known as Lower Glory Mills 1665-1865" [Topo Docs Coll: Bucks]

CAMBRIDGESHIRE
Pre-1858 Probate Jurisdictions:-
Prerogative Court: Canterbury
Consistory Courts: ELY; London; Norwich;
Rochester
Commissary Court: London (Essex & Herts)
Archdeaconry Courts: ELY; Norfolk;
Rochester; Sudbury
Peculiars, etc: Cambridge (King's College);
Cambridge (University); Ely (Dean &
Chapter); Isleham & Freckenham; Thorney
Civil Courts: Cambridge (Mayor); Wisbeach

973-1850	Jacob Index to Beneficiaries *under Jacobs' Wills in Cambs & Suffolk* (*surnames only*) (Suffolk Roots vols 6, 13 & 14) [SF/PER]
1653-1660	Cal of Invents 1653-1660 being lists of Invents exhibited in the PCC for the Commonwealth period, for the following counties: ... Cambs ... [WILLS/PCC]

Abington-juxta-Shingay
1579-1671	Wills of the Hundred of Armingford, Cambs, preserved at the Peterborough Probate Registry (*index with abst*) (E Anglian new ser vol 10) [NF/PER]

Bassingbourn
1528-1748	Wills of the Hundred of Armingford, Cambs, preserved at the Peterborough Probate Registry (*index with abst*) (E Anglian new ser vol 10) [NF/PER]

Bottisham
1516-1559	Extr from Wills in the Cole MSS (in Ely Diocesan Registry) *In* "Hist & Antiquities of the Parish of Bottisham" (Cambridge Antqn Soc Octo Pubs no 14) [CA/PER]

Burrough Green
1410-1690	Abst of Wills & Invents *In* "Hist of the Parish of Borough Green, Cambs" (Cambridge Antqn Soc Octo Pubs no 54) [CA/PER]

Cloton *see Croydon-cum-Clopton*

Croydon-cum-Clopton
1525-1767	Wills of the Hundred of Armingford, Cambs, preserved at the Peterborough Probate

Registry (*index with abst*) (E
Anglian new ser vol 10) [NF/PER]

Graveley
1521-1847 *Index to Graveley* Wills, Admons
& Invents in the Archdeaconry
Court of Ely Prob Recs *In*
"Graveley Regs" [CA/R 41]

Guilden Morden
1518-1752 Wills of the Hundred of
Armingford, Cambs, preserved at
the Peterborough Probate
Registry (*index with abst*) (E
Anglian new ser vols 10 & 11)
[NF/PER]

Hatley, East
1536-1738 Wills of the Hundred of
Armingford, Cambs, preserved at
the Peterborough Probate
Registry (*index with abst*) (E
Anglian new ser vol 10) [NF/PER]

Horningsey
1515-1589 *Abst of* Wills *In* "Hists of the
adjoining parishes of
Waterbeach, Landbeach,
Horningsey & Milton" [Mf 970]

Ickleton
1460-1743 Extr from Wills of Former
Inhabitants of Ickleton 1460-1743
In "Memoirs of Ickleton" [CA
Tracts]

Landbeach
1345-1569 Extr from Wills 1345-1569 *In*
"Hist of the Parish of Landbeach
in the County of Cambridge"
(*offprint from Cambridge Antqn
Soc Octo ser vol 6 In* Cambridge
Tracts vol 1) [CA/G 7]
1515-1589 *Abst of* Wills *In* "Hists of the
adjoining parishes of
Waterbeach, Landbeach,
Horningsey & Milton" [Mf 970]

Milton
1515-1589 Extr from Wills *In* "Hist of the
Parish of Milton in the County of
Cambridge" [CA/L 11]; *Abst of*
Wills *In* "Hists of the adjoining
parishes of Waterbeach,
Landbeach, Horningsey & Milton"
[Mf 970]

Waterbeach
1515-1589 *Abst of* Wills *In* "Hists of the
adjoining parishes of
Waterbeach, Landbeach,
Horningsey & Milton" [Mf 970]

Wisbeach
1488-1526 Extr from Some Ancient Wills
1488-1526 *In* "Wisbeach in the
Ely Episcopal Regs" (Cambridge
Tracts vol 1) [CA/G 7]

CHESHIRE
Pre-1858 Probate Jurisdictions:-
Prerogative Courts: Canterbury; York (from
1541)
Consistory Courts: CHESTER (from 1541);
Lichfield; York (Chancery - from 1541)
Archdeaconry Court: Chester (Archdeaconry
of the 12 Deaneries)
Peculiars, etc: Chester (Collegiate Church of
St John); York (Dean & Chapter - from
1541)*; see also Lancaster (Chancery)*

1322-1844 Cal of Persons Commemorated
in MI & of the abst of Wills,
Admons, etc contained in books
relating to Lancs & Cheshire
(Lancs & Cheshire Rec Soc
Procs vol 76) [CH/M 1 (*with many
ms addenda*) or LA/PER]
1396-1594 Wills in Palatinate of Chester
papers 1396-1594 *In* "List of
Wills, Admons, etc in the PRO,
London, England from 12-19th C"
[WILLS/GEN]
1486-1644 List of Cheshire Wills in Harleian
MSS 1991 in the BM (Lancs &
Cheshire Rec Soc Procs vol 2)
[LA/PER]
1519-1648 *Index to* Cheshire & Lancs Wills
in the Harleian Coll at the BM
(Cheshire Sheaf new ser vol 37)
[CH/PER]
1591-1793 Some Cheshire Wills (*will,
admon, invent & court deposition
abst*) (Cheshire Sheaf 3rd ser
vols 16, 17, 19, 22) [CH/PER]
17-19 C Beazley's Geneal Coll: this
consists of 11 ms vols, with an
index vol, mainly of will abst with
a Lancs or Cheshire connection
In "Collectanea; vols 1-12" [CH/G
1-12]
1608-1679 *Abst of* Lancs & Cheshire Wills
(Northern Genealogist vol 1)

[PER/NOR]

1621-1660 Index to Wills & Invents 1621-1650 with a list of Lancs & Cheshire Wills proved in the PCC 1650-1660 & a list of Lancs & Cheshire Admons granted in the PCC 1650-1660 (Lancs & Cheshire Rec Soc Procs vol 4) [LA/PER]

1622-1964 Indexes to the Wills, *Admons* & Will Books held by the Nantwich Group of the FHS of Cheshire (*in 2 pts*) [CH/G 41]

1633-1829 List of Wills in Shrewsbury Public Lib *for* Cheshire (Cheshire FHn no 3) [CH/PER]

1650-1660 List of Lancs & Cheshire Admons granted in the PCC 1650-1660; List of Lancs & Cheshire Wills proved in the PCC 1650-1660 (*both* Lancs & Cheshire Rec Soc Procs vol 4) [LA/PER]

1662-1835 Extr from Derbys Wills found in solicitors' old papers (*Dept of Archives, Sheffield Central Lib will index 1662, 1791-1835*) (Genealogists' Mag vol 17) [PER/GEN]

1800-1842 *Index to* Cheshire People in the PCY Wills (*A-G*) (Cheshire FHS Mag vol 12 no 1); *Index to* Cheshire Wills, *Admons & Tuits* proved at the PCY (*A-Z*) (N Cheshire FHn vols 12 & 14) [*both* CH/PER]

Backford see Stoke

Bromborough
see also the Wirral
1578-1620 List of Wills *In* "Reg of Baptisms, Marriages & Burials in the Parish of Bromborough in the County of Cheshire 1600-1726" [CH/R 8]

Bunbury
1515-1814 Extr from Wills & Admons *In* "Monuments at Bunbury Church, Cheshire" [CH/M 3]

Burton
see also the Wirral
1587-1779 Extr from Wills, Admons & Invents *In* "Notes on Burton in Wirral" [CH/L 3]

Chester City
1578-1794 Stray Chester Wills (*index of papers at St Asaph*) (Cheshire Sheaf 3rd ser vol 19) [CH/PER]

Christleton
1588-1641 *Abst of* Wills of Parishioners - Christleton (Cheshire Sheaf 3rd ser vol 31) [CH/PER]

Congleton see Newbold Astbury

Marple
1572-1839 Surnames from Simister Wills (*index for the Manchester & Marple areas*) (Manchester Genealogist vol 16 no 3) [LA/PER]

Newbold Astbury
1558-1810 Cal of Loc Wills at Chester (*including Congleton*) *In* "Newbold Astbury & its Hist" [CH/L 15]

Prestbury
1595-1690 Hidden Names in 17th C Wills; Index of Names in Orme Fam Wills 1595-1690 (N Cheshire FHn vol 20 no 1) [CH/PER]

Shotwick
see also the Wirral
1587-1830 Extr from Wills, Admons & Invents *In* "Notes on Shotwick in the County of Chester" [CH/L 20]

Stockport
1578-1650 Stockport Prob Recs (*abst of wills & invents*); vol 1: 1578-1619 (Lancs & Cheshire Rec Soc Procs vol 124); vol 2: 1620-1650 (Lancs & Cheshire Rec Soc Procs vol 131) [*both* LA/PER]

Stoke
see also the Wirral
1620-1757 Extr from Wills *In* "Monumental & other Inscriptions in the Churches of Stoak, Backford & Thornton-le-Moors in the County of Chester" (*with ms additions*) [CH/M 8]

Thornton-le-Moors see Stoke

Thurstaston
1554-1808 Extr from Wills & Admons *In*

"Thurstaston in Cheshire : an account of the parish, manor & church" [CH/L 23]

The Wirral
see also Bromborough, Burton, Shotwick & Stoke
1564-1698 Extr from Wills & Admons *In* "Wirral Recs of the 17th C" [CH/L 27]

CORNWALL
Pre-1858 Probate Jurisdictions:-
Prerogative Court: Canterbury
Consistory Court: Exeter
Episcopal Principal Registry: Exeter
Archdeaconry Courts: CORNWALL; Totnes
Peculiars, etc: Exeter (Bishop); Exeter (Dean & Chapter); St Buryan

On 5 May 1942 German aircraft bombed the Exeter Probate Registry, destroying all the probate records for Dioceses of Bath & Wells & Exeter (ie Somerset, Devon & parts of Cornwall). Since then, considerable efforts have been made to locate copies & abstracts of the lost material but researchers must be prepared to make do with the calendars & indexes although no index has survived apparently for the Archdeaconry of Totnes.

1426-1837 Cornish Wills & Admons at Somerset House & at Exeter *Episcopal Principal Registry , 1426-1822, 1837 (Glencross Card Index copies made before 1942)* [CO/G 12]
1466-1602 Abst of Wills 1466-1602 *In* "Monumental Brasses of Cornwall" [CO/M 3]
1529-1812 Index to copies of Lost Prob Recs of the Diocese of Exeter in the Library of the Society of Genealogists, London & other sources outside Devon, up to 1812 *(wills, admons, invents, etc)* [DE/G 25]
1559-1799 Cals of Wills & Admons relating to the counties of Devon & Cornwall, proved in the Court of the Principal Registry of the Bishop of Exeter 1559-1799; & of Devon only, proved in the Court of the Archdeaconry of Exeter 1540-1799; all now preserved in the Probate Registry at Exeter;

with Archdeaconry Wills 1653-1660 previously uncalendared (Trans Devon Assn extra vol for *Wills*; pts 1-4 or BRS vol 35) [DE/G 55 or BRS]; Cals of Wills & Admons relating to the counties of Devon & Cornwall, proved in the Court of the Principal Registry of the Bishop of Exeter 1559-1799; & of Devon only, proved in the Court of the Archdeaconry of Exeter 1540-1799; all now preserved in the Probate Registry at Exeter; vols 1 & 2 (*H from 1608*) (Trans Devon Assn extra vol for *Wills*) [DE/G 56 & DE/G 53]; *Corrigenda* (Devon & Cornwall N&Q vol 9) [DE/PER]
1559-1807 Index to Copies of Prob Recs relating to Cornwall in the Library of the Society of Genealogists from lost Prob Recs in the Diocese of Exeter [Apply to Staff]
1579-1646 Cornwall RO - Guide to Cornish Prob Recs [(*transcripts*) CO/G 16 & (*facsimile wills*) Apply to Staff]
1583-1834 Index of Extr from Wills & Admons of Cornish People (*W Country Studies Lib, Exeter: Moger/Murray MSS*) (Cornwall FH J no 49) [CO/PER]
1600-1649 Index to Cornish Prob Recs 1600-1649; pts 1-5: Surnames A-Z, Parishes & Occupations [CO/G 21]
1644-1659 *Abst of* Cornish Commonwealth Wills proved in the PCC 1644-1659 [CO/G 36]; *partially indexed in the GCI*
1653-1655 Cal of Invents 1653-1660 being lists of Invents exhibited in the PCC for the Commonwealth period, for the following counties: ... Cornwall ... [WILLS/PCC]
1668-1804 Devon & Cornwall Wills, not in the Cal of Wills, with Deeds in Exeter City Lib (Devon & Cornwall N&Q vol 14) [DE/PER]
1783-1797 *Abst of* Prob Recs: Cornish Peculiars (*Moger/Murray MSS*) (Cornwall FH J no 48) [CO/PER]
1800-1857 Cornish Prob recs at the Cornwall RO 1800-1857 (Mfc: BRS Mfc ser no 1) [Apply to Staff]
1807-1845 Index to Cornish Testators holding Stock in the Public Funds: *wills in Bank of England*

Regs (Cornwall FH J no 73)
[CO/PER]

1812-1857 Cornwall RO - Index to Cornish Estate Duty & Deanery of St Buryan Wills: *EDO Wills 1812-1857* [CO/G 16]; Cornish Wills (*Index to* copies of Wills made for the Stamp Duty Office 1812-1857) [Apply to Staff]

Gulval *see Madron*

Kerrier *see St Constantine*

Madron
1603-1700 Abst of some 17th C Wills, Invents & Admons held by Cornwall County RO for the Parishes of Madron & Gulval (A-J) [Apply to Staff]

Padstow district
1656-1890 Wills & Deeds - Padstow & District (*surname list*) (Cornwall FH J no 64) [CO/PER]

St Constantine
1570-1808 Index to Wills, Admons & Bonds in the Bodmin Lib *In* "Subsidy Rolls, Muster & Hearth Tax Rolls & Prob Cals of the Parish of St Constantine (Kerrier), Cornwall" (Devon & Cornwall Rec Soc *old ser vol 4*) [DE/PER]

St Winnow
1701-1777 *Index to* St Winnow Wills & Admons in the recs of the Dean & Chapter of Exeter [Topo Docs Coll: Cornwall]

CUMBERLAND
Pre-1858 Probate Jurisdictions:-
Prerogative Courts: Canterbury; York
Consistory Courts: CARLISLE; Chester (1541-1856); Durham; York (Chancery)
Archdeaconry Court: RICHMOND (for Copeland Deanery)
Peculiars, etc: York (Dean & Chapter)

1363-1858 Index & Extr of Cumbrians in Wills & *Admons* proved at the PCC *etc* [CU/G 17]
1405-1558 N Country Wills, being abst of wills relating to the counties of York, Nottingham, Northumberland, Cumberland & Westmorland at Somerset House & Lambeth Palace; *vol 1:* 1383-1558 (Surtees Soc vol 116) [DU/PER]; *see also* N Country Wills (Ancestor no 4) [PER/ANC]

16-18 C Wills, Chancery Proceedings, etc (*unindexed abst in Sherwood MSS*) [Topo Docs Coll: Cumberland]
1515-1746 Cal of the Original Deeds at Tullie House (*will & admon extr*) (Trans Cumberland & Westmorland Antqn & Archl Soc new ser vols 14, 38 & 39) [CU/PER]
1547-1844 Abst of Wills & Invents (*Gibson Coll*) (Archaeologica Aeliana 3rd ser vol 12) [NU/PER]
1558-1604 N Country Wills, being abst of wills relating to the counties of York, Nottingham, Northumberland, Cumberland & Westmorland at Somerset House & Lambeth Palace; vol 2: 1558-1604 (Surtees Soc vol 121) [DU/PER]; *see also* N Country Wills (Ancestor no 4) [PER/ANC]
1571-1856 Notes on Cumbrian Wills & Admons at Carlisle, Lancaster & Somerset House (*Moor MSS*) *In* "Nether Wasdale Parish Regs" [CU/G 33]
1603-1777 *Abst of* Cumberland & Westmorland Wills (Northern Genealogist vols 1 & 3) [PER/NOR]
1633-1855 Strays amongst the Copeland Wills (*will, admon, etc cal*) (Cumbria FHS J nos 79 & 80) [CU/PER]

Alston
1827-1842 Index of Wills, Admons, etc at the PCY (*A-G*) (Cleveland FHS J vol 2 nos 2, 3 & 5) [YK/PER]

Bewcastle
1587-1617 *Abst of* Five Bewcastle Wills 1587-1617 (Trans Cumberland & Westmorland Antqn & Archl Soc new ser vol 67) [CU Tracts or CU/PER]

Garrigill *see Alston*

Grinsdale

1708-1814 Cal of Grinsdale & Kirkandrews Docs 1635-1817 (*will & admon extr*) (Trans Cumberland & Westmorland Antqn & Archl Soc new ser vol 22) [CU/PER]

Irton

1587-1775 Old Statesmen Fams of Irton, Cumberland (*index of testators who died 1587-1775*) (Trans Cumberland & Westmorland Antqn & Archl Soc new ser vol 10) [CU/PER or CU Tracts]

Kirkandrews-upon-Eden *see Grinsdale*

DERBYSHIRE
Pre-1858 Probate Jurisdictions:-
Prerogative Court: Canterbury
Consistory Court: LICHFIELD
Peculiars, etc: Burton on Trent; Dale Abbey; Hartington; **LICHFIELD (Dean and Chapter)**; Peak Forest; Sawley

1436-1538 Extr from Wills 1436-1538 *In* "Derbys Gentry in the 15th C" (Derbys Rec Soc vol 8) [DB/PER]

1474-1920 Wills, *Invents* & Admons deposited with the Dept of Archives, Central Lib, Sheffield (*index*) [Apply to Staff]

16-19 C Oldaker Coll of Wills: *see the note on this coll in the General Collections of Wills, Indexes, etc part of the NATIONAL section*

1573-1837 List of Names mentioned in some Cresswell Fam Wills (Branch News no 21) [DB/PER]

1587-1706 *Abst of* Derbys & Leics Wills (Northern Genealogist vol 1) [PER/NOR]

1662-1835 Extr from Derbys Wills found in solicitors' old papers (*Dept of Archives, Sheffield Central Lib will index 1662, 1791-1835*) (Genealogists' Mag vol 17) [PER/GEN]

Ashover

1508-1650 List of Wills proved at Lichfield etc 1508-1650 *In* "The 'Saints & Sinners' of Ashover"; *ms index* [DB/L 4A & 4B]

Bolsover

1532-1857 Bolsover Wills & *Admons* at Lichfield: an Index [DB/L 31]

Chesterfield

1521-1603 Chesterfield wills & invents in Staffs County RO 1521-1603 (Derbys Rec Soc vol 1) [DB/PER]

Glossop

1472-1860 Index of Prob Docs for the Ancient Parish of Glossop [Apply to Staff]

Norbury

1483-1629 *Extr from* some Norbury Wills *In* "Ancient Parish of Norbury" [DB/L 13]

Pinxton

1539-1600 Coll of *Abst of* Wills & Invents of Pinxton Residents 1539-1600 [DB/L 43]

Wingfield, South

1536-1800 *Index to* S Wingfield Wills (Branch News no 54) [DB/PER]

DEVON
Pre-1858 Probate Jurisdictions:-
Prerogative Court: Canterbury
Consistory Courts: Bristol (Dorset Div - until 1836); Exeter
Episcopal Principal Registry: EXETER
Archdeaconry Courts: BARNSTAPLE; Cornwall; Dorset (until 1836); **EXETER; TOTNES**
Peculiars, etc: Exeter (Bishop); Exeter (Dean); Exeter (Dean & Chapter); Uffculme; Woodbury
Manorial Courts: Cockington; Templeton
Civil Courts: Exeter (Mayor); Exeter (Orphans)

On 5 May 1942 German aircraft bombed the Exeter Probate Registry, destroying all the probate records for Dioceses of Bath & Wells & Exeter (ie Somerset, Devon & parts of Cornwall). Since then, considerable efforts have been made to locate copies & abstracts of the lost material but researchers must be prepared to make do with the calendars & indexes although no index has survived apparently for the Archdeaconry of Totnes.

1414-1878 Devon Wills & *Admons*: a coll of

annotated testmtry abst together with the family history & genealogy of many of the most ancient gentle houses of the W of England (*Worthy MSS*) [Apply to Staff]

1529-1812 Index to copies of Lost Prob Recs of the Diocese of Exeter in the Library of the Society of Genealogists, London & other sources outside Devon, up to 1812 (*wills, admons, invents, etc*) [DE/G 25]

1539-1834 Lost Westcountry Wills in the Fothergill Coll at the Society of Genealogists (*Devon & Somerset will & admon list*) (Devon FHn no 6) [DE/PER]

1540-1799 Cals of Wills & Admons relating to the counties of Devon & Cornwall, proved in the Court of the Principal Registry of the Bishop of Exeter 1559-1799; & of Devon only, proved in the Court of the Archdeaconry of Exeter 1540-1799; all now preserved in the Probate Registry at Exeter; *with* Archdeaconry Wills 1653-1660 previously uncalendared (Trans Devon Assn extra vol for *Wills*; pts 1-4 or BRS vol 35) [DE/G 55 or BRS]; Cals of Wills & Admons relating to the counties of Devon & Cornwall, proved in the Court of the Principal Registry of the Bishop of Exeter 1559-1799; & of Devon only, proved in the Court of the Archdeaconry of Exeter 1540-1799; all now preserved in the Probate Registry at Exeter; vols 1 & 2 (*H from 1608*) (Trans Devon Assn extra vol for *Wills*) [DE/G 56 & DE/G 53]; *Corrigenda* (Devon & Cornwall N&Q vol 9) [DE/PER]

1547-1834 Lost W Country Wills in the Fothergill Colls at the Society of Genealogists (*Devon & Somerset will & admon index*) (Devon FHn no 6) [DE/PER]; Devon Will, *Admon & Inventory* Abst from the Fothergill Coll at the Society of Genealogists [DE/G 23]

1606-1782 Fam Notes (*Holworthy's Devon will & invent abst*) [FH/MISC]

1653-1655 Cal of Invents 1653-1660 being lists of Invents exhibited in the PCC for the Commonwealth period, for the following counties: ... Devon ... [WILLS/PCC]

1668-1804 Devon & Cornwall Wills, not in the Cal of Wills, with Deeds in Exeter City Lib (Devon & Cornwall N&Q vol 14) [DE/PER]

1769-1849 Devon Wills; Abst of 8 Devon Wills 1769-1849 [DE/G 24]

1812-1857 Index to the EDO Copy Wills 1812-1857 at the Devon County RO, Exeter [Apply to Staff]

Axminster
1415-1582 *Index to* PCC Wills from 1383 [Topo Docs Coll: Devon]

Barnstaple Town
1539-1733 List of Original Wills *In* "Reprint of the Barnstaple Recs vol 2" [DE/L 4]; *indexed In* Devon Tracts vol 1 [DE/G 1]

Membury
1415-1582 *Index to* PCC Wills from 1383 [Topo Docs Coll: Devon]

Moretonhampstead
1796-1811 Moretonhampstead: Death Duty Reg Wills & Admons 1796-1811 & others *in the Exeter Diocesan Registry* (*index*) [DE/L 63]

Pilton
1460-1853 Abst of a selection of Wills & Admons *In* "Pilton; its past & its people" [DE/L 68]

1489-1555 *Index to* PCC Wills from 1383 [Topo Docs Coll: Devon]

DORSET
Pre-1858 Probate Jurisdictions:-
Prerogative Court: Canterbury
Consistory Courts: Bristol (Dorset Div - from 1542); Sarum
Archdeaconry Courts: DORSET; Exeter
Peculiars, etc: Burton Bradstock; Great Canford & Poole; Chardstock & Wambrook; Corfe Castle; Fordington & Writhington; Gillingham; Lyme Regis & Halstock; Milton Abbas; Netherbury in Ecclesia; Preston; Sarum (Dean); Sarum (Dean & Chapter); Stratton; Sturminster Marshall; Wimborne Minster; Yetminster & Grimston
Manorial Court: Frampton
Civil Courts: Bridport; Dorchester (Dorset);

Lyme Regis (Mayor); Poole (Mayor); Shaftesbury; Weymouth

Note: *most parishes in the county were transferred to the Diocese of Sarum in 1836 but probate jurisdiction seems to have remained unchanged*

1287-1857 Cal of Wills & Admons relating to the County of Dorset preserved in the Probate Registry at Blandford & among the Ecclesiastical Recs of Wimborne Minster to 1857 (*Fry MSS*) [Apply to Staff]

1289-1810 *Lists of* Wills relating to Dorset Folk; pt 1: Wills .. mentioned in the PRO which cannot be traced in the Probate Courts (*1289-1711*); pt 2: Original & Copies of proved Wills in private possession which cannot be traced in Probate Courts of PCC & Blandford to which they really relate (*1546-1810*) (Somerset & Dorset N&Q vol 33) [SO/PER]

1314-1915 Abst of Wills of Dorset Folk from the PCC & various courts with indexes of testators & places (*Fry MSS in 7 pts*) [DO/G 29-35]

1359-1592 Cal of Lambeth Wills; Somerset & Dorset References at Lambeth (Somerset & Dorset N&Q vol 8) [SO/PER]

1374-1866 Dorset Wills 2: Cal of Wills & Admons relating to Dorset in the Courts of Sarum (BRS vol 53) [BRS]

1555-1810 *Index to* Testmtry Papers at Salisbury; pt 1: Berks, Dorset & Uffculme Wills, Admons, Invents, etc preserved at Sarum (Genealogists' Mag vol 5) [PER/GEN or WL/G 52]

1559-1725 Dorset Admon *Acts in the PCC* (Somerset & Dorset N&Q vols 2-6) [SO/PER]

1568-1823 Dorset Wills 1: Cal of Wills & Admons relating to the County of Dorset, proved in the Consistory Court (Dorset Div) of the late Diocese of Bristol 1681-1792, in the Archdeaconry Court of Dorset 1568-1792 & in the several peculiars 1660-1799 (BRS vol 22) [BRS]

1569-1733 Some Bequests to Dorset Churches (*extr 1569-1733*) *with*

Some Bequests to Dorset Parishes, Schools, etc (*extr 1611-1699*) (Somerset & Dorset N&Q vols 5 & 10) [SO/PER]

1636-1714 List of Windsor *CT, USA* Invents *In* appx 2 of "Dorset Pilgrims; the Story of W Country Pilgrims to New England in the 17th C" [US/NE/G 21]

1639-1699 Two 17th C Dorset Invents (*1639 & 1699*) (Dorset Rec Soc Pubs no 5) [DO/PER]

1653-1655 Cal of Invents 1653-1660 being lists of Invents exhibited in the PCC for the Commonwealth period, for the following counties: ... Dorset ... [WILLS/PCC]

1653-1759 *Abst of* some Dorset Wills at Somerset House (*1653-1656, 1728-1735, 1749-1750, 1755-1759*) (N&Q vols 169, 171, 177-179 & 192) [N&Q]; Some Dorset Wills at Somerset House reprinted from N&Q 1939-1940 (*1728-1731 & 1758-1759*) [DO/G 38]

1653-1837 Cal of Wills & Admons relating to Dorset in the Courts of Sarum; *includes: admons 1727-1729 & 1750-1784, invents 1686-1702 & guardshp bonds 1683-1803, original unproved wills 1680-1837, proved wills (originals missing) 1649-1762, copy wills (originals elsewhere) 1653-1817 & copies of wills (proved elsewhere) 1728-1788* (BRS vol 53) [BRS]

1701-1820 Cal of Dorset Wills proved in the PCC (at Somerset House); vol 2: 1701-1820 (*Fry MSS*) [Apply to Staff]

1726-1821 Dorset Admons from the Principal Probate Court 1 Jan 1726-31 Dec 1821; vol 2 [DO/G 52]

1821-1837 Index to Dorset Wills proved in the PCC; pt 1: 1821-1837 [Apply to Staff]

1821-1858 Index to Dorset Wills & Admons proved in the PCC 1821-1858 [DO/G 49]

Ashmore
1497-1740 Extr from Some Wills *In* "Ashmore, County Dorset; A Hist of the Parish" [DO/R 59]

Dorchester Town
1419-1845 List of Wills, Admons & Invents *In* "Guide to the Materials for Loc Hist in the Muniment Room of the Dorset County Museum" (*1419, 1695-1845*) [DO Tracts]

1577-1905 Cal of Dorset Wills, Admons & Invents *in* the Dorset Nat Hist & Antqn Soc *Muniment Room* [DO/G 36]

Durweston *see Stourpaine*

Fordington Town
1567-1779 List of Fordington Wills 1567-1779 *In* "Hist of Fordington" [DO/L 9]

Portland
1532-1634 Extr from Old Wills 1532-1634 *In* "Island & Royal Manor of Portland" [DO Tracts]

Stourpaine
1604-1799 Wills & Admons in the Peculiar Court of the Dean & Chapter of Sarum (relating to Stour Paine & Durweston) 1604-1799, now preserved at Somerset House, London *with invents* (BRS vol 53) [BRS]

Wambrook
1551-1622 *Index to* PCC Wills from 1383 [Topo Docs Coll: Dorset]

DURHAM
Pre-1858 Probate Jurisdictions:-
Prerogative Court: Canterbury, York
Consistory Courts DURHAM; York (Chancery)
Peculiars, etc: Craike (until 1837); Durham (Dean & Chapter); York (Dean & Chapter); *see also Durham (Chancery)*

1405-1558 N Country Wills, being abst of wills relating to the counties of York, Nottingham, Northumberland, Cumberland & Westmorland at Somerset House & Lambeth Palace (*includes Durham*); *vol 1:* 1383-1558 (Surtees Soc vol 116) [DU/PER]; *see also* N Country Wills (Ancestor no 4) [PER/ANC]

1540-1599 Index of Wills, etc in the Probate Registry, Durham & from other sources (Newcastle Rec Committee Pubs vol 8) [DU/G 27]

1547-1844 Abst of Wills & Invents (*Gibson Coll*) (Archaeologica Aeliana 3rd ser vol 12) [NU/PER]

1558-1604 N Country Wills, being abst of wills relating to the counties of York, Nottingham, Northumberland, Cumberland & Westmorland at Somerset House & Lambeth Palace(*includes Durham*); vol 2: 1558-1604 (Surtees Soc vol 121) [DU/PER]; *see also* N Country Wills (Ancestor no 4) [PER/ANC]

1651-1660 *Index to* Durham & Northumberland Wills at Somerset House (*Dale MSS*) [Apply to Staff]

1699-1857 Wills & Admons etc: listings taken from cals of the old Diocese of York & the Diocese of Lincoln (with certain additions from Durham) (*index BUR-WRI*) (Fam Hist vols 2 & 3) [PER/FAM]

1827-1842 Index of Wills, Admons, etc at the PCY (*A-G*) (Cleveland FHS J vol 2 nos 2, 3 & 5) [YK/PER]

Barnard Castle
1584-1785 *Abst of* Barnard Castle Wills 1584-1785 (Teesdale Soc Procs no 1) [DU/PER]

Darlington
1600-1625 *Abst of* Darlington Wills; vol 1: 1600-1625 (Surtees Soc vol 201) [DU/PER]

Startforth
1611-1826 *Index to* Startforth Wills, *Admons, Invents & Bonds* in the Archdeaconry of Richmond (Teesdale Soc Procs no 5) [DU/PER]

Stockton-on-Tees
see also Teesdale
1560-1588 *Extr from* Singular Wills & Invents *In* "Loc Recs of Stockton" [DU/L 19]

Teesdale
see also Stockton-on-Tees
1605-1668 *Abst of* Seven Teesdale Wills & Admons 1605-1668 (Teesdale

Soc Procs no 14) [DU/PER]

Wolsingham
1683-1766   Abst of Wills 1683-1766 *In* "Recs of Wolsingham" [DU/L 14]

ESSEX
Pre-1858 Probate Jurisdictions:-
Prerogative Court: Canterbury
Consistory Courts: London; Norwich
Commissary Courts: LONDON (Essex and Herts Div); London (London Div)
Archdeaconry Courts: COLCHESTER; ESSEX; MIDDLESEX (Essex and Herts Div); Sudbury; Suffolk
Peculiars, etc: Bocking; Creshall; Good Easter; Hornchurch; London (Dean & Chapter of St Paul's); Maldon; Newport; The Sokens (until 1851); Westminster (Abbot/Dean & Chapter); Writtle with Roxwell (until 1851)
Note: *in 1846 most parishes in the county were transferred to the Diocese of Rochester but probate jurisdiction seems to have remained unchanged*

1278-1349   Essex References in Old Wills at the Court of Husting (*abst*) (Essex Review vol 2 no 7) [ES/PER]
1511-1666   *Index to* Essex & Herts Wills at Chelmsford (*Tachell Coll*) [Topo Docs Coll: Essex]
1552-1671   Bequests relating to Essex extracted from Cals of Wills proved & enrolled in the Court of Husting, London (Trans Essex Archl Soc vols 13 & 14) [ES/PER]
1558-1603   Elizabethan Life; vol 3: Home, Work & Land from Essex Wills & Sessions & Manorial Recs (*will & invent extr*) (Essex RO Pub no 69) [ES/PER]; vol 4: *Abst of* Wills of Essex Gentry & Merchants proved in the PCC (Essex RO Pub no 71) [ES/G 34]; vol 5: *Abst of* Wills of Essex Gentry, *Merchants* & Yeomen preserved in the Essex RO (Essex RO Pub no 75) [ES/G 35]; *Abst of* Elizabethan Wills of SW Essex [ES/G 63]
1558-1603   *Abst of* Essex Wills 1558-1603; pt 1: Wills proved in the Archdeaconry of Essex, the Archdeaconry of Colchester &

the Archdeaconry of Middx (Essex Div); vol 1: 1558-1565 (Nat Geneal Soc Spec Pub no 51); vol 2: 1565-1571 (NEHG Soc *Spec Pub*); vol 3: 1571-1577 (*with additions for 1559-1571*) (NEHG Soc *Spec Pub*); vol 4: 1577-1584 (*with unregistered wills 1581-1588*) (Essex RO Pub no 96); vol 5: 1583-1592 (Essex RO Pub no 101); vol 6: 1591-1597 (Essex RO Pub no 114); vol 7: 1597-1603 (Essex RO Pub no 107); pt 2: Wills proved in the Bishop of London's Commissary Court; vol 8: 1558-1569 (*original & registered wills*) (Essex RO Pub no 124); vol 9: 1569-1578 (*original wills*) (Essex RO Pub no 127); vol 10: 1578-1588 (Essex RO Pub no 129) [*all* ES/PER]; *vols 11-12 (1589-1603) are on order*
1576-1689   *Abst of* Essex Wills (E Anglian vols 1 & 2) [NF/PER]
1580-1843   Abst of Wills of Essex Catholic Interest (Essex Recusant vols 15-17 & 19) [ES/PER]

Bobbingworth
1588-1884   Sepulchral Memorials of Bobbingworth - MI in Church & Churchyard, Pedigrees, Wills, Wood-cuts of Arms, etc *In* "List of Parish Regs & other Geneal Works" (*surname list*) (*Crisp*) [UK/R]

Chelmsford
1614-1642   Extr from Some Chelmsford Wills *In* "The Sleepers & the Shadows vol 2" (Essex RO Pub no 128) [ES/PER]

Chigwell
1518-1674   *Abst of* old Chigwell Wills (*1518-1538, 1550-1674*) (Trans Essex Archl Soc vols 10 & 11) [ES/PER]

Chingford
1283-1756   Details of Wills 1283-1756 *In* "Your Chingford Ancestors" [ES Tracts]

Colchester Town
1565-1769   Regs of the Baptisms in the Dutch Church at Colchester

(*index of "Dutch" testators'
registered wills proved 1565-
1769 & admons granted 1691-
1769 in various Essex courts with
unregistered wills 1619-1640*)
(Huguenot Soc Pubs Qto ser vol
12) [HUG/PER]

Dagenham
1430-1531   Extr from Some Wills (*1430-
1476, 1531*) *In* "Book of
Dagenham" [ES/L 67]
1533-1696   Abst of Wills 1533-1696 *In* appx
B to "Hist of Dagenham in the
County of Essex" [ES/L 10]

Fingringhoe
1401-1550   *Abst of* Fingringhoe Wills 1400-
1550 (*1401, 1501-1550*) (Trans
Essex Archl Soc vol 20)
[ES/PER, (*offprint*) ES/L 51 or (*In*
"Essex Tracts vol 1") ES/G 4]

Gestingthorpe
1385-1557   Extr from Wills 1385-1557 *In*
"Notes on the Parish of
Gestingthorpe" [ES/L 43]

Harlow
1439-1656   *Index to* PCC Wills from 1383
[Topo Docs Coll: Essex]

Henny, Great
1522-1654   *Index to* PCC Wills from 1383
[Topo Docs Coll: Essex]

Pebmarsh
1398-1558   List of Wills of Pebmarsh
Testators 1398-1558 *In*
"Pebmarsh Church, Essex" [ES/L
26]
1401-1655   *Index to* PCC Wills from 1383
[Topo Docs Coll: Essex]

Pleshey
1460-1656   *Index to* PCC Wills from 1383
[Topo Docs Coll: Essex]

Ramsden Belhouse
1419-1779   Extr from Wills of Stock Harvard
& Ramsden Belhouse *In* "Rectors
of Two Essex Parishes & their
Times" [ES/L 33]
1431-1733   Some Essex Wills (*extr*) (Essex
Review vol 56 no 224) [ES/PER]

Stock
1431-1733   Some Essex Wills (*extr*) (Essex
Review vol 56 no 224) [ES/PER]
1504-1779   Extr from Wills of Stock Harvard
& Ramsden Belhouse *In* "Rectors
of Two Essex Parishes & their
Times" [ES/L 33]

Terling
1489-1673   Abst of Wills 1489-1673 *In* "Hist
Notes & Recs of the Parish of
Terling, Essex" [ES/L 57]
1620-1717   List of Wills *In* pt 2 of "Does your
ancestor come from Terling?"
(Essex FHn nos 38) [ES/PER]

Thaxted
1546-1829   Cal of Thaxted Wills at Somerset
House (*with abst 1555-1575*) *In*
"Thaxted Notes" [ES/L 37]

Thorpe-le-Soken
1247-1847   Extr from Manorial Wills *In* "Hist
of Thorpe-le-Soken to the year
1890" [ES/L 39]

Walthamstow
1335-1559   Abst of Wills relating to
Walthamstow, County Essex
1335-1559 (Walthamstow Antqn
Soc Official Pub no 9) [ES/L 44
or (*In* "Walthamstow Regs") ES/R
83]

GLOUCESTERSHIRE
including the City of Bristol
Pre-1858 Probate Jurisdictions:-
Prerogative Court: Canterbury
**Consistory Courts: BRISTOL (City and
Deanery Div); GLOUCESTER** (from 1541);
Hereford; Wells; Worcester (until 1541)
Peculiars, etc: Bibury; Bishops Cleeve (until
1796); Child's Wickham; Withington
Manorial Court: Hawkesbury
Civil Courts: Bristol (Orphans); Gloucester
(Mayor)

1270-1810   References to Wills & *Invents* in
Gloucester Public Lib *In*
"Catalogue of the Glos Coll"
[GL/G 5]
1459-1773   Glos Wills (*misc abst*) (Glos N&Q
vols 5, 6 & 10) [GL/PER]
1473-1844   *Lists of Stray* Wills & *Invents in
parochial recs In* "Guide to the
Parish Recs of the City of Bristol

& the County of Gloucester"
(Pubs Bristol & Glos Archl Soc
Rec Sectn vol 5) [GL/R 14]

16-19 C Oldaker Coll of Wills: *see the note on this coll in the General Collections of Wills, Indexes, etc part of the NATIONAL section*

1544-1577 Some Ecclesiastical Wills (*absts for abbots & priors of suppressed Glos monasteries 1544-1545, 1577*) (Trans Bristol & Glos Rec Soc vols 49 & 52) [GL/PER]

1652-1867 List of Glos Wills in Coleman's 'Catalogue of 1000 Wills' (Glos N&Q vol 2) [GL/PER]

1653-1655 Cal of Invents 1653-1660 being lists of Invents exhibited in the PCC for the Commonwealth period, for the following counties: ... Glos ... [WILLS/PCC]

1689-1869 Testmtry Papers (*1689-1869*) *In* "Glos RO - Catalogue of Docs deposited by the Society of Genealogists" [GL/G 19]

Bagendon
1427-1787 *List of* Testators *In* "Hist of Bagendon" [GL/L 1]

Berkeley
1316-1626 Extr from Wills & Inquisitiones post mortem 1316-1626 *In* "Descriptive Catalogue of the Charters & Muniments in the possession of the Rt Hon Lord Fitzhardinge at Berkeley Castle" [GL/L 2]

Bisley
1415-1800 Lists of the Residents in the Parish of Bisley whose names *appear in* Wills proved in the PCC & *in* Wills proved in the Consistory Court of the Bishop of Gloucester 1415-1800 *In* "Hist Recs of Bisley with Lypiatt, Glos" [GL/L 3]

Bristol City
1382-1597 Wadley's Bristol Wills (*abst*); vol 1: 1382-1407; vol 2: 1407-1555; vol 3: 1564-1597 [Apply to Staff]

1473-1844 *Lists of Stray* Wills & Invents *in parochial recs In* "Guide to the Parish Recs of the City of Bristol & the County of Gloucester" (Pubs Bristol & Glos Archl Soc

Rec Sectn vol 5) [GL/R 14]

1546-1603 Tudor Wills proved in Bristol 1546-1603 (*abst*) (Bristol Rec Soc Pubs vol 44) [GL/PER]

1609-1668 Abst of Wills & Invents *In* "Merchants & Merchandise in 17th C Bristol" (Bristol Rec Soc Pubs vol 19) [GL/PER]

1793-1858 Index to Bristol Wills 1793-1858 [Apply to Staff]

Brockthrop
1598-1611 Brockthrop Wills (*abst*) (Glos N&Q vol 4) [GL/PER]

Cirencester
1541-1548 Wills of Cirencester & District 1541-1548 (*abst*) [GL/L 57]

Clifton
1609-1671 Clifton & Westbury Invents 1609-1671 (*abst*) [GL/L 46]

Elberton
1549-1670 Some Elberton & Littleton-on-Severn Wills registered in the PCC & filed at Somerset House (*index & extr*) (*Myer*) [Apply to Staff]

Frampton Cotterell
1539-1834 Goods & Chattels of our Forefathers; Frampton Cotterell & District Prob Invents 1539-1834 (*abst*) [GL/L 26]

Littleton-on-Severn *see Elberton*

Mangotsfield
1611-1760 Prob Invents for the Parish of Mangotsfield 1611-1670 (*index & extr*) (Bristol & Avon FHS J no 3) [GL/PER]

Pebworth
1510-1558 Abst of Wills of the Parish of Pebworth 1510-1558 (Trans Bristol & Glos Rec Soc vol 4) [GL/PER]

Standish
1528-1721 *Extr from* Wills *In* "Hist of Standish, Glos" [GL/L 35]

Westbury-on-Trym *see Clifton*

Wotton-under-Edge

1547-1702 *Extr from* Wills & Invents *In* "Wotton-under-Edge; men & affairs of a Cotswold wool town" [GL/L 45 or GL/L 59]

HAMPSHIRE

including the Isle of Wight ("IoW")

Pre-1858 Probate Jurisdictions:-

Prerogative Court: Canterbury

Consistory Court: Winchester

Archdeaconry Court: WINCHESTER

Peculiars, etc: Alverstoke; Old Alresford with New Alresford & Medstead; N Baddesley; Baughurst; Binstead; Bishops Waltham; Bishopstoke; Brighstone; Brixton; Burghclere with Newton; Calbourne; Cheriton with Kilmeston & Tichbourne; Chilbolton; Chilcomb; Compton; Crawley with Hunton; Droxford; Easton; Exton; Fareham; Fawley with Exbury; Hambledon; Hannington; Havant; Highclere; Houghton; Hursley with Otterbourne; Hurstbourne & Burbage; Hurstbourne Priors with St Mary Bourne; Littleton; E Meon with Froxfield & Steep; W Meon with Privett; Meonstoke with Soberton; Michelmersh; Morestead; Overton with Tadley; Ovington; Ringwood with Harbridge; St Mary Extra & S Stoneham with Weston; Sarum (Dean & Chapter); Southampton (St Mary); Twyford with Owslebury; Upham with Durley; N Waltham; Winchester (St Cross); Whitchurch; Winnall; Wonston; E Woodhay with Ashmansworth

Civil Courts: Portsmouth; Southampton

1548-1558 Hants Wills; Testamenta Vetusta 1548-1558 (*Baigent's abst*) [HA/G 72]

1571-1858 Hants RO - Index to Hants Wills, *Admons & Invents* 1571-1858: Indexes by name, occupation & place (Mfc) [Apply to Staff]

1603-1674 Cal of Wills proved in the Prerogative & Peculiar Courts of Winchester (*1603, 1644-1674*) with other Prob Docs (*1618-1632*) [HA/G 62]

1653-1660 Cal of Invents 1653-1660 being lists of Invents exhibited in the PCC for the Commonwealth period, for the following counties: ... Southants ... [WILLS/PCC]

1671-1734 Hants Wills in *the* PCC from the Prob Act Books 1671-1734 Indexed [HA/G 55]

Basingstoke

1451-1659 *Extr from* Wills of Basingstoke Worthies 1451-1659 *In* "Hist of the Ancient Town & Manor of Basingstoke ..." [HA/L 6]

Baughurst

1583-1720 Abst of Wills 1583-1720 *In* "Parish Regs of Baughurst 1678-1837" [HA/R 40]

Compton

1484-1684 Extr from Wills & Invents *In* "Compton near Winchester; being an Enquiry into the Hist of a Hants Parish" [HA/L 64]

Crondall

1490-1656 Index to PCC Wills from 1383 [Topo Docs Coll: Hants]

Holdenhurst

1560-1674 *Extr from* Wills & Invents 1560-1764 *In* appx to "Holdenhurst; mother of Bournemouth" [HA/L 24]

Micheldever

1500-1795 *Extr from* Loc Wills *In* "Hist of Micheldever" [HA/L 57]

Newchurch

1660-1699 Index to Newchurch (IoW) Prob Invents 1660-1699 (IoW FHS Mag no 23) [HA/PER]

Newport Town

1540-1750 *List of* Former Inhabitants of Newport, IoW from the Archdeacon's Wills at Winchester [Topo Docs Coll: Hants]

Sutton, Long

1502-1856 A Long Sutton Miscellany including a study of Wills 1502-1856 & Prob Invents 1558-1709 from the parishes of Long Sutton & Well, Hants [HA/L 44]

Winchester College

1290-1761 Index of Wills & *Executors' Accounts* 1290-1761 *In* "Winchester College Muniments" (*offprint from* Archives vol 5 no 28) [HA Tracts]

1308-1541 HMC National Reg of Archives - Winchester College Archives

Section: 'Pertinentia ad Alio' from
descriptive list (will cal) [Apply to
Staff]

HEREFORDSHIRE
Pre-1858 Probate Jurisdictions:-
Prerogative Court: Canterbury
Consistory Courts: HEREFORD; St Davids
Archdeaconry Court: Brecon
Peculiars, etc: Hereford (Dean); Little
Hereford with Ashford Carbonell; Upper
Bullinghope; Moreton-upon-Lugg
Civil Court: Hereford (Mayor)

1517-1598 Some 16th C Wills from NW
Herefds (*Faraday's abst*) [HR/G
21]
1534-1822 Lists of Pewterers' Invents (*to
1747*) & of Pewterers' Wills &
Letters of Admon *In* "Provincial
Pewterers: a Study of the Craft in
the W Midlands & Wales"
[PR/PEW]
1750-1800 PCC Herefds Wills (*H-M*) [Topo
Docs Coll: Herefds]

HERTFORDSHIRE
Pre-1858 Probate Jurisdictions:-
Prerogative Court: Canterbury
Consistory Courts: Lincoln; London; Ely
(from 1837)
Commissary Court: LONDON (Essex and
Herts)
Archdeaconry Court: HUNTINGDON
(including Hitchin Div from c1566);
MIDDLESEX (Essex and Herts); ST
ALBANS
Peculiars, etc: London (Dean & Chapter of St
Paul's)
Note: *in 1846 most parishes in the county
were transferred to the Diocese of
Rochester but probate jurisdiction seems to
have remained unchanged*

1349-1672 Some Notes on Herts & Middx
Wills (*extr & invents*)
(Blackmansbury vol 2 nos 1-3 &
vol 3 no 1) [PER/BLA]
1381-1432 Abst of Herts Wills of Villeins &
Copyholders *In* "Studies in
Manorial Hist" [TB/LH]
1548-1619 *Index to* Essex & Herts Wills at
Chelmsford (*Tachell Coll*) [Topo
Docs Coll: Essex]

1597-1848 Abst of Wills, Invents &
Executorship Accounts 1597-
1848 *In* Herts RO - Schedule of
Deeds deposited on permanent
loan by the Society of
Genealogists [HT/G 14]
1601-1652 Abst of Herts Wills at the Probate
Registry, Lincoln (*Peck MSS*) [Mf
922]; BRS vol 41 *indexes these
MSS* [BRS]
1610-1620 Abst of Herts Wills in Reg
"Harmer" *in the Consistory Court
of the Bishop of London* (Herts
Genealogist & Antiquary vol 3)
[HT/PER
1621-1628 Abst of Herts Wills in Reg
"Bellamy" *in the Consistory Court
of the Bishop of London* (Herts
Genealogist & Antiquary vol 3)
[HT/PER]

Barley
1592-1664 John Norden's Survey of Barley,
Herts 1593-1603 (*will extr*)
(Cambridge Antqn Rec Soc vol 2)
[CA/PER]

Harpenden *see Wheathampstead*

Hitchin
1464-1869 *Extr from* Wills & Testmts *In* "Hist
of Hitchin; vols 1 & 2" [HT/L 20-
21]

King's Langley
1498-1659 Life & Death in King's Langley:
Abst of Wills & Invents 1498-
1659 [HT/L 24]

Sandridge
1603-1775 Docs, *Abst of* Wills, Leases etc *in
Sandridge In* "The Leonard
Series; pt 4" [HT/L 64]

Sarratt
1435-1832 Pots, Platters & Ploughs: *Abst of*
Sarratt Wills & Invents 1435-
1832 [HT/L 30]

Wheathampstead
1524-1796 List of Loc Inhabitants with Info
about their Wills & Invents; pt 1:
1524-1654 *In* appx 3 to
"Wheathampstead & Harpenden
no 2: New Men & a New Society:
the 16th & 17th C" [HT Tracts]; pt
2: 1651-1796 *In* appx 8 to

"Wheathampstead & Harpenden *no 4: The Age of Independence*" [HT/L 39]

HUNTINGDONSHIRE
Pre-1858 Probate Jurisdictions:-
Prerogative Court: Canterbury
Consistory Courts: Ely (from 1837); Lincoln; Peterborough
Archdeaconry Court: Ely (from 1837); HUNTINGDON; Northampton
Peculiars, etc: Brampton; Buckden; Leighton Bromswold; Lincoln (Dean & Chapter - until 1834); Longstow

1653-1660   Cal of Invents 1653-1660 being lists of Invents exhibited in the PCC for the Commonwealth period, for the following counties: ... Hunts ... [WILLS/PCC]

Bluntisham cum Earith
1429-1725   *Extr from* Wills & Invents of Bluntisham & Earith *In* appx to "Bluntisham-cum-Earith; Recs of a Fenland Parish" [HU/L 1]

Earith *see Bluntisham*

KENT
Pre-1858 Probate Jurisdictions:-
Prerogative Court: Canterbury
Consistory Courts: CANTERBURY; London (from 1846); ROCHESTER
Commissary-General's Court: Canterbury
Archdeaconry Courts: CANTERBURY; ROCHESTER
Peculiars, etc: Canterbury (Prior/Dean & Chapter); Cliffe (until 1846); SHOREHAM; Wingham (until 1547)
Note: *in 1841 some deaneries were formed into the Archdeaconry of Maidstone (& more parishes were added in 1846) but probate jurisdiction seems to have remained unchanged*

1278-1441   *Abst of* some Early Kentish Wills (Archaeologica Cantiana vol 46) [KE/PER]
1327-1589   Catalogue of MSS in Lambeth Palace Lib - MSS 1222-1860: Kentish Wills (*index: Jenkins MS 1614*) [TB/BIB]
1384-1559   Cal of Wills relating to the County of Kent proved in the PCC 1384-1559 (Lewisham Antqn Soc Pubs vol 3) [KE/G 72]

15-16 C   Testamenta Cantiana; extr from 15th & 16th C Wills relating to church building & topography (*in 2 pts: E & W Kent*) (Testamenta Cantiana - *Archaeologica Cantiana extra vol for* 1907) [KE/PER]
1415-1442   *Abst of* some 15th C Wills *of Kentish testators (from Canterbury & York Soc vol 42)* (Archaeologica Cantiana vol 55) [KE/PER]
1440-1561   List of Clerks' Wills 1440-1561 *In* appx to "Kentish Wills ..." [KE/G 66]
1528-1797   List of Executorship Papers 1528-1797 *In* "Deeds & Cognate Docs relating to various Parishes in Kent deposited by the Society of Genealogists *in* Kent Archives Office (U1542)" [KE Tracts]
1557-1560   Testamenta Cantiana; extr from Wills of Kentish folk proved in the PCC (Misc Gen et Her 3rd ser vol 1) [PER/MIS]
1559-1603   Kentish Admons (*PCC*); pt 1: 1559-1603 (Archaeologica Cantiana vol 18) [KE/PER]
1604-1649   Kentish Admons (*PCC*); pt 2: 1604-1649 (Archaeologica Cantiana vol 20) [KE/PER]
1658-1659   Cal of Invents 1653-1660 being lists of Invents exhibited in the PCC for the Commonwealth period, for the following counties: ... Kent ... [WILLS/PCC]
1687-1766   *List of* some E Kent Invents (Kent FHS J vol 6 no 12) [KE/PER]

Appledore
1593-1669   Extr from Wills *In* "Hist of Appledore" [KE/L 118]

Ash
1470-1545   *Abst of* Ash Wills; pts 1-4 (Archaeologica Cantiana vols 34-37) [KE/PER]

Ashford
1461-1558   Ashford Wills; being abst of wills of residents in the town of Ashford, Kent 1461-1558 [KE/L 3]; *commentary* (Archaeologica Cantiana vol 51) [KE/PER]

Barham
1374-1444 *Abst of Wills In* appx to "Brasses in Barham Church" (Archaeologica Cantiana vol 40) [KE/PER]

Benenden
see also Weald of E Kent
1508-1511 *Extr from* Wills of Parishioners *In* "Parish of Benenden, Kent; its monuments, vicars & persons of note" [KE/M 35]

Bethersden *see Weald of E Kent*

Biddenden *see Weald of E Kent*

Bromley
1363-1900 Extr from Some Wills *In* "Bromley, Kent from the earliest times to the present century" (1970 ed) [KE/L 117]

Canterbury City
1586-1704 *Abst of Wills In* "Regs of the Walloon or Strangers' Church in Canterbury" (Huguenot Soc Pubs Qto ser vol 5) [HUG/PER]

Charlton
1459-1631 Extr from Wills of Former Inhabitants of Charlton, proved at Rochester, with Wills from the PCC *In* "Hasted's Hist of Kent ... corrected & enlarged ...; pt 1: Hundred of Blackheath" [KE Folio]

Cheriton
1831-1858 Extr from the Index to Archdeaconry Wills 1712-1858 (Folkestone FH J vol 3) [KE/PER]

Chislet
1636-1749 *Abst of* Wills of Parishioners *In* "Parish of Chislet; its monuments, vicars & parish officers" [KE/M 39]

Cobham
1597-1702 *Abst of* Six Wills relating to Cobham Hall (Archaeologica Cantiana vol 11) [KE/PER]; *also In* "Kentish Archaeology vol 2" [Apply to Staff]

Cowden
1456-1681 *Abst of* Wills *In* "Hist of Cowden" [KE/L 22]

Cranbrook
1396-1640 Abst of Cranbrook Wills proved in the Diocesan Courts of Canterbury & now preserved in the Kent Archives Office, Maidstone, Kent 1396-1640 [KE/L 85]

Dartford
1407-1809 Coll & Abst of all the material Deeds, Wills, Leases & Legal Docs relating to the several Donations & Benefactions to the Church & Poor of the Parish of Dartford, in Kent, & of the Spittal Alms-houses etc [KE/L 123]

Deptford
1471-1701 Extr from Wills of Former Inhabitants of Deptford, proved at Rochester, with Wills from the PCC *In* "Hasted's Hist of Kent ... corrected & enlarged ...; pt 1: Hundred of Blackheath" [KE Folio]
1571-1630 Testmtry Papers 3: Marlowe's Death at Deptford Strand - Wills of Jurors at the Inquest with some other Wills (*will & admon abst*) [KE Tracts]

Eastry
1439-1547 *Abst of* Eastry Wills (Archaeologica Cantiana vols 38-40) [KE/PER]; *also In* "Kent Tracts vol 3" (*offprint from Archaeologica Cantiana*) [KE/G 6]
1451-1617 Extr from Wills & *Invents* of the 17th C *In* "Memorials of Eastry" [KE/L 26]

Eltham
1420-1711 Extr from Wills of Former Inhabitants of Eltham, proved at Rochester, with Wills from the PCC *In* "Hasted's Hist of Kent ... corrected & enlarged ...; pt 1: Hundred of Blackheath" [KE Folio]

Folkestone
1541-1588 Folkestone Wills; Indexes to

Testators, Directions, Legatees, Pious Bequests, Executors, Legacies, etc 1541-1588 *In* "Folkestone Recs vol 1" [KE/L 34]

1831-1858 Extr from the Index to Archdeaconry Wills 1712-1858 (Folkestone FH J vol 3) [KE/PER]

Frittenden *see Weald of E Kent*

Goudhurst *see Weald of E Kent*

Halden, High *see Weald of E Kent*

Hawkhurst *see Weald of E Kent*

Headcorn *see Weald of E Kent*

Herne
1396-1527 Herne; Abst to the Wills of Parishioners 1396-1527 (Archaeologica Cantiana vols 28 & 30) [KE/PER]; *also In* "Kent Tracts vol 1" (*offprint from* Archaeologica Cantiana) [KE/G 4]

Hoath *see Reculver*

Hythe
15-16 C *Abst of* Hythe Wills; pts 1-3 (Archaeologica Cantiana vols 49-51) [KE/PER]

Kemsing
see also Seal
1457-1471 Extr from Wills *In* "Story of Kemsing in Kent" [KE/L 121]

Lee
1475-1703 Extr from Wills of Former Inhabitants of Lee, proved at Rochester, with Wills from the PCC *In* "Hasted's Hist of Kent ... corrected & enlarged ...; pt 1: Hundred of Blackheath" [KE Folio]
1584-1735 Extr from Wills & *Admons In* appx A & B to "Reg of all the Marriages, Christenings & Burials in the Church of St Margaret, Lee in the County of Kent 1579-1754" (Lewisham Antqn Soc Pubs vol 1) [KE/R 136]

Lewisham
1401-1732 Extr from Wills of Former

Inhabitants of Lewisham, proved at Rochester, with Wills from the PCC *In* "Hasted's Hist of Kent ... corrected & enlarged ...; pt 1: Hundred of Blackheath" [KE Folio]

1556-1826 *Extr from* Wills of persons residing in Lewisham *In* Appx A & B to "Reg of the Marriages, Christenings & Burials in the Church of St Mary Lewisham, Kent 1558-1756" (Lewisham Antqn Soc Pubs vol 4) [KE/R 138]

Lydd
1420-1555 *Abst of* Some Wills *In* appx to "MI in the Churchyard & Church of All Sts, Lydd, Kent" (Kent Recs *additional* vol) [KE/M 41]
1430-1484 Notes relating to Lydd Church from Wills of Parishioners (Archaeologica Cantiana vol 13) [KE/PER]

Marden *see Weald of E Kent*

Milton-next-Sittingbourne
15-16 C *Abst of* Milton Wills (next Sittingbourne); pts 1-4 (Archaeologica Cantiana vols 44-47) [KE/PER]

Newenden *see Weald of E Kent*

Newington near Hythe
1831-1858 Extr from the Index to Archdeaconry Wills 1712-1858 (Folkestone FH J vol 3) [KE/PER]

Newington near Sittingbourne
1604-1649 Extr from Kentish Admons 1604-1649 (lists Wills relating to Newington) *In* "Newington-near-Sittingbourne: Recs of Old Fams" [KE Folio]

Orpington
1464-1604 Notes from Wills *In* appx A to "Reg of the Marriages, Christenings & Burials in the Church of the Parish of All Sts, Orpington 1560-1754" (Lewisham Antqn Soc Pubs vol 8) [KE/R 150]

Reculver
1396-1549 *Abst of* Reculver & Hoath Wills
(Archaeologica Cantiana vol 32)
[KE/PER]

Rochester City
1360-1558 Extr from Wills *In* "Hist of
Rochester" [KE/L 58]

Rolvenden *see Weald of E Kent*

Ruckinge
1402-1541 Notes from Ruckinge Wills
affecting Ruckinge Church
(Archaeologica Cantiana vol 13)
[KE/PER]

Sandhurst *see Weald of E Kent*

Seal
1501-1546 *Extr from* Wills 1501-1546 *In*
"Past Generations of Seal &
Kemsing from the Memorials in
the Churches" (Seal & Kemsing
Hist Pub no 1) [KE/L 62]
1545-1610 *List of* Wills in Seal 1545-1610
with extr (NW Kent FH vol 6)
[KE/PER]

Sevenoaks
1661-1684 *Abst of* Sevenoaks Wills &
Invents in the reign of Charles II
(Kent Recs vol 25) [KE/PER]

Sittingbourne
15-16 C *Abst of* Sittingbourne Wills; pts 1-
3 (Archaeologica Cantiana vols
41-43) [KE/PER]

Smarden *see Weald of E Kent*

Staplehurst *see Weald of Kent*

Swanscombe
1563-1721 Copies of Wills *In* "Swanscombe,
Kent Parish Regs 1559-1812"
[KE/R 39]

Tenterden *see Weald of E Kent*

Weald of East Kent
1532-1598 Weald of E Kent Will Abst from
the Archdeaconry Court of
Canterbury, Kent vols 21-50; vol
1: Parish of Benenden (*1537-
1595*) (Kent FHS Rec Pub no 9);
vol 2: Parish of Bethersden

(*1536-1597*) (Kent FHS Rec Pub
no 13); vol 3: Parish of
Biddenden (*1536-1597*) (Kent
FHS Rec Pub no 20); vol 5:
Parish of Frittenden (*1537-1595*)
(Kent FHS Rec Pub no 32); vol 6:
Parish of Goudhurst (*1538-1591*)
(Kent FHS Rec Pub no 34); vol 7:
Parish of High Halden (*1537-
1595*) (Kent FHS Rec Pub no
37); vol 8: Parish of Hawkhurst
(*1536-1581*) (Kent FHS Rec Pub
no 46); vol 9: Parish of Headcorn
(*1536-1597*) (Kent FHS Rec Pub
no 49); vol 10: Parish of Marden
(*1538-1598*) (Kent FHS Rec Pub
no 53); vol 11: Parish of
Newenden (*1538-1588*) (Kent
FHS Rec Pub no 54); vol 12:
Parish of Rolvenden (*1538-1598*)
(Kent FHS Rec Pub no 56); vol
13: Parish of Sandhurst (*1535-
1597*) (Kent FHS Rec Pub no
57); vol 14: Parish of Smarden
(*1538-1597*) (Kent FHS Rec Pub
no 59); vol 15: Parish of
Staplehurst (*1536-1595*) (Kent
FHS Rec Pub no 60); vol 16:
Parishes of Tenterden (*1532-
1597*), Wittersham (*1541-1592*) &
Woodchurch (*1554*) (Kent FHS
Rec Pub no 162); Index *to vols 1-
16* (Kent FHS Rec Pub no 28)
[*for all:* Apply to Staff]
Note: *index & vols 5-16 are Mfc;
Cranbrook (vol 4): use KE/L 85*

Wittersham *see Weald of E Kent*

Woodchurch *see Weald of E Kent*

Woolwich
1455-1524 *Extr from* Curious Wills *In* "Recs
of Woolwich District vol 1" [KE/L
108]
1455-1667 Extr from Wills of Former
Inhabitants of Woolwich, proved
at Rochester, with Wills from the
PCC *In* "Hasted's Hist of Kent ...
corrected & enlarged ...; pt 1:
Hundred of Blackheath" [KE
Folio]

LANCASHIRE

Pre-1858 Probate Jurisdictions:-

Prerogative Court: Canterbury, York (from 1541)

Consistory Courts: CHESTER (from 1541); Lichfield (until 1541); York (Chancery - from 1541); York (Exchequer)

Archdeaconry Court: RICHMOND (for Amounderness, Furness & Lonsdale Deaneries)

Peculiars, etc: Chester (Archdeaconry - 12 Rural Deans); High Offley with Flixton (until 1541); York (Dean & Chapter); *see also Lancaster (Chancery)*

Manorial Courts: Halton (Lancs); Nether Kellet; Slyne with Hest; Skerton

1301-1752 Coll of Lancs & Cheshire Wills & *Invents* now not to be found in any prob registry 1301-1752 (*Earwaker's abst*) (Lancs & Cheshire Rec Soc Procs vol 30) [LA/PER]

1322-1844 Cal of Persons Commemorated in MI & of the abst of Wills, Admons, etc contained in books relating to Lancs & Cheshire (Lancs & Cheshire Rec Soc Procs vol 76) [LA/PER or CH/M 1 (*with many ms addenda*)]

1359-1858 List of Wills, *Admons, Invents, etc* relating to Lancs which are not recorded in the printed indexes of either the Chester or the Richmond Wills & which are now found among the recs deposited in the Lancs RO 1359-1858 (Lancs & Cheshire Rec Soc Procs vol 105) [LA/PER]

1476-1746 Lancs & Cheshire Wills & Invents at Chester, transcripts 1477-1746, with an appx of abst of wills now lost or destroyed 1545-1650 (Chetham Soc new ser vol 3) [LA/PER]

1483-1639 *Abst of* Lancs & Cheshire Wills & Invents from the Ecclesiastical Court, Chester (*in 3 pts: 1483-1589, 1525-1557, 1596-1639*) (Chetham Soc *original ser* vols 33, 51 & 54) [LA/PER]

1501-1788 Abst of Wills *In* "Ribblesdale Papers" [YK/L 176]

1519-1648 *Index to* Cheshire & Lancs Wills in the Harleian Coll at the BM (Cheshire Sheaf new ser vol 27)

[CH/PER]

1539-1601 List of all the Lancs entries in an early cal of wills referring generally to the eastern portion of the Archdeaconry of Richmond 1539-1601 (Lancs & Cheshire Rec Soc Procs vol 10) [LA/PER]

1551-1702 *Index to* Household Invents of the Lancs Gentry 1550-1700 (Trans Hist Soc Lancs & Cheshire vol 110) [LA/PER]

1563-1807 *Abst of* Lancs & Cheshire Wills & Invents 1563-1807 now preserved at Chester (Chetham Soc new ser vol 37) [LA/PER]

1569-1855 Index to Wills Copies from Lancs County RO, Preston in the Doc Coll in the Library of the Society of Genealogists [LA/G 61]

1571-1856 Notes on Cumbrian Wills & Admons at Carlisle, Lancaster & Somerset House (*includes N Lancs*) (*Moor MSS*) *In* "Nether Wasdale Parish Regs" [CU/G 33]

17-19 C Beazley's Geneal Coll (*11 ms vols & index, mainly of Lancs or Cheshire will abst*) *In* "Collectanea vols 1-12" [CH/G 1-12]

1603-1730 *Abst of* Lancs & Cheshire Wills (Northern Genealogist vols 1 & 2) [PER/NOR]

1621-1660 Index to Wills & Invents 1621-1650 with a list of Lancs & Cheshire Wills proved in the PCC 1650-1660 & a list of Lancs & Cheshire Admons granted in the PCC 1650-1660 (Lancs & Cheshire Rec Soc Procs vol 4) [LA/PER]

1650-1660 List of Lancs & Cheshire Admons granted in the PCC 1650-1660 (Lancs & Cheshire Rec Soc Procs vol 4); List of Lancs & Cheshire Wills proved in the PCC 1650-1660 (Lancs & Cheshire Rec Soc Procs vol 4) [*both* LA/PER]

1881-1926 Prob Indexes 1881-1926 - Taunton MA, *USA* (*list of mainly Lancs testators*) (Lancs vol 8) [LA/PER]

Blackburn

1633-1805 Abst of the original wills (unless otherwise specified) of various Priests of the Soc of Jesus which are now deposited among the archives at Stonyhurst *In* "Supp HMC Rep upon the MSS at Stonyhurst College" [Apply to Staff]

Colne District
1545-1830 Wills *Admons & Invents* of Colne & District: an index to who of where left what when (Colne Lib Pub no 2)) [LA/L 19]

Craven District
1688-1858 W Craven Wills proved at York 1688-1858 (Mfc) [Apply to Staff]

Furness District
1363-1858 Index & Extr of Cumbrian Wills & *Admons* proved at the PCC *etc* (*includes Furness*) [CU/G 17]
1571-1856 Notes on Cumbrian Wills & Admons at Carlisle, Lancaster & Somerset House (*Moor MSS*) *In* "Nether Wasdale Parish Regs" [CU/G 33]

Liverpool
1690-1760 Abst of Wills *In* appx A to "Liverpool Vestry Books 1681-1834" [LA/L 45]
1790-1800 Wealth of 33 Captains who died in the Liverpool Slave Trade 1790-1800 (Trans Hist Soc Lancs & Cheshire vol 140) [LA/PER]
1382-1655 *Abst of* Wills, admons & invents *In* "Moore MSS" (Lancs & Cheshire Rec Soc Procs vol 67) [LA/PER]

Manchester
1572-1839 Surnames from Simister Wills (*index for Manchester & Marple areas 1572-1839*) (Manchester Genealogist vol 16 no 3) [LA/PER]

Ormskirk
1580-1734 *List of copies of Loc* Invents & Wills *in Ormskirk Lib* (Ormskirk & Dist FHn no 6) [LA/PER]

Poulton
1548-1598 *Abst of* Poulton Wills dated before 1600 *In* "Hist of the Parish of Poulton-le-Fylde in the County of Lancaster" (Chetham Soc new ser vol 8) [LA/PER]

Tonge
1550-1799 Abst of Wills & Invents 1550-1799 *In* appx to "Notes on Hall i' th' Wood & its owners" [LA/L 87]

Warrington
1630-1657 Booksellers & Stationers in Warrington 1630-1657: *Abst of* Wills, Invents & Notes (*In* "Lancs Tracts vol 1") [LA/G 1]

Whittington
1580-1883 Abst of Wills *In* "Hist of Whittington" (Chetham Soc new ser vol 99) [LA/PER]

LEICESTERSHIRE
Pre-1858 Probate Jurisdictions:-
Prerogative Court: Canterbury
Consistory Court: Lincoln
Archdeaconry Court: LEICESTER
Peculiars, etc: Ashby de la Zouch; Old Dalby; Evington; Groby; Leicester (St Margaret); Lincoln (Dean & Chapter - until 1834); Merevale; Rothley

1360-1610 List of Wills & Probs in the Charter Chests of the Fam of Neville of Holt *In* "9th HMC Rep" [SP/HMC]
1384-1631 *Abst of* Leics & Rutland Wills (Leics & Rutland N&Q & Antqn Gleaner vol 3) [LA/PER]
16-19 C Oldaker Coll of Wills: *see the note on this coll in the General Collections of Wills, Indexes, etc part of the NATIONAL section*
1518-1647 Some Leics Pre-Reformation Wills ... a list of wills & *admons* ... from the Archdeaconry Court Book now marked '0.3' (*cal 1521-1522 & 1531 with extr 1518-1647*) *In* "Leics *Quaker* Recs, etc" [LE/R 19]
1576-1800 Cal of Wills & Admons relating to the County of Leicester, proved in the Archdeaconry Court of Leicester 1495-1649 & in the Peculiars of St Margaret Leicester, Rothley, Groby, Evington & unproved Wills previous to 1801 (*"incomplete wills"*); all now preserved in the Probate Registry at Leicester (BRS vol 27) [BRS]
1587-1706 *Abst of* Derbys & Leics Wills

(Northern Genealogist vol 1)
[PER/NOR]

1660-1698 *List of* Leics & Rutland Invents in the PCC (Leics FHS N/L no 42) [LE/PER]

1701-1749 *Index to* Leics & Rutland Wills in the PCC (Leics FHS N/L nos 39, 41, 43, 45 & 46) [LE/PER]

Braunstone

1532-1778 Braunstone Prob Invents 1532-1778 *In* "Leics Prob Invents" [LE/G 31]

Glenfield

1508-1834 List of Wills & Admons relating to Burials *In* "Glenfield (Leics) Parish Reg Transcripts 1604-1837" [LE/R 89]

1542-1831 Glenfield Prob Invents 1542-1831 *In* "Leics Prob Invents" [LE/G 31]

Kilworth, South

1521-1750 List of Wills & Invents *In* appx 2 of "S Kilworth Parish Reg" [LE/R 38]

Kirby Muxloe

1515-1835 Some Kirby Muxloe Wills ... (*lists & abst*) *In* appx to "Kirby Muxlow, County Leicester - Parish Reg Transcripts" [LE/R 91]

1547-1783 *Abst of* Kirby Muxloe Prob Invents 1547-1783 *In* "Leics Prob Invents" [LE/G 31]

Market Harborough

1382-1539 Extr from Wills *etc* preserved at the District Probate Registry, Leicester *In* "Market Harborough Parish Recs to 1530" [LE/L 32]

Mountsorrel

1630-1647 *Abst of* Mountsorrel Wills & Admons at Leicester *In* "Mountsorrel, County Leics Reg & Rent Rolls chiefly 1630-1676" [LE/R 13]

LINCOLNSHIRE
Pre-1858 Probate Jurisdictions:-
Prerogative Court: Canterbury
Consistory Court: LINCOLN
Archdeaconry Court: STOW (until 1834)
Peculiars, etc: Bishop Norton (until 1834); Caistor; Corringham; Heydour; Kirton-in-Lindsey; Lincoln (Dean & Chapter - until 1834); Louth; New Sleaford; Stow-in-Lindsey*; see also York (Chancery); York (Exchequer); York (PCY)*
Manorial Courts: Ingoldmells; Kirkstead Abbey
Civil Court: Lincoln (Mayor)

1474-1920 Wills, *Invents* & Admons deposited with the Dept of Archives, Central Lib, Sheffield (*index*) [Apply to Staff]

1500-1600 Lincs Wills; 1st ser (*Maddison's abst*) [LI/G 30]

16-19 C Oldaker Coll of Wills*: see the note on this coll in the General Collections of Wills, Indexes, etc part of the NATIONAL section*

16-20 C Lincs Wills Beneficiaries Index; *Coll nos 1 & 2* (also Mfc) [LI/G 28 & LI/G 29 or Apply to Staff]

1550-1639 Lincs Origins of Some Exeter, *NH (USA)* Settlers (*will abst*) (NEHGR vol 68) [US/NE/PER]

1559-1582 Analytical Cal of Lincs Wills proved in the PCC (*abst*) (Northern Genealogist vols 1-6) [PER/NOR]

1618-1716 Preambles & Bequests in Wills of the 17th C (*extr*) (Lincs N&Q vol 7) [LI/PER]

1630 List of *Lincs* Testators in the PCC "Reg Scroope" (Lincs FHS Mag vol 6 no 1) [LI/PER]

1630-1905 Wills & Admons 1630-1905 *In* Cal of Deeds on permanent loan to the Lindsey County Council sent by the Society of Genealogists [Apply to Staff]

1650-1654 Abst of Lincs *Commonwealth* Wills proved in the PCC (supps to Lincs N&Q vols 19-20, 21, 22 & 23) [LI/PER]

1662-1835 Extr from Derbys Wills found in solicitors' old papers (*Dept of Archives, Sheffield Central Lib will index 1662, 1791-1835*) (Genealogist's Mag vol 17) [PER/GEN]

1731-1858 Lincs Wills & Admons in the PCY & *Exchequer Court of York*: May 1731-Jan 1858 [Apply to Staff]

Beelsby
1591-1801 *Extr from* some Beelsby Wills *In* appx A to "Hist of Beelsby" [LI/L 3]

Bourne
1520-1836 *Extr from some Wills In* "Hist of Bourne" [LI/L 5]

Holbeach
1540-1682 Notes about past inhabitants of Holbeach ... from wills examined at Lincoln ... *In* "Holbeach Parish Reg of Baptisms, Marriages & Burials 1601 & 1613-1641" [LI/R 24]

Nettleham
1665-1666 *Abst of some* Prob Invents *In* "Hist of Nettleham" [LI/L 23]

Riseholme
1537-1826 *Abst of* Some Wills, Admons & Invents *In* "Hist of Riseholme (which includes Grange de Lings), Lincs" [LI/L 25]

LONDON and MIDDLESEX
including the City of London; see Kent or Surrey for Metropolitan areas south of the Thames
Pre-1858 Probate Jurisdictions:-
Prerogative Court: Canterbury
Consistory Courts: London; Westminster (from 1541 until 1550)
Commissary Court: LONDON (London Div)
Archdeaconry Courts: LONDON (London Div); MIDDLESEX (Middx Div)
Peculiars, etc: Croydon; London (Dean & Chapter of St Paul's); St Katherine by the Tower; Westminster (Abbot/Dean & Chapter)
City of London Jurisdictions: Arches (Deanery); London (Archdeaconry - London); London (Commissary - London); London (Dean & Chapter of St Paul's); Westminster (Abbot/Dean & Chapter)
Civil Courts: Husting (until 1688); London (Lord Mayor); London (Orphans)

13-19 C Bernau's Evidences; Misc London Will Abst (*15 vols*)

[WILLS/GEN]
16-18 C Boyd's Inhabitants of London (*238 vols & 27 index vols include Middx & Surrey probs*) [Middle Library]; Boyd's Units (*34 vols & index vols in progress, include probs*) [Upper Library]; Additional Card Index (*extra references*) [Lower Library: Index drawers 111-112]
16-19 C London Will Abst (*Whitmore MSS, in 13 pts*) [MX/G 142-154]
1617-1857 Abst of Wills (*mainly Roman Catholic priests & their fams in London*) (London Recusant vols 3-8 & new ser vol 1) [MX/PER]
1658-1665 Writing to the Court; a Scrivener's Miscellany (*scriveners' PCC prob recs extr, PRO Class PROB 24*) [MX Tracts]
18-19 C Antiquaries' List of Middx Deeds; vol 1: pts 1-8 (*Marcham's, late Coleman's, Catalogue listing wills*) [MX/G 49]

Bromley
1620-1834 Extr from Wills *In* "Hist of the Parish of Bromley St Leonard" [MX/L 8]

Edmonton
1340-1633 *Indexes of Wills of* Enfield, Edmonton, Harringay (Hornsey) & Tottenham *In* "Tottenham, Edmonton & Enfield Hist Note Book" [MX/L 178]

Enfield
1259-1579 *Indexes of Wills of* Enfield, Edmonton, Harringay (Hornsey) & Tottenham *In* "Tottenham, Edmonton & Enfield Hist Note Book" [MX/L 178]

Hampton
1374-1810 Hampton Court, Hampton Wick & Hampton on Thames Wills & Admons (*abst for* Commissary Court of London 1374-1603, PCC 1383-1655, Archdeaconry of Middx 1608-1810) *In* "Middx & City of London vol 1" [MX/L 266; *also* (supps to The Genealogist new ser vols 35-38) [PER/GEN]

Hornsey

1365-1581 *Indexes of Wills of* Enfield, Edmonton, Harringay (Hornsey) & Tottenham *In* "Tottenham, Edmonton & Enfield Hist Note Book" [MX/L 178]

London City

1272-1892 *Abst of Wills In* "Recs of St Bartholomew's Priory & the Church & Parish of St Bartholomew the Great, W Smithfield vol 1" [MX/L 111]

1274-1603 *Abst of* Wills *In* Bundle 71 of "St Bride Fleet Street; extr from the Burial Reg *called* 'From the Fleet'" [Topo Docs Coll: Middx: 'Hist of St Bride's Church' box]

1275-1759 *Abst of Wills In* "Recs of Two City Parishes ... Sts Anne & Agnes, Aldersgate" [MX/L 106]

1279-1562 St Sepulchre's, Holborn; Fresh Facts from Wills (*extr*) (Trans London & Middx Archl Soc new ser vol 8) [MX/PER]

1296-1407 Wills concerning several parishes enrolled in the Cartulary of Holy Trinity Aldgate (*abst*) (London Rec Soc vol 7) [MX/PER]

1330-1545 *Extr from* Early Wills *In* "Some Account of the Hospital of St Thomas of Acon in the Cheap, London, & of the plate of the Mercers' Co" (2nd ed) [MX/CC 46]

1349-1489 Extr of Wills enrolled in the Parish Fraternity Reg of the Fraternity of the Holy Trinity & Sts Fabian & Sebastian (*in St Botolph Aldersgate*) (London Rec Soc vol 18) [MX/PER]

1392-1712 Wills, Leases & Memoranda in the Book of Recs of the Parish of St Christopher Le Stocks in the City of London (*abst*) [MX/L 114]

1412-1685 Cal of Cutlers' Wills (*with extr*) *In* "Hist of the Cutlers' Co of London ...; vol 2: from 1500" [MX/CC 105]

1459-1480 Wills 1459-1480 *In* "Cal of Plea & Memoranda Rolls preserved among the archives of the City of London at the Guildhall 1458-1482" [Apply to Staff]

1473-1800 MI & Heraldry in St Olave's, Hart Street, London, with annotations from wills etc (*extr*) (reprinted from Misc Gen et Her 5th ser vols

2, 3 & 7 with additions) [MX/M 93]

1604-1737 Notes on London Aldermen (*Whitmore MSS, prob lists*) (6 vols) [MX/G 8-13]

1617-1727 *Abst of Wills In* "Draper's Co; Hist of the Co's Property & Trusts vol 2" [MX/CC 29]

1660-1685 Rulers of London 1660-1685; Biographical Rec of the Aldermen & Common Councilmen of the City of London (Trans London & Middx Archl Soc *extra vol*) (*prob lists*) [MX/G 17]

1723-1844 List of certified extr from wills in the PCC or the Commissary of London relating to bequests to the French Protestant Church in London (Huguenot Soc Pubs Qto ser vol 50) [HUG/PER]

Ruislip

1504-1600 16th C Ruislip Wills (*abst*) [MX/L 183]

Stoke Newington

1385-1639 *Abst of* Old Stoke Newington Wills 1386-1639 [MX/L 144]

Tottenham

1277-1600 *Indexes of Wills of* Enfield, Edmonton, Harringay (Hornsey) & Tottenham *In* "Tottenham, Edmonton & Enfield Hist Note Book" [MX/L 178]

Westminster

1540-1556 Index to Wills & Admons relating to Westminster amongst the recs of the Consistory Court of London 1540-1556 *In* "Indexes to the Ancient Testmtry Recs of Westminster" [MX/G 242]

1611-1622 *Abst of* Four Westminster Wills (Misc Gen et Her 5th ser vol 9) [PER/MIS]

NORFOLK
Pre-1858 Probate Jurisdictions:-
Prerogative Court: Canterbury
Consistory Courts: Ely; Norwich
Archdeaconry Courts: NORFOLK;
NORWICH
Peculiars, etc: Castle Rising; Great
Cressingham; Norwich (Dean & Chapter);
Thorpe-next-Norwich
Civil Courts: King's Lynn; Norwich (Mayor)

1288-1353	*Index to* Norfolk Wills in the Court of Husting, London (E Anglian new ser vol 7) [NF/PER]
14-19 C	Campling Coll [Mf 953-961] **Note:** *this coll of pedigrees of Norfolk & Suffolk fams, wills & marriage licences is indexed in the Special Colls Card Index* [Upper Library]
1485-1648	List of Norfolk Inquisitiones: Wards & Liveries ser (Henry VII to Charles I) *In* "Norfolk Recs vol 1" [NF/G 35]
1574-1657	Index to PCC Wills deposited in the *Norfolk & Norwich FHS's* Lib 1985 (Norfolk Ancestor vol 4) [NF/PER]
1582-1700	Index to the Buxton MSS in the University Lib, Cambridge relating to Norfolk (*wills*) [NF/G 7]
1583-1878	*Titlow* Index of Misc References from Norfolk & Suffolk (*wills*) (Suffolk Roots vol 8) [SF/PER]
1649-1714	Norfolk Deponents; an index to some Norfolk Depositions *in Chancery* of the period 1649-1714 [NF/G 36]; *also indexed in* The Bernau Index (Mf) [Lower Library: Bernau Index drawers]
1653-1660	Cal of Invents 1653-1660 being lists of Invents exhibited in the PCC for the Commonwealth period, for the following counties: Norfolk ... [WILLS/PCC]

Cringleford
1423-1868	Extr of Wills, Admons & Invents relating to Cringleford & District 1423-1868 [Apply to Staff]

Cromer
1374-1783	*Index to* Cromer Wills & *Admons In* "Cromer Past & Present" [NF/L 5]
1453-1574	*List of* Wills of the inhabitants

who left money to the pier *In* "Savin's Hist of Cromer" [NF/L 5]

Fincham
1321-1452	List of Fincham Wills *In* "3rd HMC Rep" [SP/HMC]

Martham
1739-1772	Invents of the Poor (*Martham Parish list*) (Norfolk Archaeology vol 35) [NF/PER]

Norwich City
1555-1715	Some Norwich Goldsmiths' Wills (*extr*) (Norfolk Archaeology vols 35 & 37) [NF/PER]
1546-1705	*Abst of* some Tombland Wills & Admons *In* "Parish Reg of St George of Tombland, Norwich 1538-1707" [NF/R 30]
1565-1852	Walloons & their Church at Norwich; references to Strangers' wills (*Huguenot will indexes for Norwich courts*) (Huguenot Soc Pubs Qto ser vol 1) [HUG/PER]

Stow Bardolph
1321-1557	Extr of wills in the Muniments Room at Stowe Bardolph (Norfolk Archaeology vol 2) [NF/PER]

NORTHAMPTONSHIRE
including the Soke of Peterborough
Pre-1858 Probate Jurisdictions:-
Prerogative Court: Canterbury
Consistory Courts: Lincoln;
PETERBOROUGH (from 1541)
Archdeaconry Court: NORTHAMPTON
Peculiars, etc: Banbury (including King's
Sutton); Gretton with Duddington; Lincoln
(Dean & Chapter - until 1834); Nassington
Civil Court: Higham Ferrers

1260-1356	Northants References in London Wills (*Court of Hustings abst*) (Northants N&Q vol 5) [NH/PER]
16-19 C	Oldaker Coll of Wills: *see the note on this coll in the General Collections of Wills, Indexes, etc part of the NATIONAL section*
1505	*Abst of* Northants Wills in the PCC (Northants N&Q vol 5) [NH/PER]
1535-1638	Abst of Wills in Northants RO (*Tachell Coll*) [Topo Docs Coll: Northants]

1558-1730 *Index to* Northants Wills, *Invents & Bonds* in Oxford RO (Footprints vol 14) [NH/PER]

1617-1783 Wills of Northants people or connections held at Bucks RO, Aylesbury (Footprints vol 17) [BU/PER]

1649-1835 Cal of Wills 1649-1835 *In* "Misc Colls, etc deposited by the Society of Genealogists in the custody of the Northants Rec Soc" [NH Tracts]

Aynho

1535-1780 *Extr from* Wills *In* "Aynho; A Northants Village" (Banbury Hist Soc vol 20) [NH/L 1]

Milton

1518-1688 Extr from Wills & *Invents In* "Story of Milton Mazor" [NH/L 7]

Northampton

1464-1554 *Abst of* Wills *In* "Hist of the Church of the Holy Sepulchre, Northampton" [NH/L 9]

Peterborough District

1609-1718 PCC Wills (*Peterborough, Werrington & District index*) (Peterborough & Dist FHS J vol 9 pt 1) [NH/PER]

Werrington *see Peterborough District*

NORTHUMBERLAND

Pre-1858 Probate Jurisdictions:-

Prerogative Courts: Canterbury; York

Consistory Courts: DURHAM; York (Chancery); York (Exchequer)

Peculiars, etc: Hexham & Hexhamshire; Tockerington; York (Dean & Chapter)

1405-1558 N Country Wills, being abst of wills relating to the counties of York, Nottingham, Northumberland, Cumberland & Westmorland at Somerset House & Lambeth Palace; *vol 1:* 1383-1558 (Surtees Soc vol 116) [DU/PER]; *see also* N Country Wills (Ancestor no 4) [PER/ANC]

1540-1599 Index of Wills, etc in the Probate Registry, Durham & from other sources (Newcastle Rec Committee Pubs vol 8) [DU/G 27]

1547-1844 Abst of Wills & Invents (*Gibson Coll*) (Archaeologica Aeliana 3rd ser vol 12) [NU/PER]

1558-1604 N Country Wills, being abst of wills relating to the counties of York, Nottingham, Northumberland, Cumberland & Westmorland at Somerset House & Lambeth Palace; vol 2: 1558-1604 (Surtees Soc vol 121) [DU/PER]; *see also* N Country Wills (Ancestor no 4) [PER/ANC]

1651-1660 *Index to* Durham & Northumberland Wills at Somerset House (*Dale MSS*) [Apply to Staff]

1711-1856 List of Northumberland Wills in Newcastle Central Lib (*Hodgson MSS*) (Northumberland & Durham FHS J vol 19 no 2) [NU/PER]

1728-1838 *Cal of* Wills in the Allendale MSS in the Northumberland RO (Northumberland & Durham FHS J vol 19 no 3) [NU/PER]

1827-1842 Index of Wills, Admons, etc at the PCY (*A-G*) (Cleveland FHS J vol 2 nos 2, 3 & 5) [YK/PER]

Berwick-upon-Tweed

1797-1803 Extr from the Principal Probate Registry relating to *Border* Wills proved in the PCC 1797-1803 (Border FH N/L no 4) [SC/PER]

Hexham District

1662-1844 Loc Wills (*abst of docs bequeathed by Jasper Gibson, a Hexham solicitor*) (Archaeologica Aeliana 3rd ser vol 12); *index (to 1828)* (Northumberland & Durham FHS J vol 19 no 2) [*both* NU/PER]

Kirkhaugh

1663-1818 *Abst of* Kirkhaugh Wills 1663-1818 (Archaeologica Aeliana 4th ser vols 40-42) [NU Tracts or (*pt 2: vol 41 only*) NU/PER]

Whittingham

1556-1600 *Extr from Wills In* "Whittingham Vale, Northumberland: its history, traditions & folk lore" [NU/L 18]

NOTTINGHAMSHIRE

Pre-1858 Probate Jurisdictions:-
Prerogative Courts: Canterbury; York
Consistory Courts: York (Chancery); **YORK (EXCHEQUER)**
Peculiars, etc: Apesthorpe; Bole; Kinoulton; Nottingham (Archdeaconry); Southwell; York (Dean & Chapter)
Manorial Courts: Clipstone; Edwinstowe; Gringley-on-the-Hill or Bawtry; Laneham; Mansfield; Ossington St Johns; Rufford Abbey; Shelford St Johns; Skegby & Teversal
Note: *in 1837 the Archdeaconry of Nottingham was transferred to the Diocese of Lincoln but probate jurisdiction seems to have remained unchanged*

1405-1558	N Country Wills, being abst of wills relating to the counties of York, Nottingham, Northumberland, Cumberland & Westmorland at Somerset House & Lambeth Palace; *vol 1:* 1383-1558 (Surtees Soc vol 116) [DU/PER]; *see also* N Country Wills (Ancestor no 4) [PER/ANC]
1415-1482	Abst of Notts Wills at York (Trans Thoroton Soc vol 21) [NT/PER]
1474-1920	Wills, *Invents* & Admons deposited with the Dept of Archives, Central Lib, Sheffield (*index*) [Apply to Staff]
16-20 C	Coll of Misc Lists & Abst of Wills, etc for Notts & elsewhere 16-20th C [Apply to Staff]
1512-1568	*Abst of* Notts Household Invents (Thoroton Soc rec ser vol 22) [NT/PER]
1558-1604	N Country Wills, being abst of wills relating to the counties of York, Nottingham, Northumberland, Cumberland & Westmorland at Somerset House & Lambeth Palace; vol 2: 1558-1604 (Surtees Soc vol 121) [DU/PER]; *see also* N Country Wills (Ancestor no 4) [PER/ANC]
1569-1583	Notts Wills not all at Nottingham (*surname list*) (Notts FHS N/L vol 2 no 6) [NT/PER]

Edwinstowe
1346-1584	Testmtry Burials (*will extrs*) *In* "Regs of Edwinstow in the County of Nottingham 1634-

1758" [NT/R 8]

Kirkby-in-Ashfield
1608-1853	*Extr from* Kirkby Wills & Invents *In* "Kirkby-in-Ashfield A interesting township" [NT/L 31]

Newark-upon-Trent
1429-1557	Newark Wills & Admons preserved at York *In* "Hist of Newark-upon-Trent vols 1 & 2" [Apply to Staff]

Shelton
1483-1624	Testmtry Burials (*extr from wills*) *In* "Parish Regs of Shelton in the County of Nottingham 1592-1812" [NT/R 33]

Tollerton
1529-1723	*Abst of* some Tollerton Wills *In* "Hist of Tollerton" [NT/L 24]

OXFORDSHIRE

Pre-1858 Probate Jurisdictions:-
Prerogative Court: Canterbury
Consistory Courts: Oxford (from 1542); Lincoln
Archdeaconry Court: OXFORD
Peculiars, etc: Banbury (including Cropredy, Horley & Hornton); Dorchester (Oxon); Langford Ecclesia; Lincoln (Dean & Chapter - until 1834); Monks Risborough; Oxford (University); Thame
Civil Court: Oxford (Mayor)
Manorial Court: Sibford

1340-1706	*List of* some Wills, *Admons* & *Invents* in Lincs Archives Office (Oxon FHn vol 2 no 4) [OX/PER]
1391-1807	Snell's Geneal Coll*: this consists of 48 ms vols including will abst with an Oxon connection* [BK/G 1-48 or Apply to Staff]: *see the note on this coll under BERKSHIRE*
1393-1510	*Abst of* some Oxon Wills proved in the PCC (Oxford Rec Soc vol 39) [OX/PER]
1494-1764	*Indexes to* Oxon Prob Invents in the recs of the PCC (*1494, 1557, 1580, 1661-1764*) (Oxon Loc Hist vol 1 no 2 & vol 2 no 3) [OX/PER]
1550-1590	*Abst of* Household & Farm Invents in Oxon 1550-1590 (Oxford Rec Soc vol 44)

[OX/PER]

1557-1937 *Index to* Stray, *Draft & other* Wills & *Admons* in the Oxford RO; pts 1 & 2 (Oxon FHn vol 2) [OX/PER]

1750-1800 Oxon Testators in the PCC (*index A-Sh*) (Oxon FHn vols 1 no 6, 3 no 6, 4 no 9 & 16) [OX/PER]
Note: *index Si-Z on order*

1801 *Index to* Berks & Oxon Wills & Admons in the PCC (Oxon FHn vol 1 no 8) [OX/PER]

Banbury Town

1493-1723 *Index to* Wills of Banbury inhabitants not appearing in the Burial Reg *In* "Banbury Baptism & Burial Reg of 1558-1723"; vol 1: 1493-1653 (Banbury Hist Soc no 7); vol 2: 1654-1723 (Banbury Hist Soc no 9); Addenda & Corrigenda (Cake & Cockhorse vol 11) [*all* OX/PER]

1571-1590 *Index to* Banbury parishioners leaving wills and/or invents 1571-1590 (Banbury Hist Soc no 13) [OX/PER]

1591-1650 *Abst of* Banbury Wills & Invents 1591-1650; vol 1: 1591-1620 (Banbury Hist Soc no 13); vol 2: 1621-1650 (Banbury Hist Soc no 14) [*both* OX/PER]

1591-1723 *Index to* Wills of Banbury parishioners proved in the PCC; pt 1: 1591-1620 (Banbury Hist Soc no 13); pt 2: 1621-1650 (Banbury Hist Soc no 14); *supp 1701-1723* (Cake & Cockhorse vol 5) [*all* OX/PER]

1663-1707 Index of Wills for residents of Banbury, *Grimsbury, Neithrop, Calthorpe, Nethercote, Hardwick & Wickam* (Cake & Cockhorse vol 9) [OX/PER]

1677-1722 Living in Banbury 1660-1730: a foretaste (*invents abst*) (Cake & Cockhorse vol 10) [OX/PER]

Begbroke

1535-1544 *Extr from* some Wills of Begbroke People (Oxford Hist Soc vol 24) [OX/PER]

Burford

1468-1531 *Extr from Wills In* "Burford Recs; study in minor town government" [OX/L 9]

Calthorpe *see Banbury*

Enstone

1531-1545 Extr from Wills proved in the Court of the Archdeacon of Oxford 1531-1545 *In* "Account of Church Enstone" [OX Tracts]

Faringdon *see BERKSHIRE*

Grimsbury *see Banbury*

Hardwick *see Banbury*

Milton, Great

1562-1673 Benefactors & Wills (*extr*) *In* appx E to "Great Milton (Oxon) Parish Regs" [OX/R 84]

Neithrop *see Banbury*

Nethercote *see Banbury*

Oxford City

1600-1936 Social Hist of Property & Possessions; pt 1: Invents & Wills including Renaissance Lib Catalogues from the Bodleian Lib, Oxford 1436-1814 consisting of an index to Wills proved in the Court of the Chancellor of the University of Oxford & to such of the recs of that Court as relate to matters or causes testmtry (with ms annotations) & *index to The Bodleian Lib Benefactors' Reg 1600-1936* [Mf 1768]

Wheatley

1583-1750 *Abst of* some Wills & *Invents* in "Wheatley Recs" (Oxford Rec Soc vol 37) [OX/PER]

Wickham *see Banbury*

Woodstock

1607-1635 List of Woodstock Invents 1607-1635 *In* "Farming Activities at Thame & Woodstock in the early 17th C: the evidence of Prob Invents" (Oxon Loc Hist vol 3 no 7) [OX/PER]

RUTLAND
Pre-1858 Probate Jurisdictions:-
Prerogative Court: Canterbury
Consistory Courts: Lincoln,
  PETERBOROUGH (from 1541)
Archdeaconry Court: Northampton
Peculiars, etc: Caldecott; Empingham; Ketton
  with Tixover; Liddington; Lincoln (Dean &
  Chapter - until 1834)

1384-1631	*Abst of* Leics & Rutland Wills (Leics & Rutland N&Q & Antqn Gleaner vol 3) [LE/PER]
1660-1698	*List of* Leics & Rutland Invents in the PCC (Leics FHS N/L no 42) [LE/PER]
1701-1749	*Index to* Leics & Rutland Wills in the PCC (Leics FHS N/L nos 39, 41, 43, 45 & 46) [LE/PER]

Egleton
1502-1845	Abst of some Wills & Admons *In* pt 2 of "Transcript of the Parish Regs of Egleton, Rutland" [RU/R 6]

SHROPSHIRE
Pre-1858 Probate Jurisdictions:-
Prerogative Court: Canterbury
Consistory Courts: HEREFORD;
  LICHFIELD; St Asaph
Peculiars, etc: Astley Abbotts; Bridgnorth;
  Buildwas; Little Hereford with Ashford
  Carbonell or Hereford (Chancellor); Lichfield
  (Dean); Lichfield (Dean & Chapter); Prees;
  Shrewsbury (St Mary); Wombridge
Civil Courts: Shrewsbury (Mayor)
Manorial Courts: Ellesmere; Hampton &
  Colemere; Longdon-upon-Tern; Lyneall;
  Ruyton-of-the-Eleven-Towns; Tyrley

1304-1591	Old Salop Wills; pt 1: *will cal in Ludlow & the Palmer's Guild Deeds 1304, 1321-1499* (Trans Salop Archl & Nat Hist Soc 1st ser vol 5); pt 2: *will cals in the PCC 1402-1499, at Lambeth Palace 1387-1591 & in Mytton MSS 1316-1461* (Trans Salop Archl & Nat Hist Soc 1st ser vol 6); pt 3: *PCC will cal 1391-1499* (Trans Salop Archl & Nat Hist Soc 2nd ser vol 9) [*all* SH/PER]
1363-1591	Index of Salop Wills at Lambeth Palace (Trans Salop Archl & Nat

Hist Soc 3rd ser vol 2) [SH/PER]

1529-1650	*Cal of* Clerical Wills at Lichfield (Salop N&Q 3rd ser vol 3) [SH/PER]
1534-1822	List of Pewterers' Invents (*to 1747*) & List of Wills & Letters of Admon consulted *In* "Provincial Pewterers: a Study of the Craft in the W Midlands & Wales" [PR/PEW]
1641-1660	Cal of Salop Wills in the PCC 1641-1660 (Trans Salop Archl & Nat Hist Soc 3rd ser vols 1 & 2) [SH/PER]
1700-1749	*Index to* Salop Probs in the PCC 1700-1749 (*Matthews MSS*) [SH/G 22]

Alveley
1605-1821	*Abst of* Wills *In* "King's Ley; Story of the Ancient Parish of Alveley, Shrops" [SH/L 1]

Baschurch
1472-1858	Complete Listing of all Probs from the Cal of Wills at Lichfield Joint RO for the Parishes of Baschurch, Fitz, Great Ness, Little Ness, Montford & Shrawardine, Shrops, 1472-1858 [SH/G 16]
1630-1700	*Cal of* PCC Wills 1630-1700 for the parishes of Fitz, Montford, Shrawardine, Great Ness, Little Ness, Baschurch, in the County of Salop [Apply to Staff]

Dawley *see Telford*

Diddlebury
1404-1842	Extr from Wills 1404-1842 *In* "Hist of the Manor of Westhope, County Salop" [Apply to Staff]

Fitz
1472-1858	Complete Listing of all Probs from the Cal of Wills at Lichfield Joint RO for the Parishes of Baschurch, Fitz, Great Ness, Little Ness, Montford & Shrawardine, Shrops, 1472-1858 [SH/G 16]
1630-1700	*Cal of* PCC Wills 1630-1700 for the parishes of Fitz, Montford, Shrawardine, Great Ness, Little Ness, Baschurch, in the County of Salop [Apply to Staff]

Highley

1544-1771   Extr from Wills & Invents *In* "Highley; development of a community 1550-1880" [SH/L 28]

Lilleshall *see Telford*

Montford

1472-1858   Complete Listing of all Probs from the Cal of Wills at Lichfield Joint RO for the Parishes of Baschurch, Fitz, Great Ness, Little Ness, Montford & Shrawardine, Shrops, 1472-1858 [SH/G 16]

1630-1700   *Cal of* PCC Wills 1630-1700 for the parishes of Fitz, Montford, Shrawardine, Great Ness, Little Ness, Baschurch, in the County of Salop [Apply to Staff]

Ness, Great and Little

1472-1858   Complete Listing of all Probs from the Cal of Wills at Lichfield Joint RO for the Parishes of Baschurch, Fitz, Great Ness, Little Ness, Montford & Shrawardine, Shrops, 1472-1858 [SH/G 16]

1630-1700   *Cal of* PCC Wills 1630-1700 for the parishes of Fitz, Montford, Shrawardine, Great Ness, Little Ness, Baschurch, in the County of Salop [Apply to Staff]

Shrawardine

1472-1858   Complete Listing of all Probs from the Cal of Wills at Lichfield Joint RO for the Parishes of Baschurch, Fitz, Great Ness, Little Ness, Montford & Shrawardine, Shrops, 1472-1858 [SH/G 16]

1630-1700   *Cal of* PCC Wills 1630-1700 for the parishes of Fitz, Montford, Shrawardine, Great Ness, Little Ness, Baschurch, in the County of Salop [Apply to Staff]

Shrewsbury Town

1307-1900   List of Wills & Marriage Settlements in the Loc Hist Coll of Shrewsbury Public Lib [Apply to Staff]

1833-1847   Shrewsbury Canal Co - Copy Reg of Probs (*will & admon abst*) [SH/L 18]

Telford

1650-1750   Yeomen & Colliers in Telford; *Abst of* Prob Invents for Dawley, Lilleshall, Wellington & Wrockwardine 1650-1750 [SH/L 26]

Uffington

1192-1471   Abst of Wills) enrolled *In* "Cartulary of Haughmond Abbey" (Salop Archl Soc *vol*) [WS/G 69]

Wellington *see Telford*

Wrockwardine *see Telford*

SOMERSET
Pre-1858 Probate Jurisdictions:-
Prerogative Court: Canterbury
Consistory Courts: Bristol (City & Deanery Div); **WELLS**
Archdeaconry Courts: TAUNTON; WELLS
Peculiars, etc: Ashill; Banwell; Buckland Dinham; Compton Bishop; Compton Dundon; Cudworth; Easton-in-Gordano; Fordington & Writhlington; E Harptree; Hazlebere; Henstridge; Ilminster; Ilton; Kingsbury Episcopi & E Lambrook; Litton; W Lydford; Pilton & N Wootton; St Decumans; Timberscombe; Wells (Dean); Wells (Dean & Chapter); White Lackington; Witham Friary; Wiveliscombe; Wookey; Yatton
Civil Courts: Bridgwater

On 5 May 1942 German aircraft bombed the Exeter Probate Registry, destroying all the prob recs for Dioceses of Bath & Wells & Exeter (ie Somerset, Devon & parts of Cornwall). Since then, considerable efforts have been made to locate copies & abst of the lost material but researchers must be prepared to make do with the cals & indexes.

14-18 C   Somerset Parishes; a handbook of historical references to all places in the county *with bibliography of wills in print, arranged by parishes*; vols 1 & 2 [SO/G 35 & SO/G 36]

1311-1823   *List of* Somerset Wills *in print* (N&Q vol 185) [N&Q]

1359-1592   Cal of Lambeth Wills; Somerset & Dorset References at Lambeth (Somerset & Dorset N&Q vol 8) [SO/PER]

1363-1558 Somerset Medieval Wills; 1st ser: *Abst of PCC wills 1392-1500* (Somerset Rec Soc vol 16); 2nd ser: *Abst of PCC wills 1488-1530 & Lambeth Palace wills 1363-1491* (Somerset Rec Soc vol 19); 3rd ser: *Abst of PCC wills 1410-1558* (Somerset Rec Soc vol 21); *Vacancy ser:* Somerset Medieval Wills & other recs at Canterbury *(listing from the Prior & Chapter's Court 1500-1501)* (Somerset & Dorset N&Q vol 24) [*all* SO/PER]

16-18 C Brown Coll: Abst of Somerset Wills etc copied from the ms colls of the late Rev Frederick Brown; 1st-6th ser (6 vols) [SO/G 28-33]; Somerset Wills - six vols of wills at Somerset House, Taunton, etc *In* "List of Parish Regs & other Geneal Works" (*surnames only*) [UK/R]; Somerset Wills - *Crisp's Surname List In* "List of Parish Regs & other Geneal Works" (*1897 ed*) [UK/R]; (*1904 & 1908 eds*) [TB/BIB]; Rev Frederick Brown's Coll of ms Somerset Wills & Pedigrees preserved at Taunton Castle (*index from temp Henry VIII, no dates*) (Procs Somerset Archl & Nat Hist Soc vol 57) [SO/PER or (reprint *In* "Somerset Tracts" vol 1) SO/G 1]

1531-1850 Somerset Wills Index: Printed & MS Copies (also Mfc) [SO/G 70 or Apply to Staff]

1534 *Extr from* some Early *Somerset* Wills *In* "Somerset Tracts vol 3" [SO/G 3]

1536-1597 Abst of Wills from the Holworthy Coll 1536-1597 (*parishes A-E*) (Somerset Rec Soc vol 62) [SO/PER]

1539-1541 *Abst of some* Somerset Wills (N&Q 3rd ser vols 3 & 4) [N&Q]

1539-1834 Lost Westcountry Wills in the Fothergill Coll at the Society of Genealogists (*Devon & Somerset will & admon index*) (Devon FHn no 6) [DE/PER]

1603-1641 Sales of Wardships in Somerset (Somerset Rec Soc vol 67) [SO/PER]

1653-1655 Cal of Invents 1653-1660 being lists of Invents exhibited in the PCC for the Commonwealth period, for the following counties:

... Somerset [WILLS/PCC]

1729-1747 Studies in Somerset Hist from Loc Recs 1971 *no* 6: *Cal of* Somerset Prob Invents 1729-1747 [SO/G 39]

1805-1857 Index of Somerset EDO Wills; vol 1: Wills & Letters of Admon 1805-1811 & vol 2: Wills 1812-1857 [SO/G 71]; EDO Wills: Somerset 1812-1857 (Prov List) SO/G 34]

1815-1845 *Index to* Somerset Wills in the EDO but not at Taunton (Greenwood Tree vol 15 no 1) [SO/PER]

Bath City
1765-1827 Catalogue of Docs relating to the City of Bath (*with probs*) [SO/R 15]

Buckland, West *see Wellington*

Chew Magna
1534-1799 List of wills of the inhabitants of Chew Magna, Chew Stoke, Dundry & Stowey 1534-1799 *In* "Colls for a parochial history of Chew Magna" (Somerset Archl & Nat Hist Soc, Northern Branch *vol*) [SO/L 6]

1530-1599 *Abst of* 16th C Chew Magna Wills (Somerset Rec Soc vol 62) [SO/PER]

Chew Stoke *see Chew Magna*

Dundry *see Chew Magna*

Keynsham
1557-1700 Some Early Keynsham (Somerset) Fams: PCC Will Extr 1557-1700 [SO/L 47]

Staple Fitzpaine
1593-1702 Extr from Wills 1593-1702 *In* "Staple Fitzpaine & the Forest of Neroche" [SO/L 19]

Stowey *see Chew Magna*

Wellington
1372-1811 Materials for the Hist of the Town & Parish of Wellington in the county of Somerset; pt 1: *Abst of* Wills (Wellington & W Buckland) 1372-1811 [SO/L 27]

1543-1661 Extr from Wills 1543-1661 *In* "Materials for the Hist of the Town of Wellington, County Somerset" [SO/L 26]

STAFFORDSHIRE

Pre-1858 Probate Jurisdictions:-
Prerogative Court: Canterbury
Consistory Courts: LICHFIELD; Worcester
Peculiars, etc: Alrewas & Weeford; Colwich; Eccleshall; Gnosall; Handsacre & Armitage; Lichfield (Dean); Lichfield (Dean & Chapter); Longdon; High Offley & Flixton; Pattingham; Penkridge; Prees; Stafford (Commissary); Tettenhall; Whittington & Baswich; Wolverhampton
Manorial Courts: Burton-on-Trent; Newcastle-under-Lyme; Sedgley; Tyrley

16-19 C Oldaker Coll of Wills: *see the note on this coll in the General Collections of Wills, Indexes, etc part of the NATIONAL section*
1539-1639 Abst of Wills in Lichfield Joint RO *(index to Tachell Coll)* [Topo Docs Coll: Staffs]
1558-1579 *Abst of Staffs* Chancery Proceedings; ser 2 'temp Elizabeth'; pts 2 & 3 *(D-Z)* (Wm Salt/Staffs Rec Soc 3rd ser vols for 1926, 1931 & 1938) [ST/PER]
1597-1614 Typical Invents of Clergymen c1600 *In* "Clerical Invents" (appx 4 to Wm Salt/Staffs Rec Soc 3rd ser vol for 1915) [ST/PER]
1662-1835 Extr from Derbys Wills found in Solicitors' old papers *(Dept of Archives, Sheffield Central Lib will index 1662, 1791-1835)* (Genealogists' Mag vol 17) [PER/GEN]

Alrewas
1540-1548 Extr from Wills & Admons *In* "Lichfield Probate Registry Extracts vol 2" [ST/G 30]
1558-1595 Alrewas Parish Reg; vol 2: Abst of Wills, Admon & other Bonds also Invents in the Parish Chest in the Church at Alrewas [ST/R 92]

Hamstall Ridware
1640-1649 Extr from Wills & Admons *In* "Lichfield Probate Registry Extracts vol 2" [ST/G 30]

Haywood, Great and Little
1549-1696 A True & Perfect Inventory ... a glimpse of life in the Haywoods in the 17th C from wills of that period *(will & invent abst)* [Apply to Staff]

Mavesyn Ridware
1626-1649 Extr from Wills & Admons *In* "Lichfield Probate Registry Extracts vol 2" [ST/G 30]

Pipe Ridware
1628-1647 Extr from Wills & Admons *In* "Lichfield Probate Registry Extracts vol 2" [ST/G 30]

Rugeley
1619-1650 Extr from Wills & Admons *In* "Lichfield Probate Registry Extracts vol 2" [ST/G 30]

Tamworth
1619-1718 Extr from Wills & Admons *In* "Lichfield Probate Registry Extracts vol 2" [ST/G 30]

Willenhall
see also Wolverhampton
1728-1811 Abst of Willenhall Wills 1728-1811 *from* Lichfield Peculiar Court [Apply to Staff]

Wolverhampton Town
1444-1592 *Abst of* Wolverhampton Wills in the PCC (Wolverhampton Antiquary vol 1) [ST/PER]

SUFFOLK

Pre-1858 Probate Jurisdictions:-
Prerogative Court: Canterbury
Consistory Courts: Ely (from 1837); Norwich; Rochester
Archdeaconry Courts: Ely (from 1837); Norwich; SUDBURY; SUFFOLK
Peculiars, etc: Bocking; Isleham & Freckenham; *see also Huntingdon (Archdeaconry)*
Civil Court: Orford

10-19 C County of Suffolk: its Hist as disclosed by existing Recs & other docs, being *material* for the history of Suffolk *with many probs arranged by localities*; vols 1-6 [SF/G 34-39]

973-1850 Jacob Index to Beneficiaries *under Jacobs' Wills in Cambs & Suffolk* (*surnames only*) (Suffolk Roots vols 6, 8, 13 & 14) [SF/PER]

13-18 C Suffolk Manorial Fams being the County Visitations & other Pedigrees; vols 1, 2 & 3 pt 3 (*Muskett's will abst*) [SF/G 27-28]

14-19 C Campling Coll [Mf 953-961] Note: *this coll of pedigrees of Norfolk & Suffolk fams, wills & marriage licences is indexed in the Special Colls Card Index* [Upper Library]

1383-1604 Cal of Wills relating to the County of Suffolk proved in the PCC 1383-1604 (English MI Soc Pub) [SF/G 66]

1383-1837 Index to Names in Wills & Admons 1383-1837: Arch*deacnry of Suff*; Arch*deaconry of* Sudbury; PCC [Apply to Staff]

1533-1543 *Abst of* Suffolk Wills *at Ipswich* 1533-1543 [SF/G 70]

1583-1878 *Titlow* Index of Misc References from Norfolk & Suffolk (*wills*) (Suffolk Roots vol 8) [SF/PER]

1631-1700 Checklist of Invents of 17th C Suffolk Grocers *In* "Suffolk Grocers in the 17th C" (Suffolk Review new ser no 20) [SF/PER]

1653-1660 Cal of Invents 1653-1660 being lists of Invents exhibited in the PCC for the Commonwealth period, for the following counties: ... Suffolk ... [WILLS/PCC]

1700-1749 *Cal of* Suffolk Probs in the PCC 1700-1749 (*Matthews MSS*) [SF/G 73]

Buxhall
1441-1710 Early Wills with extr relating to property in the parish *In* "Hist of the Parish of Buxhall in the County of Suffolk" [SF/L 3]

Denham
1522-1678 *Abst of* Wills *In* "Denham Parish Reg" (Suffolk Green Books vol 8) [SF/PER]

Hardwick *see Hawsted*

Hawstead
1381-1557 Ancient Wills (*1381, 1493 & 1552-1557*) *In* "Hist & Antiquities

of Hawsted & Hardwick in the County of Suffolk" (2nd ed) [SF/L 38]

Icklingham
1481-1665 *Abst of* Icklingham Wills *In* "Icklingham Papers" [SF/L 7]

Ipswich
1583-1631 Ipswich Prob Invents 1583-1631 (Suffolk Rec Soc vol 22) [SF/PER]

Kirkley
1382-1542 List of Kirkley Wills *In* "Flinten Hist being the story of Pakefield & its church" [SF/L 14]

Kirton
1507-1601 Cal of Kirton Wills *In* "Shotley Parish Recs" (Suffolk Green Books vol 16 pt 2) [SF/PER]

Orford Town
1405-1776 *Abst of* Suffolk Wills (Orford) proved in the PCC 1387-1800 (English MI Soc Pub) [SF/L 13]

1580-1862 Abst of Some Wills *In* "MI remaining in the church of St Bartholomew at Orford in the County of Suffolk (English MI Soc Pub) [SF/M 7]

Pakefield
1372-1545 List of Pakefield Wills *In* "Flinten Hist being the story of Pakefield & its church" [SF/L 14]

Playford
1444-1800 *Abst of* Playford Wills at Ipswich 1444-1800 [Mf 815]

Rattlesden
1361-1631 Extr from Old Wills *In* "Notes on the Hist of the Church & Parish of Rattlesden in the County of Suffolk" [SF/R 89]

Rushbrook
1504-1780 *Abst of* Wills *In* "Rushbrook Parish Reg" (Suffolk Green Books vol 6) [SF/PER]

Shotley
1375-1630 *Abst of* Wills *In* "Shotley Parish Recs" (Suffolk Green Books vol 16 pt 2) [SF/PER]

1463-1538 *Abst of* Shotley Wills 1463-1538
(N&Q 10th ser vol 3) [N&Q]

Stow, West
1557-1752 *Abst of* Wills *In* "W Stow &
Wordwell Parish Reg" (Suffolk
Green Books vol 7) [SF/PER]

Wordwell *see Stow, West*

Welnetham
1350-1776 Abst of Wills 1350-1776 *In*
"Welnetham Parish Regs"
(Suffolk Green Books no 15)
[SH/PER]

Wingfield
1375-1504 Extr from Some Old Wingfield
Wills *In* "Wingfield its Church,
Castle & College" [SF/R 107]

Witnesham
1440-1900 *Cal of* Witnesham Wills 1444-
1900 *with* Admons in the Acta
Book 1609-1699 *In* "Witnesham
& the Meadows Fam" [SF/L 20]

SURREY
Pre-1858 Probate Jurisdictions:-
Prerogative Court: Canterbury
Consistory Courts: Canterbury (from 1837);
London (from 1845); Winchester
Commissary Court: SURREY
Archdeaconry Courts: Canterbury (from
1837); SURREY
Peculiars, etc: Croydon

1383-1568 Some Surrey Wills in the PCC
(*Hooper's abst*); pt 1: 1413-1568
(Surrey Archl Colls vol 51)
[SR/PER or (reprint *In* "Surrey
Wills") SR/G 56]; pt 2: 1383-1570
(Surrey Archl Colls vol 52)
[SR/PER or (reprint *In* "Surrey
Wills") SR/G 56]
1469-1649 Union Index of Surrey Prob Recs
which survive before the year
1650 (BRS vol 99) [BRS]
1497-1522 Coll of Wills of Persons resident
in Surrey (*abst*) (Surrey Archl
Colls vol 1) [SR/PER]
16-18 C Boyd's Inhabitants of London
(*238 vols & 27 index vols include
Middx & Surrey probs*) [Middle
Library]; Boyd's Units (*34 vols &
index vols in progress, include*

probs) [Upper Library]; Additional
Card Index (*extra references*)
[Lower Library: Index drawers
111-112]
16-19 C Index to Surrey Prob Invents, 16-
19th C [SR/G 26 or SR/G 46]
1505-1748 Abst of Surrey, Sussex & other
Wills & various Admons
(*Garraway Rice Coll*) [Apply to
Staff]
1555-1856 Wills & Admons (1555-1856) *In*
"Cal of Docs deposited by the
Society of Genealogists at Surrey
RO, Kingston-upon-Thames" [SR
Tracts]
1600-1608 Surrey Wills collected by
Frederick Arthur Crisp (*PCC abst*)
(Surrey Archl Colls vols 10-13)
[SR/PER]
1609-1611 Surrey Wills collected by Ethel
Stokes (*PCC abst*) (Surrey Archl
Colls vols 23-24 & 35) [SR/PER]
1610 Surrey Wills proved in the PCC in
1610 (*Stokes's abst*) (Surrey
Archl Colls vol 24) [SR/PER]
1650-1700 Index of Surrey Wills proved in
the PCC 1650-1700 (W Surrey
FHS rec ser no 9) [SR/PER]
1651-1827 *Cal of* Surrey Wills & Admons in
the Court of Delegates (Root &
Branch vol 15) [SR/PER]
1655-1811 Wills & Admons of Surrey &
Sussex - Bax Papers; vol 1:
1655-1665 & 1760-1792; vol 2:
1793-1811 & Index [SR/G 48-49]
1760-1781 Surrey Admons in the PCC 1760-
1781 (W Surrey FHS rec ser no
17) [SR/PER]; *also In* "Surrey
Wills" [SR/G 56]

Carsholton
1391-1664 Extr from Some Wills 1391-1664
In "Some Particulars relating to
the Hist & Antiquities of
Carshalton" (2nd ed 1882) [SR/L
9]

Clapham
1579-1808 *Abst of* Clapham Wills [SR/G 37]

Dunsfold
1483-1533 *Extr from* Dunsfold Wills (Surrey
Archl Colls vol 31) [SR/PER]

Kingston
1498-1795 *List of* Wills & Complimentary
Docs *In* "County of Surrey -

Invents of Borough Recs with some illustrative extr; vol 3" (Surrey Rec Soc *extra vol* no 29) [SR/G 18 or SR/PER]

Mitcham
16-18 C   Misc Wills & Admons - Mitcham, Surrey (*Rice Coll*) [Apply to Staff]

Richmond
1486-1871   Index to the Wills & Admons, Abst of which appear in Mr JC Challenor Smith's Coll in the Lib of the Surrey Archl Soc [SR/L 55]

Southwark
1082-1659   Coll of Wills relating to Southwark (*abst 1082-1563, 1659*) (Surrey Archl Colls vol 1) [SR/PER]
1657-1803   *Abst of* Southwark Wills (Surrey Archl Colls vol 22) [SR/PER]

Stockwell
1413-1568   Some Surrey Wills in the PCC (*Hooper's abst for Stockwell*); pt 1: 1413-1568 (Surrey Archl Colls vol 51) [SR/PER or (reprint *In* "Surrey Wills") SR/G 56]

Stoke d'Abernon
1413-1568   Some Surrey Wills in the PCC (*Hooper's abst for Stoke d'Abernon*); pt 1: 1413-1568 (Surrey Archl Colls vol 51) [SR/PER or (reprint *In* "Surrey Wills") SR/G 56]

Streatham
1383-1570   Some Surrey Wills in the PCC (*Hooper's abst for Streatham*); pt 2: 1383-1570 (Surrey Archl Colls vol 52) [SR/PER or (reprint *In* "Surrey Wills") SR/G 56]
1538-1601   *Abst of* Wills in the PCC relating to the village of Streatham [Topo Docs Coll: Surrey]

Sutton
1383-1570   Some Surrey Wills in the PCC (*Hooper's abst for Sutton*); pt 2: 1383-1570 (Surrey Archl Colls vol 52) [SR/PER or (reprint *In* "Surrey Wills") SR/G 56]

Wimbledon
1627-1825   Wimbledon Names in the Prob Recs of the Deanery of Croydon

(*1627-1780, 1825*) [Topo Docs Coll: Surrey]

SUSSEX
Pre-1858 Probate Jurisdictions:-
Prerogative Court: Canterbury
Consistory Courts: *see the Archdeaconries*
Archdeaconry Courts: CHICHESTER;
   LEWES; Rochester
Peculiars, etc: Battle; Chichester (Dean); S Malling; Pagham & Tarring
Civil Court: Rye

14 C-1550   Transcripts of Sussex Wills up to 1560 (*parish-by-parish extr, Garraway Rice Coll*); vols 1-4: (Sussex Rec Soc vols 41-43 & 45) [*all* SX/PER]
1366-1794   *List of* Sussex Wills in the *PRO* (*1380-1592*) & *the* BM (*1366, 1446-1794*) (Sussex N&Q vol 6) [SX/PER]
1500-1503   *Extr from* some Sussex 'Sede Vacante' Wills *in the archives of Dean & Chapter, Canterbury during 1500 & 1503 vacncies* (Sussex N&Q vol 5) [SX/PER]
16-18 C   Index to the Garraway Rice Bequest (2 vols, *including probs*) [SX Folio]
1505-1748   Abst of Surrey, Sussex & other Wills & various Admons (*Garraway Rice Coll*) [Apply to Staff]
1520-1800   *Index to* Wills & *Admons* of Sussex Clergy (Sussex N&Q vol 8) [SX/PER]
1521-1834   W Sussex Prob Invents 1521-1834: a catalogue (Mfc) [Apply to Staff]
1553-1601   Index to some Wills proved & Admons granted in the peculiar of the Deanery of S Malling & an Index to 216 other *16th C* Sussex Wills (Sussex Archl Colls vol 50) [SX/G 51 or SX/PER]
1565-1742   *Abst of* some Sussex Wills (*Dobell MSS*) (Sussex Rec Soc vol 29) [SX/PER]
1621-1731   *List of* Stray Invents at *the* WSRO (Sussex Geneal & Loc Hn vol 2) [SX/PER]
1623-1685   *Abst of* some Sussex Wills in the PCC (Sussex Archl Colls vol 28) [SX/PER]
1655-1811   Wills & Admons of Surrey &

Sussex - Bax Papers; vol 1:
1655-1665 & 1760-1792; vol 2:
1793-1811 & Index [SR/G 48-49]
1661-1725 *List of* Sussex Invents in the PCC
1661-1725 (Sussex Geneal &
Loc Hn vol 7) [SX/PER]

Herstmonceux
1540-1548 *Extr from* Wills of Inhabitants of
Herstmonceux (Sussex Archl
Colls vol 4) [SX/PER]

Kirdford
1611-1776 *Extr from* Kirdford Invents
(Sussex Archl Colls vol 93)
[SX/PER]

Pagham Town
1283-1619 Pagham Wills: List of Testators
(*1283-1424, 1521-1619*) *In* appx
F to "Hist of Pagham in Sussex
vol 3" [SX/L 30]

Petworth
1610-1760 Petworth Town & Trades (*abst of
tradesmen's invents*) (Sussex
Archl Colls vols 96, 98 & 99)
[SX/PER]

Rye Town
1497-1510 Abst of Rye Townsmen's Wills
1497-1510 (Sussex Archl Colls
vol 17) [SX/PER]
1530-1603 *Extr from Wills In* "Tudor Rye"
[SX/L 54]

Steyning
1559-1787 Steyning Town & its Trades
1597-1787 *with a list of invents*
(Sussex Archl Colls vol 130)
[SX/PER]

Wivelsfield
1542-1777 Extr from Wills for a Hist of
Wivelsfield in the County of
Sussex (Misc Gen et Her 2nd ser
vol 1) [PER/MIS]

WARWICKSHIRE
Pre-1858 Probate Jurisdictions:-
Prerogative Court: Canterbury
Consistory Courts: LICHFIELD (until 1837);
Worcester
Peculiars, etc: Alveston with Wasperton;
Bishops Itchington; Bishops Tachbrook;
Hampton Lucy; Lichfield (Dean & Chapter);

Merevale; Packwood; Stratford-upon-Avon;
Ufton Cantoris; Ufton Decani
Manorial Courts: Baddesley Clinton; Barston;
Knowle; Temple Balsall

16-19 C Oldaker Coll of Wills*: see the
note on this coll in the General
Collections of Wills, Indexes, etc
part of the NATIONAL section*
1529-1650 *Cal of* Clerical Wills at Lichfield
(Salop N&Q 3rd ser vol 3)
[SH/PER]
1534-1822 List of Pewterers' Invents (*to
1747*) & List of Wills & Letters of
Admon consulted *In* "Provincial
Pewterers: a Study of the Craft in
the W Midlands & Wales"
[PR/PEW]
1591-1869 Warwks County Council: County
Muniments - Deed coll from the
Society of Genealogists -
Schedule [WA/G 10]

Atherstone District
1690-1718 Extr from Wills & Admons *In*
"Lichfield Probate Registry
Extracts vol 2" [ST/G 30]

Austrey
1528-1775 Extr from Wills & Admons *In*
"Lichfield Probate Registry
Extracts vol 1" [ST/G 30]
1570-1896 Testmtry Papers; *abst for*
"Austrey, County Warwks etc"
(*Oldaker MSS*) [WA/L 1]

Beaudesert *see Henley-in-Arden*

Birmingham
1551-1600 *Abst of* Birmingham Wills &
Invents [WA/L 7]

Edgbaston
1647-1812 Wills - *Cal of* Edgbaston &
Harborne *Wills & Admons* (*1647-
1650, 1675-1812*) *In* "Regs of
Edgbaston Parish Church 1631-
1812 vol 1" (Procs Dugdale Soc
vol 8) [WA/PER]

Fillongley
1702-1749 List of Fillongley Wills at Lichfield
followed by abst of such wills
[Apply to Staff]

Grendon
1680-1750 Extr from Wills & Admons *In*

45

"Lichfield Probate Registry Extracts vol 2" [ST/G 30]

Harborne *see Edgbaston*

Henley-in-Arden
1507-1688   *Abst of* Beaudesert & Henley
            Wills *In* "Recs of Beaudesert,
            Henley-in-Arden, County
            Warwick" [WA/L 5]

Kenilworth
1599-1624   Will Abst - Kenilworth &
            Stoneleigh Parishes (*Holworthy
            Papers*) [WA/L 73]

Ladbroke
1309-1720   Abst of Wills 1309-1720 *In*
            "Ladbroke & its Owners" [Apply
            to Staff]

Lillington
1533-1634   *Abst of* Wills 1533-1634 *In* "Hist
            of Lillington, Leamington Spa"
            [WA/L 76]

Newton Regis
1680-1750   Extr from Wills & Admons *In*
            "Lichfield Probate Registry
            Extracts vol 2" [ST/G 30]

Polesworth
1680-1750   Extr from Wills & Admons *In*
            "Lichfield Probate Registry
            Extracts vol 2" [ST/G 30]

Stoneleigh *see Kenilworth*

Stratford-upon-Avon
1578-1615   Testmtry Papers (*abst*); *pt* 1:
            Wills from Shakespeare's Town &
            Time; *pt* 2: Wills from
            Shakespeare's Town & Time 2nd
            ser [*both* WA Tracts]

Tamworth *see STAFFORDSHIRE*

Tysoe
1508-1684   Cal of Tysoe Wills 1508-1684 *In*
            "Parish Regs of Tysoe, Warwks
            (Fam Hist Pub)" [WA/R 30]

Wolfamcote
1524-1775   *Extr from* Wolfamcote Parish
            Wills *In* appx A to "Wolfamcote
            Parish Regs; pt 1: 1558-1768"
            [WA/R 34 or WA/R 46]

Yardley *see WORCESTERSHIRE*

WESTMORLAND
Pre-1858 Probate Jurisdictions:-
Prerogative Courts: Canterbury; York
Consistory Courts: CARLISLE; Chester
   (from 1541); Lichfield (until 1541); York
   (Chancery); York (Exchequer)
Archdeaconry Court: RICHMOND (for
   Kendal & Lonsdale Deaneries)
Peculiars, etc: York (Dean & Chapter)
Manorial Courts: Docker; Ravenstonedale;
   Temple Sowerby

1363-1858   Index & Extr of Cumbrians in
            Wills & *Admons* proved at the
            PCC *etc* [CU/G 17]
1405-1604   N Country Wills, being abst of
            wills relating to the counties of
            York, Nottingham,
            Northumberland, Cumberland &
            Westmorland at Somerset House
            & Lambeth Palace; *vol 1:*
            1383-1558 (Surtees Soc vol
            116); vol 2: 1558-1604 (Surtees
            Soc vol 121) [*both* DU/PER]; *see
            also* N Country Wills (Ancestor
            no 4) [PER/ANC]
1571-1856   Notes on Cumbrian Wills &
            Admons at Carlisle, Lancaster &
            Somerset House (*Moor MSS*) *In*
            "Nether Wasdale Parish Regs"
            [CU/G 33]
1603-1795   *Abst of* Cumberland &
            Westmorland Wills (*1603-1680,
            1727-1736, 1746-1795*)
            (Northern Genealogist vols 1 & 2)
            [PER/NOR]
1686-1738   Some Westmorland Wills 1686-
            1738: *Extr from* Quaker Wills &
            Invents in the possession of the
            Soc of Friends at Kendal [Mf
            2721 or WE/G 16]
1697-1777   Book of Quaker Wills (*extr mainly
            for Westmorland*) (Trans
            Cumberland & Westmorland
            Antqn & Archl Soc new ser vol
            29) [CU/PER]

Dufton
1560-1852   *Index to* Wills, Admons & Bonds
            In "Dufton Regs 1571-1837 &
            Wills 1560-1852" [WE/R 13]

WILTSHIRE
Pre-1858 Probate Jurisdictions:-
Prerogative Court: Canterbury
Consistory Courts: Gloucester (from 1541);
   Hereford (until 1541); Sarum; Winchester;
   Worcester (until 1541)
Archdeaconry Courts: SARUM; WILTSHIRE
Peculiars, etc: Bishopstone; Calne; Castle
   Combe (until 1786); Chute & Chisenbury;
   Coombe & Harnham; Corsham; Durnford;
   Highworth; Hurstbourne & Burbage;
   Netheravon; Sarum (Bishop); Sarum
   (Dean); Sarum (Dean & Chapter); Sarum
   (Precentor); Sarum (Sub Dean); Savernake
   Forest (until 1829); Wantage (Dean &
   Canons of Windsor); Wilsford & Woodford

1383-1604 *Index to* Wilts Wills proved in the
   PCC; pt 1: 1383-1558 (Wilts N&Q
   vols 1-2 & 5); pt 2: 1558-1583
   (Wilts N&Q vol 5); pt 3: 1584-
   1604 (Wilts N&Q vols 6-8) [*all*
   WL/PER]
1462-1799 Wilts Wills & other Geneal
   Evidences *including* Wills in the
   Peculiar Court of the Perpetual
   Vicar of Corsham & Misc items
   (*abst & extr 1548-1749*)
   (*Sherwood MSS*) [Apply to Staff]
1505-1769 Index of Copies of Wills in the
   Wilts Archl Soc Lib, Devizes
   (*1505-1553, 1610-1698, 1769*)
   (Wilts FHS J no 16) [WL/PER]
1540-1831 Index to Wilts Wills etc still
   preserved in the Diocesan
   Registry, Salisbury [WL/G 52]
1547-1865 Sarum Wills; abst of wills,
   admons, invents & bonds of Wilts
   testators 16-19th C [WL/G 47]
   Note: in this book, numbered
   abst refer to facsimile copies in
   "Wilts Wills, copies of original
   recs 16-19th C" (*Bignold Coll*);
   vol 1: *1558-1799* nos 1-94; vol 2:
   1700-1730 nos 101-194; vol 3:
   1663-1679 nos 201-294 [WL/G
   49-51]
1653-1660 Cal of Invents 1653-1660 being
   lists of Invents exhibited in the
   PCC for the Commonwealth
   period, for the following counties:
   ... Wilts ... [WILLS/PCC]
1836-1885 Abst of Docs, MI & other Geneal
   Material relative to Wilts (*wills*)
   [WL/G 41]

Farley
1598-1740 Wills & Invents (*extr 1598-1697*)
   In "Noble Achievements" *with*
   Some interesting wills of
   parishioners (*abst 1696-1740*) *In*
   appx 2 to "Most Worthy
   Gentlemen" *both In* "Farley with
   Pitton (Monographs in Loc Hist of
   some Parishes on the borders of
   SE Wilts & Hants) [WL/L 31]

Garsden *see Malmesbury*

Hazelbury
1285-1625 Wardship Deeds & Evidences *In*
   appx to "Hist of the Manor of
   Hazelbury" [WL/L 14]

Lea *see Malmesbury*

Malmesbury
1522-1791 Geneal Notes from Wills of
   Persons from Malmesbury, the
   Lea, Garsden, etc County Wilts
   (*abst*) [WL Tracts]

Pitton *see Farley*

Semington
1631-1740 Notes on Semington MI (*will &
   admon abst*) (The Genealogist
   new ser vol 27) [PER/GEN]

Wraxall, North
1528-1745 Extr from Docs in the BM & the
   PRO (*will abst*) *In* "Notes of the
   Parish of N Wraxall" [WL/R 8]

WORCESTERSHIRE
Pre-1858 Probate Jurisdictions:-
Prerogative Court: Canterbury
Consistory Courts: Gloucester (from 1541);
   HEREFORD; WORCESTER
Peculiars, etc: Alvechurch; Bredon with
   Norton & Cutsdean; Charlcote; Fladbury;
   Hanbury; Hartlebury; Ripple with Queenhill
   & Holdfast; Stratford-upon-Avon; Tredington
   with Shipston-upon-Stour; Worcester (Dean
   & Chapter); Worcester (St Swithin)

16-19 C Oldaker Coll of Wills*: see the
   note on this coll in the General
   Collections of Wills, Indexes, etc
   part of the NATIONAL section*
1534-1822 List of Pewterers' Invents (*to
   1747*) & List of Wills & Letters of

Admon consulted *In* "Provincial Pewterers: a Study of the Craft in the W Midlands & Wales" [PR/PEW]

1545-1614 Prob Invents of Worcs Tradesmen 1545-1614 *In* "Miscellany 2" (Worcs Hist Soc new ser vol 5) [WO/PER]

1555-1584 Index to vol 6 of Worcs Wills & *Admons* [Apply to Staff]

1558-1633 *Extr from* Ancient Wills & *Invents In* "Worcs Relics" [WO/G 17]

1665-1840 Worcester Wills; vol 1: 1665, 1725, 1770-1833 (*Phillips MS 18920*); vol 2: 1704, 1745, 1753-1840 (*Phillips MS 18950*) [WO/G 40-41]
Note: this Coll is indexed in the GCI

1697-1903 N Worcs *Prob* Index (*surname list*) (Midland Ancestor vol 5) [WA/PER]

Bewdley
1660-1760 Index of Wills & Invents *In* "Bewdley in its Golden Age" [WO/L 51]

Bretforton
see also Evesham
1528-1858 List of Bretforton Wills with some abst *In* appx to "Transcript of the Reg of the Parish Church, Bretforton in the County & Diocese of Worcester 1538-1837" [WO/R 10]

Clent
1538-1642 Extr from Early Clent Wills & Invents *In* "Short Hist of Clent" [WO/L 34]

Evesham
1529-1759 *Abst of* 16th C Evesham Wills (*1529-1533, invent 1615, 1721, 1759*) (Evesham & 4 Shires N&Q vols 1 & 3) [WO/L 14 & WO/L 16]

Hampton
1529-1593 *Abst of* some Hampton Wills & *Invents* (Evesham & 4 Shires N&Q vols 2 & 3) [WO/L 15 & WO/L 16]

Yardley
1510-1559 *Extr from* Wills & Invents of Peasants *In* "Medieval Yardley" [WO/L 39]

YORKSHIRE
Pre-1858 Probate Jurisdictions:-
Prerogative Court: Canterbury; York
Consistory Courts: Chester (from 1541); Durham; **YORK (Chancery)**; **YORK (Exchequer)**
Archdeaconry Courts: RICHMOND (for the Boroughbridge, Catterick, Lonsdale & Richmond Deaneries)
Peculiars, etc: Acomb; Allerton & Allertonshire (Durham Bishop - until 1846); Allerton & Allertonshire (Durham Dean & Chapter - until 1846); Alne & Tollerton; Ampleforth; Barnby (until 1736); Beverley (until c1560); Bilton; Bishop Wilton; Bugthorpe; S Cave; Crayke or Craike (until 1837); Driffield; Dunnington (until 1729); Fenton; Fridaythorpe (until 1730); Givendale (until 1670); Grindal (until 1628); Holme Archiepiscopi; Howden & Howdenshire; Husthwaite; Knaresborough (Prebend); Langtoft; Laughton en le Morthen; Linton-on-Ouse; Mappleton; Masham; Mexborough; Middleham; N Newbald; Nottingham (Archdeaconry); Osbaldwick; Preston in Holderness; Riccall; Ripon; Salton; Selby; Snaith; Stillington; Strensall; Ulleskelf; Wadworth; Warthill; Weighton; Wetwang; Wistow; York (Dean); York (Dean & Chapter); York (St Leonard's Hospital)
Manorial Courts: Aldborough; Altofts in Normanton; Arkengarthdale with New Forest & Hope; Askham Bryan; Barnoldswick; Batley; Beeford; Cold Kirby; Crossley with Bingley, Cottingley & Pudsey; Hunsingore; Knaresborough (Honour); Marsden; Newton-on-Ouse with Beningbrough; Shipton & Overton; Silsden; Temple Newsam; Town End in Bolsterstone; Wakefield; Warmfield with Heath; Westerdale
Civil Courts: Kingston-upon-Hull

1359-1589 Wills deposited at Lambeth (*Yorks will index, mainly clergy*) (Yorks Arch & Topo J vol 24) [YK/PER]

1405-1558 N Country Wills, being abst of wills relating to the counties of York, Nottingham, Northumberland, Cumberland & Westmorland at Somerset House & Lambeth Palace; *vol 1:* 1383-1558 (Surtees Soc vol 116) [DU/PER]; *see also* N Country

Wills (Ancestor no 4) [PER/ANC]

1474-1920 Wills, *Invents* & Admons deposited with the Dept of Archives, Central Lib, Sheffield (*index*) [Apply to Staff]

1501-1788 Abst of Wills *In* "Ribblesdale Papers" [YK/L 176]

1539-1745 Coll of Wills (*abst*) *In* "W Riding Cartulary" (Bradford Antiquary new ser vol 3) [YK/PER]

1542-1689 Yorks Prob Invents 1542-1689 (*Yorks Archl Soc abst*) (Yorks Archl Soc rec ser vol 134) [YK/PER]

1557-1588 Yorks Wills (*Holworthy's abst York Registry wills*); Book 1: vols 15-19 (*1557-1588*); Book 2: vols 20-22 (*1569-1586*) [YK/G 83-84]

1558-1604 N Country Wills, being abst of wills relating to the counties of York, Nottingham, Northumberland, Cumberland & Westmorland at Somerset House & Lambeth Palace; vol 2: 1558-1604 (Surtees Soc vol 121) [DU/PER]; *see also* N Country Wills (Ancestor no 4) [PER/ANC]

1648-1659 Abst of Yorks Wills in the time of the Commonwealth, at Somerset House, London, chiefly illustrative of Sir William Dugdale's Visitation of Yorks in 1665-1666 (Yorks Archl Soc rec ser vol 9) [YK/PER] **Note:** *see Surtees Soc vol 36 for the Visitation & there is an ms index to vol 36* [both DU/PER]

1649-1660 Catalogue of the Yorks Wills at Somerset House (Yorks Archl Soc rec ser vol 1) [YK/PER]

1827-1842 Index of Wills, Admons, etc at the PCY (*A-G*) (Cleveland FHS J vol 2 nos 2, 3 & 5) [YK/PER]

1850-1900 NZ Probs/Intestacies 1850-1900 (*index: people of Yorks origins*) (Yorks FHn vol 21) [YK/PER]

Abbotside

1552-1688 Abst of Abbotside Wills, *Admons, Bonds* & *Invents* 1552-*1558, 1571-1642, 1654*-1688 (Yorks Archl Soc rec ser vol 130) [YK/PER]

Barwick-on-Elmet

1420-1748 *Abst of Wills 1420-1748 with cal of Admons 1510-1745 In* "Wills, Regs & MI of the Parish of Barwick-on-Elmet, County York" [YK/R 181]

Bradford

1392-1460 Translation of the earliest Loc Wills in the York Registry (*will & admon abst*) (Bradford Antiquary vols 1 & 2) [YK/PER]

1433-1612 List of Vicars, Rectors & Testmtry Burials (*will abst*) (Bradford Antiquary new ser vol 1) [YK/PER]

1722-1848 *List of* copies of Loc Wills in the Bradford Archives *In* "Retracing Your Bradford Ancestors" [YK/L 177]

Craven District

1688-1858 W Craven Wills proved at York 1688-1858 (Mfc) [Apply to Staff]

Darfield *see Silkstone*

Doncaster

1694-1728 Doncaster people of ten generations ago (selection *of abst* of Doncaster Prob Invents) [YK/L 192]

Halifax

1562-1601 Gleanings from Loc Elizabethan Wills (*extr*) (Halifax Antqn Soc Papers for 1915) [YK/PER]

Holderness

1390-1454 *Extr from* Holderness Wills (Trans E Riding Antqn Soc vols 10 & 11) [YK/PER]

Huddersfield

1612-1926 *Huddersfield & District* Wills Beneficiaries Index (*A-C*) (Huddersfield & Dist FHS J vol 5 no 4) [YK/PER]

Hull *see Kingston-upon-Hull*

Kingston-upon-Hull

1546-1651 *Abst of* Kingston-on-Hull Wills from the coll of Richard Holworthy (*1546, 1588-1651*) [YK/L 137]

Kirkby Malhamdale

1400-1551 *Abst of* Wills *In* "Parish of Kirkby Malhamdale in the W Riding of Yorks" [YK/L 52]

Kirkby Underdale
1506-1635 *Abst of* some Typical Wills *In* "Hist of Kirkby Underdale" [YK/L 49]

Leeds and District
1391-1552 *Abst of* Wills, *of Prob & Admon Acts* of Leeds District *arranged by places*; pt 1-4 (Thoresby Soc Pubs vols 22, 24, 26 & 33) [YK/PER]
1391-1561 Testamenta Leodiensia (*abst of wills for Leeds, Pontefract, Wakefield, Otley & District*); pt 1: 1391-1495 (Thoresby Soc Pubs vol 2); pt 2: 1496-1524 (Thoresby Soc Pubs vol 4); pt 3: 1515-1531 (Thoresby Soc Pubs vol 9); pt 4: 1531-1538 (Thoresby Soc Pubs vol 11); pt 5: 1538-1539 (Thoresby Soc Pubs vol 15); pt 6: 1539-1553 (Thoresby Soc Pubs vol 19); pt 7: 1554-1561 (Thoresby Soc Pubs vol 27); Note on Leeds Wills 1539-1561 (Thoresby Soc Pubs vol 50) [*all* YK/PER]

Morley
1650-1660 *Cal of* Morley & District Wills 1650-1660 (Cameo for 1993 no 3) [YK/PER]

Otley *see Leeds*

Pontefract *see Leeds*

Scarborough
1364-1667 *Extr from* Wills of Scarborough Men & Women *In* "Hist of Scarborough" [YK/L 81]

Sheffield
1440-1553 Catalogue of the Ancient Charters belonging to the twelve Capital Burgesses & Commonality of the Town & Parish of Sheffield, usually known as the Church Burgesses, with Abst of all Sheffield Wills proved at York prior to 1554 [YK/L 86]
1474-1920 Wills, *Invents* & Admons deposited with the Dept of Archives, Central Lib, Sheffield (*index*) [Apply to Staff]
1521-1553 Sheffield Wills extracted from

Yorks Archl Soc rec ser vol 9 (Index to Wills in York Registry 1514-1553) (Flowing Stream vol 7) [YK/PER]
1532-1757 Descriptive Catalogue of the Edmunds Coll ... including Deeds & Wills relating to Sheffield (*abst*) [YK/L 89]
1554-1560 Descriptive Catalogue of Misc Charters & other Docs relating to the districts of Sheffield & Rotherham with abst of Sheffield Wills proved at York 1554-1560 [YK/L 92]
1560-1566 City of Sheffield Descriptive Catalogue of Charters, Copy Court Rolls & Deeds forming the Wheat Coll at the Public Reference Lib, Sheffield also others from private colls, with Abst of Sheffield Wills proved at York 1560-1566 & 285 genealogies deduced therefrom [YK/L 85]
1800-1842 Index to Wills & Admons at the PCY (*Sheffield & District, A-G*); pt 1: 1800-1826; pt 2: 1827-1842 (Flowing Stream vol 4 nos 4 & 3) [*both* YK/PER]

Silkstone
1680-1750 Yorks Prob Invents: Silkstone, Worsborough & Darfield (*surnames list*) (Flowing Stream vol 8 no 1) [YK/PER]

Wakefield *see Leeds*

Whitby
1701-1792 A Yorks Town of the 18th C; the Prob Invents of Whitby, N Yorks 1700-1800 (*abst*) [YK/L 159]

Worsborough *see Silkstone*

York City
1285-1840 Testmtry Business (*extr*) *In* "Guide to the Archives of the Co of Merchant Adventurers of York" (Borthwick Texts & Cals no 16) [YK/PER]
1385-1447 *Abst of* some Early Civic Wills of York (Associated Archl Socs Reps & Papers vols 28 & 31-35) [PER/ASS]
1387-1456 Abst of Wills in the York Memorandum Book 1387-1456

(Surtees Soc vol 186) [DU/PER]

1500-1600 York Clergy Wills 1520-1600; vol 1: Minster Clergy (Borthwick Texts & Cals no 10); vol 2: City Clergy (Borthwick Texts & Cals

no 15) [*both* YK/PER]

1607-1768 Some Physicians' Wills (*abst of wills proved at York*) (Northern Genealogist vol 2) [PER/NOR]

THE CHANNEL ISLANDS
only a few probate cases were referred to the Consistory Court of Winchester; see also the NATIONAL section

1642-1762 Channel Island Wills at the PRO (*index*) (Channel Islands FHS J no 57) [CI/PER]

1837-1854 "Foreign" Wills proved at Carlisle (*will & admon index to persons who died in Channel Islands*) (Genealogists' Mag vol 15) [PER/GEN]

GUERNSEY
including Alderney, Sark, Herm & Jethou
Probate Jurisdictions:-
Prerogative Court: Canterbury (to 1858)
Consistory Court: Winchester (to 1858)
Ecclesiastical Court: GUERNSEY (Deanery)

JERSEY
Pre-1949 Probate Jurisdictions:-
Prerogative Court: Canterbury (to 1858)
Consistory Court: Winchester (to 1858)
Ecclesiastical Court: JERSEY (Deanery)

1583-1867 *Abst of* Invents of Household Effects (Société Jersiaise Annual Bull vol 20) [CI/PER]

THE ISLE OF MAN
see also the NATIONAL section
Pre-1847 Probate Jurisdictions:-
Prerogative Courts: Canterbury; York
Consistory Courts: SODOR and MAN; York (Chancery)
Archdeaconry Court: ISLE OF MAN
Peculiars, etc: York (Dean & Chapter)

Note: *for probate off the island see also Armagh (PCA); Carlisle (Consistory); Chester (Consistory); Richmond; Edinburgh (Commissariot)*

1663-1831 *Abst of Manx* Wills *etc* (Manx Museum J vols 2 & 4) [IM/PER]

IRELAND

During the Irish Civil War the Four Courts building in Dublin, which housed the PRO of Ireland & the Principal Probate Registry, was gutted by fire on 30 Jun 1922. As a result, virtually all the records of the Prerogative, Consistory & Peculiar Courts in Ireland as well as the Principal Probate Registry, Dublin were destroyed. Since then, considerable efforts have been made to locate copies & abstracts of the lost material but researchers must be prepared to make do with surviving cals & indexes.

PRE-1858 PROBATE JURISDICTIONS
After the Reformation all Irish probate courts were administered by the established Church of Ireland and, although the Roman Catholic provinces & dioceses had the same titles as the established church, they had no probate

jurisdiction at all. Whilst the PCA held island-wide probate jurisdiction over Ireland, many Irish wills were proved in other courts in the British Isles especially in the PCC where wills were identified either as "Parts" or as "Ireland". It should be noted that the established church's Archbishops of Cashel, Dublin & Tuam did not have any probate jurisdiction outside their dioceses.

IRISH PROBATE PAPERS IN LONDON
In addition to the PCC records, many Irish wills can be found in other London repositories -
Principal Probate Registry, London: *from 1859, many Irish Wills & Admons were re-sealed in London & Irish testators may be found amongst the indexes to the Principal Probate Registry, London (qv); after 1877*

these names are found after the letter "Z"
Estate Duty Office: *there are many Irish references in the indexes to the records of the EDO (qv) particularly for 1812-1857*

NATION-WIDE COLLECTIONS
see also the NATIONAL section

14-19 C   Irish Wills in the PCC (*undated index to Culleton's abst*) (Fam Hist vol 11 no 73) [PER/FAM]

1404-1700   Irish Wills & Admons in the PCC (*Garrett's abst: wills 1404-1660 & admons 1559-1660; wills list 1661-1700*) [IR/G 94]

1406-1859   Irish Geneal Guides; vol 1: Guide to Copies & Abst of Irish Wills (1st ser) (*Clare MSS*) [IR/G 92 & IR/G 118]

1484-1802   *Index to* Irish PCC Wills & Admons [Topo Docs Coll: Ireland]

1543-1851   *Index to* Welply Will Abst in the Representative Church Body Lib (Irish Genealogist vols 6 & 7) [IR/PER]

1550-1909   *Index to* the Thrift Abst *of Wills In* "55-57th, Reps of Deputy Keeper of Public Recs in Ireland" [*all* IR/K]

1551-1837   *Abst of* Wills & Admons 1551-1837 *In* "Inchquin MSS" (IMC *vol*) [IR/G 32]

1563-1831   List of Wills printed in "Irish Memorials J" (Irish Memorials Assn J vol 12 pt 6) [IR/M 6A]

1569-1909   Welply's Irish Wills & Pleadings 1569-1909; vols 1-18: Irish Wills & Pleadings (*will & admon abst*) [IR/G 96-113]; vol 19: Pedigrees & Plea Rolls of Ireland (*enrolled will abst c1460-c1570*) [IR/G 114]; vol 20: Irish Wills & Pleadings (*supp*) [IR/G 115]; An Index to Welply's Irish Wills & Pleadings; vols 1-19 [IR/G 116]; An Index to Wills & Pleadings; *vol* 5 [IR/G 95]; An Index to Welply's Irish Wills & Pleadings; vol 20 [IR/G 117]

1597-1645   *Irish* Wills & Admons from the Registry at York prior to 1660 (*ie PCY Cal*) (Procs & Papers Royal Soc of Antiquaries of Ireland vol 33) [IR/PER]

1597-1849   Geneal Abst of Irish Wills *from various sources* (Irish Genealogist vols 1 & 2) [IR/PER]

17-18 C   Household Stuff (*invent abst*) (Irish Ancestor vol 1); Quaker Invents of the 17th & 18th C (Irish Ancestor vol 3) [*both* IR/PER]

1612-1805   *Index to* Will Abst in the Lane-Poole Papers *in the National Lib of Ireland* (Irish Genealogist vol 8) [IR/PER]

1612-1843   Index to Irish Wills in the Carrigan MSS at St Kieran's College, Kilkenny (Irish Genealogist vol 4) [IR/PER]

1613-1777   *Abst of* Original Wills (Irish Memorials Assn J vol 11 pts 5-6 & vol 13 pt 1) [IR/M 6A]

1613-1857   Abst of Wills *sent in by readers* (Irish Ancestor vols 2-8 & 14) [IR/PER]

1613-1878   *Index to* the Crosslé MSS (*abst of wills, grants, etc*) *In* "Reps of Deputy Keeper of Public Recs (Northern Ireland) for the Years 1925 & 1933*" [both* IR/K]

1619-1784   Index of Wills in the Burke MSS at Mount Mellery Abbey, County Waterford (Irish Genealogist vol 4) [IR/PER]

1633-1855   *Index to the* Stewart Kennedy Notes (extr from wills of Ulster testators in the PRO, Dublin) *In* "Rep of Deputy Keeper of Public Recs (Northern Ireland) for the Year 1935" [IR/K]

1637-1849   Abst of Wills from the Swanzy Coll (Irish Genealogist vols 1, 3 & 9) [IR/PER]

1650-1877   Abst from some Irish Wills (*Clare MSS*) [IR/G 89]

1660-1845   Synopsis of the Davies Abst in the State Lib at Melbourne, *Australia* (*lists Irish will abst, mainly PCA*) (Irish Genealogist vol 4) [IR/PER]

1665-1869   List of Misc Quaker Wills in the Hist Lib, Eustace Street, *Dublin In* appx 2 to "Quaker Recs, Dublin" (IMC *vol*) [IR/G 76]

1665-1879   *Abst of* Wills 1665-1879 *In* "Guide to Irish Quaker Recs 1654-1860" (IMC *vol*) [IR/G 75]

1684-1757   Abst of Wills & *Invents In* "Quaker Recs Dublin: Abst of Wills" (IMC *vol*) [IR/G 76]

1689-1872   Irish Wills in England; *post-1858 index 1864-1872; Court of Delegates index 1689-1820; India Office Lib (Bombay) index 1774-1779* (Irish Geneal Res Soc

18-19 C N/L vol 1 no 5) [IR/PER] Rosbottom Coll; *indexed* Abst of about 4,000 Irish Wills compiled by Lorna Rosbottom & now in the Library of the Society of Genealogists (also Mfc) [Mf 2030 or Apply to Staff]

1703-1903 List of Probs & Admons, etc ... *granted outside Ireland In* appx 2B to "55th Rep of Deputy Keeper of Public Recs in Ireland" [IR/K]

1714-1726 Extr from Invents 1714-1726 *In* "Immigration of the Irish Quakers into PA 1682-1750 with their Early Hist in Ireland" [US/PA/G 10]

1726-1758 Irish Wills from Barcelona (*will abst in the Archiva Historicó de Protocolos*) (Irish Genealogist vol 6) [IR/PER]

1749-1847 *Index to* Wills of Irish Interest in the Probate Registry at Halifax, NS, Canada (Irish Ancestor vol 1) [IR/PER]

1750 Irish References in PCC Wills proved in 1750 (*abst*) (Irish Genealogist vol 7) [IR/PER]

1771-1852 Index to the Hawkins Coll of Wills 1771-1852 *In* "Index to the Prerogative Wills of Ireland 1536-1810" [IR/G 93 or IR/G 150]

1776-1783 Irish Will *Abst* proved in the PCC (A-E) (*Walton MSS*) [Topo Docs Coll: Ireland]

1793-1859 Extr of Wills & Deeds in Newfoundland Provincial Archives (*300 British & Irish will abst*) (Newfoundland Ancestor vols 8-11) [CAN/NL/PER]

1802-1849 "Foreign" Wills proved at Carlisle (*will & admon index to persons who died in Ireland, etc*) (Genealogists' Mag vol 15) [PER/GEN]

Registry of Deeds, Dublin
1679-1738 *Irwin's Abst of* Irish Wills (*in Registry of Deeds etc*) (Misc Gen et Her 5th ser vol 4) [PER/MIS]

1708-1729 Wills 1708-1729 on record at the Registry of Deeds, Dublin (*index & abst*) [IR/G 83]

1708-1785 Alphabetical List of Wills in the Registry of Deeds with dates of registration; pt 1: 1708-1785 [IR/G 82]

1708-1832 Registry of Deeds; Abst of Wills (*all* IMC *vols*); vol 1: 1708-1745; vol 2: 1746-1785; vol 3: 1785-1832 [IR/G 90-91 & IR/G 131]

Genealogical Office, Dublin
16-19 C Consolidated Index to the Recs of the Genealogical Office, Dublin, Ireland (*wills' surname index*); Chapters A-O [IR/G 214A-C]*; chapters N-Z on order*

1536-1858 Index of Will Abst in the Genealogical Office, Dublin (Analecta Hibernica no 17) [IR/PER]

Public Record Office of Ireland, Dublin
now the National Archives of Ireland; see also PRO Belfast below

1270-1799 Index to the Act or Grant Books & to the Original Wills & *Admons* of the Diocese of Dublin to the Year 1800 (*wills copied from the Chancery & the Exchequer*) (appx to "26th Rep of Deputy Keeper of Public Recs in Ireland") [IR/K]

1556-1882 Irish FH: 17th, 18th & 19th C Wills (*will, admon, invent abst & indexes in the PRO, Dublin for 1556, 1605-1829, 1869-1882*) (N&Q vols 146-151, 154, 159 & 180-181) [N&Q]

1569-1909 Welply's Irish Wills & Pleadings 1569-1909; vols 1-18: Irish Wills & Pleadings (*will & admon abst*) [IR/G 96-113]; vol 19: Pedigrees & Plea Rolls of Ireland (*enrolled will abst c1460-c1570*) [IR/G 114]; vol 20: Irish Wills & Pleadings (*supp*) [IR/G 115]; An Index to Welply's Irish Wills & Pleadings; vols 1-19 [IR/G 116]; An Index to Wills & Pleadings; *vol 5* [IR/G 95]; An Index to Welply's Irish Wills & Pleadings; vol 20 [IR/G 117]

1569-1922 List of Original Prob, Letters of Admon wills annexed & intestate, Marriage Licence Grants & Official Copies of Wills, Grants, etc presented *to the PRO* during the period from the destruction of the RO to the end of 1927 *In* appx 2B to "55th Rep of Deputy Keeper of Public Recs in Ireland"; *additions for* 1928 *In* appx 1A to

"56th Rep"; *additions for* 1929 &
1930 *In* appx 1A to "57th Rep"
[*all* IR/K]

1584-1922 List of Original Unproved Wills
(never lodged for prob),
Duplicates of Wills & Plain
Copies of Wills, Grants, etc
presented *to the PRO* 1922-1927
In appx 2C to "55th Rep of
Deputy Keeper of Public Recs in
Ireland"; *additions for* 1928 *In*
appx 1B to "56th Rep"; *additions
for* 1929 & 1930 *In* appx 1B to
"57th Rep" [*all* IR/K]

1681-1846 Surname Index to the Swanzy
MSS (*these MSS include will abst
from the PRO, Dublin for the PCA
& the Dioceses of Clogher,
Kilmore as well as a few from
Connor, Down & Dromore*) [IR/G
143]

Public Record Office of Northern Ireland, Belfast
see also PRO, Dublin above
16-19 C Index to docs deposited in the
PRO of Northern Ireland during
the year *with probs* (appx 1 to
"Rep of Deputy Keeper of Public
Recs (Northern Ireland) for"
1924); *additions:* appx F to "Reps
of Deputy Keeper of Public Recs
(Northern Ireland) for 1925-1937"
[*all* IR/K]

ANTRIM
including the City of Belfast
Pre-1858 Probate Jurisdictions:-
Prerogative Court: Armagh
Consistory Courts: CONNOR; Derry; Down;
Dromore

18-19 C Extr from Wills & Admons *In*
"Gravestone Inscriptions, County
Antrim vols 1-3" [IR/M 12-13 &
IR/M 13A]

Belfast City
18-19 C Extr from Wills & Admons *In*
"Gravestone Inscriptions, Belfast
vols 1-4" [IR/M 14-15, IR/M 25 &
IR/M 29]

ARMAGH
Pre-1858 Probate Jurisdictions:-
Prerogative Court: Armagh
Consistory Courts: ARMAGH; Dromore

Ballyhagan near Lisburn
1685-1740 Will Book of Ballyhagan Meeting
of the Soc of Friends (*wills &
invent abst*) (Irish Genealogist vol
2) [IR/PER]; List of Quaker Wills
preserved at Lisburn *In* appx 1 to
"Quaker Recs Dublin: Abst of
Wills" (IMC *vol*) [IR/G 76]

CARLOW
Pre-1858 Probate Jurisdictions:-
Prerogative Court: Armagh
Consistory Courts: Dublin; Ferns; **LEIGHLIN**

CAVAN
Pre-1858 Probate Jurisdictions:-
Prerogative Court: Armagh
Consistory Courts: Ardagh; **KILMORE**;
Meath

1681-1846 Surname Index to the Swanzy
MSS (*these MSS include will abst
from the PRO, Dublin concerned
with the county of Cavan, etc*)
[IR/G 143]

CLARE
Pre-1858 Probate Jurisdictions:-
Prerogative Court: Armagh
**Consistory Courts: KILLALOE and
KILFENORA**; Limerick

CORK
Pre-1858 Probate Jurisdictions:-
Prerogative Court: Armagh
**Consistory Courts - E Riding: CLOYNE;
CORK and ROSS**; Limerick; Waterford &
Lismore; **CLOYNE; CORK and ROSS**
Consistory Courts - W Riding: Ardfert &
Aghadoe; **CLOYNE; CORK and ROSS**

1536-1810 Index to the Prerogative Wills of
Ireland 1536-1810 relating to
Cork & Kerry (*DEL-Z*) *In* "O'Kief,
Coshe Mang, Slieve Lougher &
Upper Blackwater in Ireland; vol
6: Hist & Geneal Items relating to
N Cork & E Kerry" [IR/G 196]

1548-1628 *Abst of* Wills & Invents of Cork,
temp Mary, Elizabeth, James I &
Charles I (Gentleman's Mag new
(*1856*) ser vols 11-13) [GM]

Mallow
1716-1805 Mallow Testmtry Recs in Mallow
Castle (*will & invent abst*) (Irish
Ancestor vol 1) [IR/PER]

DERRY, COUNTY *see LONDONDERRY*

DONEGAL
Pre-1858 Probate Jurisdictions:-
Prerogative Court: Armagh
Consistory Courts: Clogher; Derry; **RAPHOE**

DOWN
Pre-1858 Probate Jurisdictions:-
Prerogative Court: Armagh
Consistory Courts: Connor; **DOWN**; Dromore
Peculiars, etc: Newry & Mourne
see ANTRIM for the City of Belfast

18-19 C Extr from Wills & Admons *In*
"Gravestone Inscriptions, County
Down; vols 1-21" [IR/M 17-22,
IR/M 28 & IR/M 32]

Downpatrick
19th C Old Fams of Downpatrick &
District from Gravestone
Inscriptions, Wills & Biographical
Notes (*extr*) *In* "Gravestone
Inscriptions, County Down vol 21"
[IR/M 32]

DUBLIN
including the City of Dublin
Pre-1858 Probate Jurisdictions:-
Prerogative Court: Armagh
Consistory Court: DUBLIN
Civil Court: Dublin (Lord Mayor)

1270-1799 Index to the Act or Grant Books &
to the Original Wills & *Admons* of
the Diocese of Dublin to the Year
1800 *including the Inquisitions of
Dublin, Kildare & Wicklow*) (appx
to "26th Rep of the Deputy
Keeper of Public Recs in Ireland")
[IR/K]

Dublin City
1270-1799 Index to the Act or Grant Books &
to the Original Wills & *Admons* of
the Diocese of Dublin to the Year
1800 (*wills amongst Christ
Church Deeds*) (appx to "26th
Rep of the Deputy Keeper of
Public Recs in Ireland") [IR/K]
1665-1869 List of Misc Quaker Wills in the

Hist Lib, Eustace Street, *Dublin
In* appx 2 to "Quaker Recs
Dublin: Abst of Wills" (IMC *vol*)
[IR/G 76]
1684-1695 *Extr from* Invents of Five Dublin
Quaker merchants in the late
17th C (Irish Ancestor vol 10)
[IR/PER]

FERMANAGH
Pre-1858 Probate Jurisdictions:-
Prerogative Court: Armagh
Consistory Courts: CLOGHER; Kilmore

1612-1858 Indexes to Some Wills *In* "Hist
Gleanings from County Derry (&
some from Fermanagh)" [IR/L 29]
1681-1846 Surname Index to the Swanzy
MSS(*these MSS include will abst
from the PRO, Dublin concerned
with the county of Fermanagh,
etc*) [IR/G 143]

GALWAY
Pre-1858 Probate Jurisdictions:-
Prerogative Court: Armagh
Consistory Courts: CLONFERT; Elphin;
Killaloe & Kilfenora; **TUAM**

1681-1846 Surname Index to the Swanzy
MSS (*these MSS include will abst
& occasional items for County
Galway*) [IR/G 143]

KERRY
Pre-1858 Probate Jurisdictions:-
Prerogative Court: Armagh
Consistory Courts: ARDFERT and
AGHADOE; Cork & Ross; Limerick

1536-1810 Index to the Prerogative Wills of
Ireland 1536-1810 relating to
Cork & Kerry (*DEL-Z*) *In* "O'Kief,
Coshe Mang, Slieve Lougher &
Upper Blackwater in Ireland; vol
6: Hist & Geneal Items relating to
N Cork & E Kerry" [IR/G 196]

KILDARE
Pre-1858 Probate Jurisdictions:-
Prerogative Court: Armagh
Consistory Courts: DUBLIN; KILDARE;
Leighlin

1270-1799 Index to the Act or Grant Books &
to the Original Wills of the
Diocese of Dublin to the Year

1800 (*wills in the Inquisitions of Dublin, Kildare & Wicklow*) (appx to "26th Rep of the Deputy Keeper of Public Recs in Ireland") [IR/K]

KILKENNY
Pre-1858 Probate Jurisdictions:-
Prerogative Court: Armagh
Consistory Courts: Cashel & Emly; LEIGHLIN; OSSORY

KING'S COUNTY
now COUNTY OFFALY
Pre-1858 Probate Jurisdictions:-
Prerogative Court: Armagh
Consistory Courts: Clonfert; KILDARE; KILLALOE and KILFENORA; MEATH; Ossory

LEITRIM
Pre-1858 Probate Jurisdictions:-
Prerogative Court: Armagh
Consistory Courts: ARDAGH; KILMORE

LEIX/LAOIS *see QUEEN'S COUNTY*

LIMERICK
Pre-1858 Probate Jurisdictions:-
Prerogative Court: Armagh
Consistory Courts: CASHEL and EMLY; Cloyne; Killaloe & Kilfenora; LIMERICK

Limerick City
1361-1475 List of Medieval Wills of Citizens of Limerick *in the Patent Rolls (Ireland)* (Procs & Papers Royal Soc of Antiquaries of Ireland vol 28) [IR/PER]
1403-1717 List & Abst of Wills *In* "Notes on the Chapels of St Mary's Cathedral, Limerick" (Procs & Papers Royal Soc of Antiquaries of Ireland vol 28) [IR/PER]

LONDONDERRY
Pre-1858 Probate Jurisdictions:-
Prerogative Court: Armagh
Consistory Courts: ARMAGH; CONNOR; DERRY

1612-1858 Indexes to Some Wills *In* "Hist Gleanings from County Derry (& some from Fermanagh)" [IR/L 29]

LONGFORD
Pre-1858 Probate Jurisdictions:-
Prerogative Court: Armagh
Consistory Courts: ARDAGH; Meath

LOUTH
Pre-1858 Probate Jurisdictions:-
Prerogative Court: Armagh
Consistory Courts: ARMAGH; Clogher

Kilsaran District
1562-1907 *Extr from* Wills of Residents *In* appx 6 to "Hist of Kilsaran Union of Parishes in the County of Louth" [IR/L 58]

MAYO
Pre-1858 Probate Jurisdictions:-
Prerogative Court: Armagh
Consistory Courts: KILLALA and ACHONRY; TUAM

MEATH
Pre-1858 Probate Jurisdictions:-
Prerogative Court: Armagh
Consistory Courts: Armagh; Kilmore; MEATH

MONAGHAN
Pre-1858 Probate Jurisdictions:-
Prerogative Court: Armagh
Consistory Courts: CLOGHER

1681-1846 Surname Index to the Swanzy MSS (*these MSS include will abst from the PRO, Dublin concerned with the county of Monaghan, etc*) [IR/G 143]

OFFALY *see KING'S COUNTY*

QUEEN'S COUNTY
now COUNTY LEIX/LAOIS
Pre-1858 Probate Jurisdictions:-
Prerogative Court: Armagh
Consistory Courts: Dublin; KILDARE; Killaloe & Kilfenora; LEIGHLIN; OSSORY

ROSCOMMON
Pre-1858 Probate Jurisdictions:-
Prerogative Court: Armagh
Consistory Courts: Ardagh; Clonfert; ELPHIN; Killala & Achonry; Tuam

1681-1846 Surname Index to the Swanzy MSS (*these MSS include will abst* with occasional items for County Roscommon) [IR/G 143]

SLIGO
Pre-1858 Probate Jurisdictions:-
Prerogative Court: Armagh
Consistory Courts: Ardagh; ELPHIN; KILLALA and ACHONRY; Kilmore

TIPPERARY
Pre-1858 Probate Jurisdictions:-
Prerogative Court: Armagh
Consistory Courts - Tipperary N Riding: CASHEL & EMLY; KILLALOE & KILFENORA
Consistory Courts - Tipperary S Riding: CASHEL & EMLY; WATERFORD & LISMORE

TYRONE
Pre-1858 Probate Jurisdictions:-
Prerogative Court: Armagh
Consistory Courts: ARMAGH; CLOGHER; DERRY

WATERFORD
Pre-1858 Probate Jurisdictions:-
Prerogative Court: Armagh
Consistory Courts: Cloyne; WATERFORD & LISMORE
Peculiars, etc: Lismore

1579-1926 Wills & Admons Relating to Waterford; pt 4: Unpublished Abst in the Jennings MSS (index: L-Z, 1583 & 1626-1842) (extr from Decies no 20) [IR/PER]; pt 5: Misc Wills in the Jennings MSS (list B-S, 1579 & 1630-1839) (extract from Decies no 22) [Apply to Staff]; pt 6: Coll of Waterford Wills in the National Lib of Ireland (list 1773-1926) (extr from Decies no 23) [Apply to Staff]; pt 7: Marriage Licence Bonds, Chancery Bills & Miscellanea in the Jennings MSS (Chancery parties list 1597-1738) (extr from Decies no 23) [Apply to Staff]

WESTMEATH
Pre-1858 Probate Jurisdictions:-
Prerogative Court: Armagh
Consistory Courts: Ardagh; MEATH

WEXFORD
Pre-1858 Probate Jurisdictions:-
Prerogative Court: Armagh
Consistory Courts: Dublin; FERNS; Leighlin

WICKLOW
Pre-1858 Probate Jurisdictions:-
Prerogative Court: Armagh
Consistory Courts: DUBLIN; FERNS; LEIGHLIN; Kildare

1270-1799 Index to the Act or Grant Books & to the Original Wills of the Diocese of Dublin to the Year 1800 (wills in the Inquisitions of Dublin, Kildare & Wicklow) (appx to "26th Rep of the Deputy Keeper of Public Recs in Ireland") [IR/K]

SCOTLAND

PRE-1823 PROBATE JURISDICTIONS
After the Reformation neither the established Church of Scotland nor the Episcopal Church of Scotland exercised probate jurisdiction in Scotland & probate administration was undertaken by Commissariots from 1560 to 1823 when jurisdiction passed to Sheriff's Courts. Some records dating from the earlier ecclesiastical administration survive but these were absorbed into commissariots' papers in the 16th C. Although there was no prerogative jurisdiction in Scotland, the Commissariot of Edinburgh may be regarded as the principal court as it had jurisdiction over persons dying "furth of Scotland". In addition, many Scottish wills were proved in other courts in the British Isles especially in the PCC where wills were identified as "Parts", "Scotland", "North Britain" or just by the name of the commissariot. Under border law, probates granted in border commissariots could be re-sealed at Carlisle, Durham or the PCY but not vice versa.

NATION-WIDE COLLECTIONS
see THE REGISTERS OF SCOTLAND for probate records amongst the Regs other than of Testments ie of Deeds, of Services of Heirs, etc; see also the NATIONAL section.

1392-1789 *Index to* Testmts of Individuals *In* "Scottish Texts & Cals; an analytical guide to serial pubs" (Royal Hist Soc Guides & Handbooks no 14) [Apply to Staff]

1481-1740 *Cal of* Misc Executry Papers preserved in HM Reg House (Scottish Rec Soc vol 24) [SC/PER]

16-19 C Macleod Coll *includes a large number of Scottish Will abst (33 bound vols & 82 boxes)* [Upper Library: Special Colls]

1571-1775 Invents from Craftsmen's Wills *In* appx 1 to "Scottish Arms Makers" *(extr from invents of Scottish armourers, bowyers, bucklermakers, cutlers, gunners, gunmakers, lorimers, sheathmakers & sword stoppers)* [PR/ARM]

1585-1749 *Extr from* Testmts & Invents of various *fams In* appx to "Some Old Fams; a contribution to the general history of Scotland" [SC/G 46]

1600-1700 Some Loc Wills in the PCC *(index to the Tay Valley area)* (Tay Valley FHn no 15) [SC/PER]

1650-1900 Scottish American Wills 1650-1900; Index to testmts & invents registered & confirmed in the Commissariot & Sheriff courts of Edinburgh with supp data from the Index to Personal Estates of Defuncts 1846-1866 of Scots resident in N America [US/G 147]

1668-1699 Scottish-Jamaican Testmts *(index to wills in the Jamaican RO)* (Scottish Genealogist vol 35 no 1) [SC/PER]

1680-1830 Directory of Scots in the Carolinas 1680-1830 *(prob extr)* [US/NC/G 9]

1700-1893 Abst of Wills & Admons in the PCC & elsewhere with Extr from Testmts in Scottish Commissariots; vols 1-2: 1700-1893 *(Hargreaves-Mawdeley Colls)* [WILLS/GEN]

1796-1802 Death Duty Reg extr 1796-1801 *(N Scottish wills in the PCC to 1801)* (Highlands FHS J no 9); Extr from the Estate Duty Regs at the PRO London relating to *Scottish* Wills proved in the PCC (Scottish Genealogist vol 30 nos 3 & 4); Scottish Wills proved in Canterbury *(PCC abst)* (Aberdeen & NE Scotland FHS N/L nos 8, 11 & 14) *[all* SC/PER]

1800-1830 Index to Testmts 1800-1830 *(Macleod MSS)* [SC/G 118]

1820-1853 "Foreign" Wills proved at Carlisle *(will & admon index to persons who died in Scotland 1820-1853)* (Genealogists' Mag vol 15) [PER/GEN]

1827-1842 PCY Index of Scotsmen 1827-1842 *(A-G)* (Scottish Genealogist vol 29 no 2) [SC/PER]

1876-1913 Wealthy Scots 1876-1913 *(index of invents in the Cal of Confirmations)* (Bull Inst Hist Res vol 58 no 137) [PER/INS]

THE REGISTERS OF SCOTLAND
see also under individual counties

1502-1700 Inquisitionum ad capellam Domini Regis Retornatarum quae Scotiae adhuc servantur, abbreviatio (vols 1-3: *Record of Retours by counties)* [SC Folio]

1625-1825 Directory of Scottish Settlers in N America 1625-1825; vol 4: *Abst of N American Services of Heirs, Testmts & Admons in Edinburgh & the PCC;* vol 6: *Abst of N American docs in the Edinburgh Reg of Deeds including wills* [US/MIG 20 & 87]

1673-1696 Index to Regs of Deeds; vols 13-20 *(annually 1673-1680),* & vol 36 *(1696)* (Regs & Recs of Scotland Indexes nos 22, 24, 26, 28, 30, 32, 34, 35 & 70) *[all* SC/PER]

1683-1883 Scottish American Heirs *(abst of Decennial Indexes of Returns of Heirs)* [US/G 184]

1700-1799 N American Residents in Retours 1700-1799 *(index)* (Scottish Genealogist vol 13 no 1) [SC/PER]

1800-1819 Scottish American Heirs 1800-1819 (continuation of the Decennial Indexes of Returns of Heirs) (Scottish Genealogist vol 14 no 4) [SC/PER]

1829-1859 Scottish Australasian Heirs before 1860 *(index 1829-1859)* (Scottish Genealogist vol 15 no 1) [SC/PER]

ABERDEENSHIRE
Pre-1823 Jurisdictions:-
Commissariots: ABERDEEN; Moray

ANGUS
Pre-1823 Probate Jurisdictions:-
Commissariots: BRECHIN; Dunkeld; ST
  ANDREWS

1565-1800   Examples of Testmts (*index*) *In*
    "Pre-1855 Gravestone
    Inscriptions in Angus; vol 1:
    Strathmore" (*index 1565-1800*);
    "vol 2: Seacoast" (*index 1579-
    1793*); "vol 4: Broughty Ferry"
    (*index 1576-1770*) [SC/M 27, 28
    & 40]

ARGYLLSHIRE
Pre-1823 Probate Jurisdictions:-
Commissariots: ARGYLL; THE ISLES

AYRSHIRE
Pre-1823 Probate Jurisdiction:-
Commissariot: GLASGOW

BANFFSHIRE
Pre-1823 Probate Jurisdictions:-
Commissariots: ABERDEEN; Moray

BERWICKSHIRE
Pre-1823 Probate Jurisdiction:-
Commissariot: LAUDER

1797-1803   Extr from the Death Duty Regs
    relating to *Border* Wills proved in
    the PCC (Borders FH N/L no 4)
    [SC/PER]

BUTESHIRE
Pre-1823 Probate Jurisdiction:-
Commissariot: THE ISLES

1661-1800   Examples of Testmts (*a parish-
    by-parish index*) *In* "Pre-1855
    Gravestone Inscriptions in Bute &
    Arran" [SC/M 52]

CAITHNESS
Pre-1823 Probate Jurisdiction:-
Commissariot: CAITHNESS

CLACKMANNANSHIRE
Pre-1823 Probate Jurisdictions:-
Commissariots: Dunblane; STIRLING

CROMARTY *see ROSS & CROMARTY*

DUMFRIESSHIRE
Pre-1823 Probate Jurisdiction:-
Commissariot: DUMFRIES

Applegarth
1624-1797   Commissariot Rec of Dumfries;
    Extr from Reg of Testmts *In*
    "Memorials of Applegarth &
    Sibbaldie Parish" [SC/M 2]

Corrie *see Hutton*

Eskdalemuir
1656-1793   Commissariot Rec of Dumfries;
    Extr from Reg of Testmts *In*
    "Memorials of Eskdalemuir"
    [SC/M 2]

Hutton
1624-1800   Extr from the Reg of Testmts
    1624-1800; Commissariot Rec of
    Dumfries *In* "Memorials of Hutton
    & Corrie Parishes" [SC/M 1]

Kirkpatrick-Juxta
1624-1800   Commissariot Rec of Dumfries;
    Extr from the Reg of Testmts
    1624-1800 *In* "Memorials of
    Kirkpatrick-Juxta Parish" [SC/M
    2]

Langholm
1624-1800   Commissariot Rec of Dumfries;
    Extr from the Reg of Testmts
    1624-1800 *In* "Memorials of
    Langholm vol 1: Wauchope"
    [SC/M 1]
1643-1712   Commissariot Rec of Dumfries;
    Extr from the Reg of Testmts *In*
    "Memorials of Langholm Parish
    vol 3: Staplegordon" [SC/M 2]

Mouswald
1625-1793   Commissariot Rec of Dumfries;
    Extr from the Reg of Testmts *In*
    "Memorials of Mouswald Parish"
    [SC/M 11]

Ruthwell
1624-1800   Commissariot Rec of Dumfries;
    Extr from Reg of Testmts
    (*including adjacent parishes*) *In*
    "Memorials of Ruthwell Parish"
    [SC/M 11]

St Mungo
1624-1800   Commissariot Rec of Dumfries;

Extr from Reg of Testmts In
"Memorials of St Mungo Parish"
[SC/M 11]

Sibbaldie see Applegarth

Torthorwald
1625-1797 Commissariot Rec of Dumfries;
Extr from Reg of Testmts In
"Memorials of Torthorwald
Parish" [SC/M 11]

Trailflatt
1674-1777 Commissariot Rec of Dumfries;
Extr from Reg of Testmts In
"Memorials of Trailflatt Parish"
[SC/M 2]

Tundergarth
1624-1800 Commissariot Rec of Dumfries;
Extr from Reg of Testmts In
"Memorials of Tundergarth
Parish" [SC/M 11]

Wamphray
1658-1798 Commissariot Rec of Dumfries;
Extr from Reg of Testmts In
"Memorials of Wamphray Parish"
[SC/M 11]

Westkirk
1640-1797 Commissariot Rec of Dumfries;
Extr from Reg of Testmts In
"Memorials of Westkirk Parish"
[SC/M 2]

DUNBARTONSHIRE
Pre-1823 Probate Jurisdictions:-
Commissariots: GLASGOW; Hamilton &
  Campsie

EDINBURGHSHIRE see MIDLOTHIAN

ELGIN see MORAYSHIRE

FIFE
Pre-1823 Probate Jurisdictions:-
Commissariots: Dunkeld; ST ANDREWS;
  Stirling

1550-1822 Examples of Testmts (parish-by-
parish index) In "MI (pre-1855) in
E Fife" [SC/M 33]
1578-1820 Examples of Testmts (parish-by-
parish index) In "MI (pre-1855) in
W Fife" [SC/M 33]

FORFARSHIRE see ANGUS

HADDINGTONSHIRE see LOTHIAN, EAST

INVERNESS
Pre-1823 Probate Jurisdictions:-
Commissariots: Argyll; INVERNESS; Moray;
THE ISLES

KINCARDINESHIRE
Pre-1823 Probate Jurisdictions:-
Commissariots: BRECHIN; ST ANDREWS

1661-1800 Examples of Testmts (parish-by-
parish index) In "Pre-1855
Gravestone Inscriptions in
Kincardineshire" [SC/M 52]

KINROSSSHIRE
Pre-1823 Probate Jurisdictions:-
Commissariots: Dunblane; ST ANDREWS;
  Stirling

KIRKCUDBRIGHTSHIRE
Pre-1823 Probate Jurisdictions:-
Commissariots: Dumfries;
KIRKCUDBRIGHT; Wigtown

1572-1797 Examples of Testmts (parish-by-
parish index) In "Pre-1855
Gravestone Inscriptions; an index
for the Stewartry of
Kirkcudbrightshire; vols 1-3 & 6"
[SC/M 76]
Note: vols 4-5 on order

LANARKSHIRE
including the City of Glasgow
Pre-1823 Probate Jurisdictions:-
**Commissariots: GLASGOW; HAMILTON
and CAMPSIE; LANARK**

1799-1799 Abst of Retours of Heirs 1700-
1799 In "MI (pre-1855) in the
Upper Ward of Lanarkshire"
[SC/M 9]

LINLITHGOWSHIRE see LOTHIAN, WEST

LOTHIAN, EAST
Pre-1823 Probate Jurisdictions:-
Commissariots: EDINBURGH; Dunkeld

LOTHIAN, WEST
Pre-1823 Probate Jurisdictions:-
Commissariots: EDINBURGH; Dunkeld

MIDLOTHIAN
Pre-1823 Probate Jurisdiction:-
Commissariot: EDINBURGH

Edinburgh City
1557-1687 Coll of the Wills of Printers &
Booksellers in Edinburgh 1557-
1687 (*abst*) *In* "Bannantyne
Miscellany vol 2" [SC/G 142]

MORAYSHIRE
Pre-1823 Probate Jurisdiction:-
Commissariot: MORAY

NAIRNSHIRE
Pre-1823 Probate Jurisdiction:-
Commissariot: MORAY

ORKNEY
Pre-1823 Probate Jurisdiction:-
Commissariot: ORKNEY and SHETLAND
Sheriff's Court: Orkney

PEEBLESHIRE
Pre-1823 Probate Jurisdiction:-
Commissariot: PEEBLES

1797-1803 Extr from the Death Duty Regs
relating to *Border* Wills proved in
the PCC (Borders FH N/L no 4)
[SC/PER]

PERTHSHIRE
Pre-1823 Probate Jurisdictions:-
Commissariots: DUNBLANE; DUNKELD; ST
ANDREWS

1596-1800 Examples of Testmts (*parish-by-
parish index*) *In* "MI (pre-1855) in
N Perthshire" [SC/M 12]
1595-1800 Examples of Testmts (*parish-by-
parish index*) *In* "MI (pre-1855) in
S Perthshire" [SC/M 13]

RENFREWSHIRE
Pre-1823 Probate Jurisdictions:-
Commissariots: GLASGOW; Hamilton &
Campsie
see LANARKSHIRE for the City of Glasgow

ROSS and CROMARTY
Pre-1823 Probate Jurisdiction:-
Commissariot: ROSS; The Isles

ROXBURGHSHIRE
Pre-1823 Probate Jurisdiction:-
Commissariot: PEEBLES

1636-1847 *Reg of* Services of Heirs -
Roxburghshire 1636-1847
(Scottish Rec Soc vol 69)
[SC/PER]; Notes of the Services
of Heirs - Roxburghshire; in the
Sheriff Clerk's Office, Jedburgh
(*Macleod MSS*) [SC/L 184]
1797-1803 Extr from the Death Duty Regs
relating to *Border* Wills proved in
the PCC (Borders FH N/L no 4)
[SC/PER]

SELKIRKSHIRE
Pre-1823 Probate Jurisdiction:-
Commissariot: PEEBLES

1797-1803 Extr from the Death Duty Regs
relating to *Border* Wills proved in
the PCC (Borders FH N/L no 4)
[SC/PER]

SHETLAND
Pre-1823 Probate Jurisdiction:-
Commissariot: ORKNEY and SHETLAND

STIRLINGSHIRE
Pre-1823 Probate Jurisdiction:-
Commissariots: Glasgow; Hamilton &
Campsie; STIRLING

1672-1791 Examples of Testmts (*parish-by-
parish index*) *In* "MI (pre-1855) in
E Stirlingshire" [SC/M 15]
1549-1796 Examples of Testmts (*parish-by-
parish index: 1549, 1610-1796*)
In "MI (pre-1855) in W
Stirlingshire" [SC/M 16]

SUTHERLAND
Pre-1823 Probate Jurisdiction:-
Commissariot: CAITHNESS

WIGTOWNSHIRE
Pre-1823 Probate Jurisdiction:-
Commissariot: WIGTOWN

1843-1925 Wills & Bequests *In* "Wigtown
Free Press Index vol 4: Subject
Index 1843-1925" [SC/L 192]

WALES

NATION-WIDE COLLECTIONS
see also the NATIONAL section

1463-1551 *Abst of* Early Wills of W Wales (W Wales Hist Rec vol 7) [WS/PER]

1519-1648 *Index to* Cheshire & Lancs Wills in the Harleian Coll at the BM (*including pts of Wales*) (Cheshire Sheaf 3rd ser vol 27) [CH/PER]

1523-1540 *Abst of* Wills of Welsh Ecclesiastics holding appointments in England (Archaeologia Cambrenis vol 82 for 1927) [WS/PER]

1541-1828 Abst of Wills, Admons & Invents *In* "National Lib of Wales - Cal of Deeds & Docs; vol 3: Hawarden Deeds" [WS/G 16]

1545-1858 Welsh Wills proved at Chester 1545-1858 (*will, admon, invent, bond, etc index*) [WS/G 127]

1546-1855 Abst of Wills, Admons & Invents *In* "National Lib of Wales - Cal of Deeds & Docs; vol 2: Crosswood Deeds" [WS/G 15]

1568-1650 Wills, admons & invents of persons belonging to places outside the Diocese of Chester 1568-1650 & now preserved at Chester (Lancs & Cheshire Rec Soc Procs vol 4) [LA/PER]

1622-1872 Abst of Wills, Admons & Invents *In* "National Lib of Wales - Cal of Deeds & Docs; vol 1: Coleman Deeds" [WS/G 14]

1821-1837 *Index to* Welsh Wills proved in the Archdeaconry of Chester (Hel Achau no 38) [WS/PER]

ANGLESEY
Pre-1858 Probate Jurisdictions:-
Prerogative Court: Canterbury
Consistory: BANGOR

1684-1855 List of Wills, Admons & other Prob Recs of Anglesey Seamen, Allied Trades & Professions (Gwynedd Roots no 1) [WS/PER]

BRECONSHIRE
Pre-1858 Probate Jurisdictions:-
Prerogative Court: Canterbury

Archdeaconry: BRECON

CAERNARVONSHIRE
Pre-1858 Probate Jurisdictions:-
Prerogative Court: Canterbury
Consistory Courts: BANGOR; St Asaph

CARDIGANSHIRE
Pre-1858 Probate Jurisdictions:-
Prerogative Court: Canterbury
Consistory Court: St David's
Archdeaconry Court: CARDIGAN

1546-1855 Abst of Wills, Admons & Invents *In* "National Lib of Wales - Cal of Deeds & Docs; vol 2: Crosswood Deeds" [WS/G 15]

Llanllwchaern
1684-1721 1670 Hearth Tax at Llanllwchaern & *abst of* some contemporary wills (Dyfed FHS J vol 5 no 2) [WS/PER]

CARMARTHENSHIRE
Pre-1858 Probate Jurisdictions:-
Prerogative Court: Canterbury
Consistory Court: St David's
Archdeaconry Court: CARMARTHEN

Llannon
1838-1858 Index to Wills & Letters of Admon - St David's Diocese: Llannon & Llanelli 1838-1858 (Dyfed FHS J vol 3) [WS/PER]

Llanelly *see Llannon*

DENBIGHSHIRE
Pre-1858 Probate Jurisdictions:-
Prerogative Courts: Canterbury; York (from 1541)
Consistory Courts: BANGOR; Chester (from 1541); Lichfield (until 1541); **ST ASAPH**; York (Chancery)
Peculiars, etc: York (Dean & Chapter - from 1541)

FLINTSHIRE (Flints)
Pre-1858 Probate Jurisdictions:-
Prerogative Courts: Canterbury; York
Consistory Courts: CHESTER (from 1541); Lichfield; **ST ASAPH**; York (Chancery)

Peculiars, etc: Hawarden; York (Dean & Chapter)

1541-1828 Abst of Wills, Admons & Invents *In* "National Lib of Wales - Cal of Deeds & Docs; vol 3: Hawarden Deeds" [WS/G 16]

GLAMORGAN (Glam)
Pre-1858 Probate Jurisdictions:-
Prerogative Court: Canterbury
Consistory Courts: LLANDAFF; St David's
Archdeaconry Court: Carmarthen

1392-1600 Glam Wills proved in the PCC: Interim Cal (*abst*); vol 1: 1392-1571; vol 2: 1572-1600 [WS/L 78 & 77]
1601-1770 Alphabetical Index to Glam Testators of Wills proved in the PCC; pt 1: 1601-1700 (Glam FHS J no 13); pt 2: 1701-1770 (Glam FHS J no 12) (*both* Mfc) [*both* WS/PER or Apply to Staff]

Cowbridge
1575-1799 *Index to* Cowbridge Wills & Admons *In* "Old Cowbridge Borough, Church & School" [WS/L 15]

MERIONETHSHIRE
Pre-1858 Probate Jurisdictions:-
Prerogative Court: Canterbury
Consistory Courts: BANGOR; ST ASAPH

MONMOUTHSHIRE (Mons)
Pre-1858 Probate Jurisdictions:-
Prerogative Court: Canterbury
Consistory Courts: Hereford until 1836); LLANDAFF
Archdeaconry Court: Brecon (until 1836)

1404-1560 Mons Wills proved in the PCC 1404-1560 (*cal with abst*) [WS/G 71]

Llanthewy Skirrid *see St Teilo*

Llantillio Pertholey *see St Teilo*

St Teilo
1690-1826 Llantillio Pertholey (St Teilo *including Llanthewy Skirrid*): Removal Orders 1799-1814, *Abst*

of Wills & other Docs 1690-1826, Constables 1673 & 1725 & Glebe Lands 1765 [WS/L 71]

MONTGOMERYSHIRE (Montgomery)
Pre-1858 Probate Jurisdictions:-
Prerogative Court: Canterbury
Consistory Courts: BANGOR; Hereford; ST ASAPH
Archdeaconry Court: Brecon

1443-1747 *Abst of* Early Montgomery Wills at Somerset House (Montgomery Colls vols 24 & 26) [WS/PER]
1701-1749 *Cal of* Montgomery Wills at the PRO (Montgomery Colls vol 63) [WS/PER]

Cemmaes
1661-1729 Early Cemmaes Wills in the St Asaph Reg (*will & admon index*) (Cronicl no 15) [WS/PER]

PEMBROKESHIRE (Pembroke)
Pre-1858 Probate Jurisdictions:-
Prerogative Court: Canterbury
Consistory Court: St David's
Archdeaconry Court: ST DAVID'S

1620-1714 Index to Chancery Court Proceedings of Pembroke Interest [WS/G 91]
1701-1800 Pembroke Wills 1701-1800 proven in the PCC [Apply to Staff]

RADNORSHIRE (Radnor)
Pre-1858 Probate Jurisdictions:-
Prerogative Court: Canterbury
Consistory Court: Hereford
Archdeaconry Court: BRECON

1452-1604 Index to Radnor Wills *in the PCC* (Radnor Soc Trans vol 3) [WS/PER]
1452-1651 *Abst of* Radnor Wills *in the PCC* (Radnor Soc Trans vols 7-8, 11, 13, 17 & 21-23) [WS/PER]
1539-1600 *Abst of Radnor Wills in* Hereford Probate Court (Radnor Soc Trans vols 24, 26-36 & 38) [WS/PER]
1543-1589 *Abst of* Radnor Wills in the Archdeaconry of Brecon (Radnor Soc Trans vols 20-21, 38-42, 44, 47-49 & 51-58) [WS/PER]

OVERSEAS

At the date of publication of this Guide the only probate material in the Society's Overseas collections were for the following countries but people from the British Isles dying abroad often had probate granted or re-granted in a British court - particularly, prior to 1858, in the PCC (as foreign "Parts"); see also the NATIONAL section & the Nation-Wide Collections of the IRELAND, SCOTLAND & WALES sections

ANTIGUA
see also WEST INDIES

1637-1820   Wills & Admons *In* appx to "Hist of the Island of Antigua, one of the Leeward Caribbees in the WI, from the First Settlement in 1635 to the Present Time vol 3"; pt 1: Extr from such of the earlier Recs of Wills as are now extant (*1670-1820*); pt 2: Abst of PCC Wills & Admons (*1637-1774*) [WI Folio]

1641-1812   Antigua: List of Wills relating to this island proved in the PCC down to 1812 (Caribbeana vol 3) [WI/G 3]

1766-1789   Indentures, Wills, etc at Dominica RO (*Antiguan wills extr*) (Caribbeana vol 4) [WI/G 4]

AUSTRALIA
NSW = New South Wales, NT = Northern Territory, QL = Queensland, SA = South Australia, V = Victoria

1829-1859   *Index to* Scottish Australasian *Return of* Heirs before 1860 (Scottish Genealogist vol 15 no 1) [SC/PER]

New South Wales
1800-1806   *Abst of* Early Sydney Wills (Australian Genealogist vol 4 pts 1-8) [AUA/PER]

1800-1901   NSW Prob List 1800-1901 (*wills & admons A-BRE*) (Australian Genealogist vols 2 pts 4-7, 3 pts 2-12 & 4 pts 1-8) [AUA/PER]

1800-1982   Supreme Court of NSW: Prob Index 1800-1982 (Mfc) [Lower Library: Australia Mfc drawer]

1831-1901   Index to NSW Probs (*testators late of NZ A-C*) (NZ Genealogist vol 16 no 157) [NZ/PER]

1862-1989   Unrelated Wills (*index to strays in Nepean FHS Lib*) (Timespan no 59) [AUA/NSW/PER]

Northern Territory
1885-1941   Supreme Court of the NT: Prob Indexes 1885-1941 (ie an index of persons whose wills have been granted prob, an index of legatees & other persons mentioned in the wills & an index of first & second witnesses) (Mfc) [Lower Library: Australia Mfc drawer]

1954-1962   Admons granted & sealed by the Supreme Court of the NT 1954-1962 (Mfc) [Lower Library: Australia Mfc drawer]

Queensland
1796-1801   Death Duty Recs (*PCC will extr*) (QL FHn vol 7 no 5) [AUA/QL/PER]

1878-1909   Transmission of Real Estate by Death (*will & admon cal*) (Yesteryear Links: QL Rec ser A) (Mfc); vol 1: 1878-1889 [Lower Library: Australia Mfc drawer]; **Note:** *vols 2 & 3: 1890-1904 on order*; vol 4: 1905-1909 [Lower Library: Australia Mfc drawer]

South Australia
1846-1909   Wills amongst Land Recs (*cal of wills & admons in the Registrar-General's Dept, Adelaide*) (S Australian Genealogist vol 1 nos 1 & 2) [AUA/SA/PER]

Victoria
1841-1892   Probate Office of the Supreme Court of V: Index to Grants of Representations 1841-1892 (Mfc) [Lower Library: Australia Mfc drawer]

1862-1888   Prob Recs, PRO V (*index to testators late of NZ*) (NZ Genealogist vol 16 no 154) [NZ/PER]

BANGLADESH *see India*

BARBADOS
see also WEST INDIES

1614-1853 *Abst of* Wills *In* "Genealogies of Barbados Fams" [WI/L 5]
1628-1799 List of Wills relating to Barbados proved *in the* PCC (*index*) (Caribbeana vol 2) [WI/G 2]
1639-1725 *Abst of* Barbados Recs - Wills & Admons; vol 1: 1639-1680; vol 2: 1681-1700; vol 3: 1701-1725 [WI/L 12-14]
1647-1799 List of Wills recorded in Barbados down to the year 1800 (*2-pt index to Barbados Probate Registry*) (Caribbeana vols 4 & 5) [WI/G 4-5]
1676-1739 Abst of Jewish Wills for Bridgetown 1676-1739, Speightstown 1695-1735, etc *In* "Review of the Jewish Colonists in Barbados in the Year 1680" (Trans Jewish Hist Soc Eng vol 13) [WI/L 11 or JR/PER]

BELIZE
formerly British Honduras; see WEST INDIES

BERMUDA
see also WEST INDIES

1629-1835 *Nominal Indexes to* Early Bermuda Wills & *Admons* 1629-1835 [WI/L 40]

BURMA
now Myanmar; see India

CANADA
see also UNITED STATES
AB = Alberta, BC = British Columbia, NL = Newfoundland & Labrador, NS = Nova Scotia, ON = Ontario, QB = Quebec

1625-1825 Directory of Scottish Settlers in N America 1625-1825; vol 4: *Abst of N American Services of Heirs, Testmts & Admons in Edinburgh & the PCC*; vol 6: *abst of N American docs in the Edinburgh Reg of Deeds including wills* [US/MIG 20 & 87]
1650-1900 Scottish American Wills 1650-1900; Index to testmts & invents registered & confirmed in the Commissariot & Sheriff courts

of Edinburgh with supp data from the Index to Personal Estates of Defuncts 1846-1866 of Scots resident in N America [US/G 147]
1700-1799 *Index to* N American Residents in Retours 1700-1799 (Scottish Genealogist vol 13 no 1) [SC/PER]

British Columbia
1868-1876 Intestate Estates in BC 1868-1876: an index (BC Genealogist vol 14 no 3) [CAN/BC/PER]

Newfoundland and Labrador
1793-1859 Extr of Wills & Deeds in Newfoundland Provincial Archives (*300 British & Irish will abst*) (NL Ancestor vols 8-11) [CAN/NL/PER]
1826-1865 Wills & FH (*extr from Provincial Archives of Newfoundland & Labrador*) (NL Ancestor vols 10-12) [CAN/NL/PER]

Nova Scotia
1749-1799 Deaths, Burials & Prob of Nova Scotians, 1749-1799, from Primary Sources; vols 1 & 2 (Geneal Assn of NS Pubs 14 & 15) [CAN/NS/R 1]
1749-1847 *Index to* Wills of Irish Interest in the Probate Registry at Halifax, NS, Canada (Irish Ancestor vol 1) [IR/PER]

Ontario
1793-1858 Index to Surrogate Court Recs - Upper Canada/Canada West now ON: 1793-1858 (Mfc) [Apply to Staff]

CEYLON
now Sri Lanka; see India

DOMINICA
see also WEST INDIES
1766-1789 Indentures, Wills, etc at Dominica RO (*Antiguan will extr*) (Caribbeana vol 4) [WI/G 4]

GIBRALTAR

1809-1815 Cal of Naval Hospital Wills at Gibraltar 1809-1815 (*abst of* "An account of wills executed by patients of this hospital 17 Jul

1809-2 Nov 1815") (*PRO Class ADM 105/40*) [GIB/G 3]; *also In* "List of Wills, Admons, etc in the PRO, London, England from 12-19th C" [WILLS/GEN]

GUYANA
formerly British Guiana & Demerara; see WEST INDIES

INDIA

1766-1857 "Foreign" Wills proved at Carlisle (*index to wills & admons of persons who died in the E Indies*) (Genealogists' Mag vol 15) [PER/GEN]
1775-1926 *Extr from* Wills & Admons *In* "Anglo-Indian Colls vol 3" [IND/R 10]

Bombay
1723-1900 Bombay Wills 1723-1900 (*A-C*) *In* "E India Co's Service" [IND/RIN/LST]
1774-1779 Irish Wills in England; *India Office Lib (Bombay index) 1774-1779* (Irish Geneal Res Soc N/L vol 1 no 5) [IR/PER]

Hyderabad
1775-1926 Wills & Admons of the Nizam's Loc officers (*abst for 1775, 1805-1887, 1926*) *In* "Anglo-Indian Colls vol 3" [IND/R 10]

Madras
1711-1780 Some Extr from Wills *In* "Vestiges of Old Madras" (vols 1-3 & index) [IND/L 1-4]
1735-1746 Recs of Fort St George; Copies of Wills, Probs & Letters of Admon, Mayor's Court of Madraspatam; vol 1: 1735-1744; vol 2: 1744-1746 [IND/G 84-85]

JAMAICA
see also WEST INDIES

1625-1792 Abst of Jamaica Wills in the BM 1625-1792 (*Vernona Smith Coll, Add MSS 34,181*) [Mf 1101]
1655-1810 List of Wills relating to this Island proved in the PCC from 1655-1810 (Caribbeana vol 2) [WI/G 2]
1663-1699 Names of Persons whose Wills are registered in Jamaica

previous to 1700 (*lists names in 9 vols in the BM commencing 1663, 1672, 1682, 1683, 1687, 1688, 1691, 1694 & 1697*) (Caribbeana vol 1) [WI/G 1]
1668-1699 Scottish-Jamaican Testmts (*will index in the Jamaican RO*) (Scottish Genealogist vol 35 no 1) [SC/PER]
1674-1701 Jamaican Invents of Probated Estates (*lists, 1674-1694 & 1699-1701*) (Caribbean Hist & Geneal J vol 2 no 2) [WI/PER]
1731-1750 List of all Testators whose wills are on record in the Office of the Island Secretary, Jamaica from 1731-1750 (Caribbeana vol 2) [WI/G 2]

NETHERLANDS

16-19 C English Adventurers & Colonial Settlers; abst of Legal Proceedings in 17th C English & Dutch Courts *from Amsterdam & Rotterdam Notarial Books* [US/G 74]

NEVIS and ST CHRISTOPHER
see also WEST INDIES

Nevis
1629-1733 Abst of Nevis Wills in the PCC; pt 1: 1629-1678 (Caribbeana vol 4); pts 2 & 3: 1679-1733 (Caribbeana vols 5 & 6) [WI/G 4-6]
1631-1799 List of Wills relating to Nevis & St Kitts proved *in the* PCC (Caribbeana vol 2) [WI/G 2]

St Christopher
1628-1799 List of Wills relating to Nevis & St Kitts proved *in the* PCC (Caribbeana vol 2) [WI/G 2]

NEW ZEALAND

1831-1901 Index to NSW Probs (*testators late of NZ, A-C*) (NZ Genealogist vol 16 no 157) [NZ/PER]
1840-1859 Scottish Australasian *Return of Heirs before 1860* (*index*) (Scottish Genealogist vol 15 no 1) [SC/PER]
1843-1869 Intestate Estates notified in "NZ Gazette" 1843-1869 (Mfc) [Lower

Library: NZ Mfc drawer]

1850-1900 NZ Probs/Intestacies 1850-1900 (*index to people of Yorks origin*) (Yorks FHn vol 21) [YK/PER]

1862-1888 Prob Recs, PRO V (*index to testators late of NZ*) (NZ Genealogist vol 16 no 154) [NZ/PER]

1866-1900 *Index to* Deceased Estates notified in "NZ Gazette" 1866-1900 *ie* (a) estates placed under the charge of the Curator of Intestate Estates 1866-1873, (b) estates placed under the charge of the Public Trustee 1873-1900 & (c) estates where death occurred before 1901 but notified later (Mfc) [Lower Library: NZ Mfc drawer]

Canterbury

1867-1914 Canterbury Death Duty Regs Index 1867-1914 (Mfc) [Lower Library: NZ Mfc drawer]

1887-1914 Deceased Persons' Estates, Canterbury, 1887-1914 (copied from the "NZ Mercantile Gazette" *with absts*) (Mfc) [Lower Library: NZ Mfc drawer]

1901-1958 Public Trust Deceased Estates, Canterbury 1901-1958 (extracted from "NZ Gazette") (Mfc) [Lower Library: NZ Mfc drawer]

Wellington

1833-1910 *Index to* Wills at Lands & Deeds Office, Wellington 1833-1910 (Mfc) [Lower Library: NZ Mfc drawer]

NICARAGUA
see WEST INDIES for the Mosquito Shore

PAKISTAN see India

RUSSIA

1817-1861 Wills in the British Consular Archives for Russia 1817-1861 *In* "List of Wills, Admons, etc in the PRO, London, England from 12-19th C" [WILLS/GEN]

ST CHRISTOPHER or ST KITTS see
NEVIS; WEST INDIES

ST HELENA

1706-1833 St Helena Wills & Admons 1706-1833 (*A-I*) *In* "E India Co's Service" [IND/RIN/LST]

SOUTH AFRICA

Cape of Good Hope

1795-1815 Extr from the *Orphan Chamber* Reg of Deaths at the Cape of Good Hope 1795-1815 [AFR/R 1 or AFR/R 3]

SPAIN

Barcelona

1726-1758 Irish Wills from Barcelona (*will abst in Archiva Historicó de Protocolos*) (Irish Genealogist vol 6) [IR/PER]

TUNISIA

1699-1885 Wills in Tunis Consular Archives 1699, 1848, 1866-1885 *In* "List of Wills, Admons, etc in the PRO, London, England from 12-19th C" [WILLS/GEN]

UNITED STATES
CA = California, CO = Colorado, CT = Connecticut, DC = District of Columbia (see also Maryland), DE = Delaware, GA = Georgia, IN = Indiana, KY = Kentucky, LA = Louisiana, MA = Massachusetts, MD = Maryland, ME = Maine, MI = Michigan, MN = Minnesota, MO = Missouri, MS = Mississippi, NC = North Carolina, NE = New England states, NH = New Hampshire, NJ = New Jersey, NY = New York, OH = Ohio, OR = Oregon, PA = Pennsylvania, RI = Rhode Island, SC = South Carolina, TX = Texas, VA = Virginia; VT = Vermont, WV = West Virginia (see also Virginia)

Nation-Wide Items
see also 'American Probates in the PCC' under Canterbury (PCC) in the COURTS section

1461-1777 English Wills of Colonial Fams (*Currer-Briggs's abst*) [US/G 80]

1464-1721 Lea's Geneal Gleanings (*colls of notes & abst of wills, admons & invents*) (NEHGR vols 54-59) [US/NE/PER]

16-18 C	Immigrants to America Appearing in English Recs (*will extr*) [US/G 77]
16-19 C	American Colonists in English Recs: a Guide to direct references in authentic recs, Passenger Lists not in "Hotten", &c, &c, &c (*will abst*); 1st ser; 2nd ser; 1st & 2nd ser *combined reprint* [US/G 71-73]
16-19 C	English Adventurers & Colonial Settlers; abst of Legal Proceedings in 17th C English & Dutch Courts [US/G 74]
16-19 C	Geneal Gleanings in England (new ser) (reprinted from the Geneal Mag) (*will abst A-ANY*) [US/G 82]
16-19 C	*Waters's* Geneal Gleanings in England (*will abst*); vols 1 & 2 [US/G 83-84]; Waters's Geneal Gleanings (*mainly PCC abst*) (NEHGR vols 37-52 indexed in vol 52) [US/NE/PER]
16-19 C	Gleanings from English Recs about New England Fams (offprint from Essex Inst Hist Colls vol 17) [Apply to Staff]
1569-1675	Withington's Abst of English Wills (NEHGR vols 51-54) [US/NE/PER]
1610-1799	English Estates of American Colonists; *cal of* American Wills & Admons in the PCC; vol 1: 1610-1699; vol 2: 1700-1799 [US/G 78-79]
1610-1857	American Wills & Admons in the PCC 1610-1857 (*list with extr*) [US/G 81]
1611-1693	*Americans in* London Commissary Court Recs (*prob abst*) (Nat Geneal Soc Qtrly vol 76) [US/PER]
1611-1775	*Abst of* American Wills proved in London 1611-1775 [US/G 126 & WILLS/PCC]
1625-1825	Directory of Scottish Settlers in N America 1625-1825; vol 4: *Abst of N American Services of Heirs, Testmts & Admons in Edinburgh & the PCC*; vol 6: *Abst of N American docs in the Edinburgh Reg of Deeds including wills* [US/MIG 20 & 87]
1641-1736	Lord Mayor's Court of London Depositions relating to Americans 1641-1736 (*with* PCC testmtry cases) [US/G 76]
1642-1809	American Wills contested in the PCC (*abst of Depositions 1657-1809 & Cause Papers 1642-1722*) (Nat Geneal Soc Qtrly vol 66) [US/PER]
1650-1900	Scottish American Wills 1650-1900; Index to testmts & invents registered & confirmed in the Commissariot & Sheriff courts of Edinburgh with supp data from the Index to Personal Estates of Defuncts 1846-1866 of Scots resident in N America [US/G 147]
1671-1689	Some Early Invents in the PCC (*index to US testators*) (Nat Geneal Soc Qtrly vol 67) [US/PER]
1683-1883	Scottish American Heirs (*abstract of Decennial Indexes of Returns of Heirs*) [US/G 184]
18-19 C	Abst of Admons & other Prob Recs amongst Deeds & Indentures *In* "Lost Links - New Recordings of Old Data from Many States" [US/G 28]
1700-1799	*Cal of* American Admons & Prob Acts in the PCC; pt 1: 1700-1710 (*A-HAS*) (Nat Geneal Soc Qtrly vol 61); pts 2: 1711-1715, 3: 1716-1720 & 4: 1721-1725 (Nat Geneal Soc Qtrly vol 62); pts 5: 1726-1730 & 6: 1731-1740 (Nat Geneal Soc Qtrly vol 64); pts 7: 1741-1750 & 8: 1751-1760 (Nat Geneal Soc Qtrly vol 65); pts 9: 1761-1770 & 10: 1771-1780 (Nat Geneal Soc Qtrly vol 66); pt 12: 1791-1799 (Nat Geneal Soc Qtrly vol 68) [*all* US/PER]
1700-1799	*Index to* N American Residents in Retours 1700-1799 (Scottish Genealogist vol 13 no 1) [SC/PER]
1772-1858	*Index to* American Invents in the PCC (Nat Geneal Soc Qtrly vol 69) [US/PER]
1784-1853	"Foreign" Wills proved at Carlisle (*index to wills & admons of persons who died in the USA*) (Genealogists' Mag vol 15) [PER/GEN]
1799-1986	Wills of the Rich & Famous (*1799, 1826, 1910-1986*) [US/G 142]
1800-1819	Scottish American Heirs 1800-1819 (continuation of the

Decennial Indexes of Returns of Heirs) (Scottish Genealogist vol 14 no 4) [SC/PER]

1814-1858 Extr from Some Slaveowners' Wills & Invents 1814-1858 *In* appx A to "Slave Genealogy: a Res Guide with Case Studies" [US/G 106]

1828-1849 *Abst about* Americans in Litigation Papers in the PCC (Nat Geneal Soc Qtrly vol 80) [US/PER]

Alabama

1815-1853 Wills & Abst of Wills *In* "Lost Links - New Recordings of Old Data from Many States" [US/G 28]

California

Orange County:

1889-1927 Index to Orange County Prob Recs 1889-1927 (*1927: A-EPP only*) (Orange County CA Geneal Soc Qtrly vols 6-9) [US/CA/PER]

Colorado

Gilpin County:

1862-1888 *Index to* Gilpin County Misc Prob Papers (CO Genealogist vol 51) [US/CO/PER]

Old Arapahoe County:

1867-1873 Abst of Early Prob Recs of Old Arapahoe County (*filed accounts, invents, etc*) (CO Genealogist vols 5-8, 10-12, 17-19, 21-23 & 25) [US/CO/PER]

Connecticut

1633-1892 Mayflower Deeds & Probs from the files of George Ernest Bowman at the MA Soc of Mayflower Descendants (*lists & extr*) [US/MA/G 36]

1700-1800 Cal of Sample Estates (*extr*) *In* "Prob Invents as a Source for Economic Hist in 18th C CT" (Connecticut Hist Soc Bull vol 37 no 1) [US/CT/PER]

New Haven:

1647-1687 Abst of Early Prob Recs of New Haven; Book I (*pt 1 only: wills & invents*) (NEHGR vol 81) [US/NE/PER]

New London:

1691-1711 Prob Recs in New London, CT County Court recs now in the

State Lib, Harford (*abst of wills, invents, admons, etc*) (American Genealogist vols 9-15, 17-18, 20-21 & 29) [US/PER]

Sharon:

1757-1759 Sharon, CT Prob Recs (*will abst*) (American Genealogist vol 10) [US/PER]

Windham:

1723-1746 Windham, CT Prob Recs (*will abst*) (American Genealogist vol 23) [US/PER]

Windsor:

1636-1714 *List of* Windsor Invents *In* appx 2 of "Dorset Pilgrims; Story of W Country Pilgrims to New England in the 17th C" [US/NE/G 21]

Delaware

Deale County: see Sussex County

New Castle County:

1682-1800 Cal of DE Wills - New Castle County - 1682-1800 [Apply to Staff]

Sussex County:

1681-1704 Notes from the Probate Court of Sussex County, DE: The First Record (*extr*) (County Court Note-Book vol 9 no 9) [US & CAN GEN PER box]

1682-1751 Abst of Wills & Admons of Sussex County (*1682-1719 & 1722-1751*) (Pubs of the Geneal Soc of PA vols 11-13) [US/PA/PER]

1683-1695 *Abst of* Prob Recs 1683-1695 *In* "Some Recs of Sussex County, DE" [US/DE/L 1]

District of Columbia *see Maryland*

Florida

1833-1848 Wills & Abst of Wills *In* "Lost Links - New Recordings of Old Data from Many States" [US/G 28]

Georgia

1772-1955 Index to GA Wills; *Will Books index for counties formed before the 1832 Land Lottery Act* [US/GA/G 3]

1803-1871 Wills & Abst of Wills *In* "Lost Links - New Recordings of Old Data from Many States" [US/G 28]

Burke County:
1790-1830   Index to Burke County, GA
            Admon of Estates (Nat Geneal
            Soc Qtrly vol 54) [US/PER]
1791-1823   Abst of Burke County Wills
            probated in Jefferson County, GA
            (Nat Geneal Soc Qtrly vol 54)
            [US/PER]
Green County:
1796-1877   Abst of the Green County, GA
            Will Book 1794-1819 Geneal Soc
            Qtrly vol 40) [US/PER]
Jefferson County: see Burke County
Liberty County:
1777-1887   Liberty County, GA Wills Index
            (Nat Geneal Soc Qtrly vol 44)
            [US/PER]
Oglethorpe County:
1794-1806   Orphans of Oglethorpe County,
            GA (abst of Inferior Court
            Minutes) (Nat Geneal Soc Qtrly
            vol 41) [US/PER]

Kentucky
1782-1911   Abst of some KY Wills & other
            testmtry recs In "KY Pioneers &
            Their Descendants" [US/KY/G 1]
1785-1853   Extr from Some KY Wills (Geneal
            Qtrly vol 2) [PER/GEN]
1808   Wills & Abst of Wills In "Lost
            Links - New Recordings of Old
            Data from Many States" [US/G
            28]
Allen County:
1826-1885   List of Wills In "In the Hills of the
            Pennyroyal" [US/KY/L 1]
Fayette County:
1820   Abst of Wills, Fayette County,
            KY; Will Book E (with invents)
            (Nat Geneal Soc Qtrly vol 29)
            [US/PER]
Knotts County:
1892-1895   Abst of Last Wills & Testmts
            (Knotts Gentlefolk & Flowers of
            the Forest vol 1 nos 1-2)
            [US/KY/PER]

Louisiana
Baton Rouge:
1816-1818   Abst of E Baton Rouge Prob
            Recs (1816 & 1818) (LA Geneal
            Reg vols 18 & 21) [US/LA/PER]
1811-1924   Index to E Baton Rouge Parish
            Prob Recs (FOW-GUI) (LA
            Geneal Reg vols 18 & 19)
            [US/LA/PER]

Feliciana:
1817-1905   Index to E Feliciana Parish
            Probate Court Recs (LA Geneal
            Reg vol 22) [US/LA/PER]
Jackson:
1881-1901   Abst of Prob Recs of Jackson
            Parish (LA Geneal Reg vols 18 &
            19) [US/LA/PER]
New Orleans:
1806-1846   General Index to all Successions
            in the Parish of Orleans (M-S)
            (New Orleans Genesis vol 7)
            [US/LA/PER]
Opelousas:
1815-1841   Index to Marriage Contracts &
            Wills from the Labyche Isles of
            Opelousas (LA Geneal Reg vol
            18) [US/LA/PER]

Maine
1623-1660   Abst of Wills, Admons & Invents
            In "Pioneers of ME & NH"
            [US/ME/G 2]
1640-1760   Abst of ME Wills 1640-1760
            [US/ME/G 3]
Hancock County:
1789-1800   ME Prob Abst; vol 2 [US/ME/G 5]
Kennebec County:
1799-1800   ME Prob Abst; vol 2 [US/ME/G 5]
Washington County:
1789-1800   ME Prob Abst; vol 2 [US/ME/G 5]
York County:
1687-1800   ME Prob Abst; vol 1 1687-1775;
            vol 2: 1775-1800 [US/ME/G 4-5]

Maryland
including the District of Columbia
1721-1723   MD's Next of Kin (extr from invent
            cals, incomplete) (County Court
            Note-Book vol 6 nos 2 & 4, vol 7
            nos 1 & 3, vol 8 no 6 & vol 9 no
            6) [US & CAN GEN PER box]
1733-1848   Wills & Abst of Wills In "Lost
            Links - New Recordings of Old
            Data from Many States" [US/G
            28]
Baltimore:
1755-1765   Heirs to Baltimore Estates (cal of
            Admon Books) (Nat Geneal Soc
            Qtrly vol 53) [US/PER]
District of Columbia:
1818-1846   DC Balances & Distributions
            Book (prob accounts summary)
            (American Genealogist vol 50)
            [US/PER]
Somerset County:
1667-1742   Index to Wills proved at Snow

Hill, *Somerset now* Worcester
County, MD (Pubs of the Geneal
Soc of PA vol 7) [US/PA/PER]
Worcester County: see Somerset County

Massachusetts
1621-1727 *Abst of Wills, Admons, Invents,*
Estate Settlements of Mayflower
Passengers & their Heirs In
"Mayflower Reader (Selection of
Articles from Mayflower
Descendant Excerpted from vols
1-8, 1899-1905)" [US/MA/G 6]
1633-1892 Mayflower Deeds & Probs from
the files of George Ernest
Bowman at the MA Soc of
Mayflower Descendants (*lists &*
extr) [US/MA/G 36]
1643-1694 17th C Wills: Death Bed, Sick
Bed or Prudent? (*will & admon*
list) (Nexus vol 3) [US/NE/PER]
Barnstable County:
1694-1695 Abst of Barnstable County, MA
Prob Recs (Mayflower
Descendant vol 24 no 2)
[US/MA/PER]
Berkshire County:
1760-1804 Berkshire County, MA Prob Recs
(*will & invent abst*) (Nat Geneal
Soc Qtrly vol 31) [US/PER]
Boston:
1644-1651 Prob Cases *In* "Vol relating to the
Early Hist of Boston containing
the Aspinwall Notarial Recs
1644-1651" [US/MA/L 4]
Bristol County:
1693-1699 Abst from the First Book of Bristol
County Prob Recs (NEHGR vols
62-64) [US/NE/PER]
1698-1710 Bristol County, MA Prob Recs
(*will, admon & invent abst*) (Nat
Geneal Soc Qtrly vol 73)
[US/PER]
1751-1755 *Abst of* Bristol County, MA
Guardnshp Recs (Nat Geneal
Soc Qtrly vol 74) [US/PER]
1762-1764 Bristol County Prob Abst 1762-
1765 (Mayflower Descendant vol
45) [US/MA/PER]
1881-1926 Prob Indexes 1881-1926 -
Taunton MA (*list of mainly Lancs*
testators) (Lancs vol 8) [LA/PER]
Cambridge: see Middlesex County
Essex County:
1638-1840 Essex County, MA Prob Indexes
1638-1840; vols 1 & 2 [US/MA/L
53 & US/MA/L 54]

1643-1648 Prob Recs of Essex County, MA
(*will & invent abst, incomplete*)
(Essex Inst Hist Colls vols 50 &
51) [US/MA/PER]
Hampshire County:
1708-1760 Hampshire County, MA Estates
(*will abst*) (Nat Geneal Soc Qtrly
vol 32) [US/PER]
Middlesex County:
1649-1665 Ancient Wills in Middlesex (*abst:*
1649 & 1665) (NEHGR vol 3)
[US/NE/PER]
1651-1655 Abst of the Earliest Wills in E
Cambridge, Middlesex County,
MA (NEHGR vols 16-17, 19 & 30)
[US/NE/PER]
Plymouth:
1633-1678 Abst of the First Wills in the
Probate Office, Plymouth *with*
invents (NEHGR vols 4-7)
[US/NE/PER]
1672 Plymouth Colony Wills & Invents
(Mayflower Descendant vol 24 no
2) [US/MA/PER]
1899-1928 Plymouth, MA Probs (*will abst*)
(RotaGene vol 14 no 5)
[US/PER]
Suffolk County:
1639-1659 Abst of the Earliest Wills upon
Record in the County of Suffolk,
MA (NEHGR vols 2-13, 15-20,
30-32 & 48) [US/NE/PER]
1685-1688 *Abst of* Stray Wills in Suffolk
County Probate Registry
(American Genealogist vols 13 &
14) [US/PER]
1686-1692 Suffolk County Prob Index
(American Genealogist vols 12 &
13) [US/PER]
Worcester County:
1740-1741 *Abst of* Early Worcester County
Prob Recs (Mayflower
Descendant vol 45 no 1)
[US/MA/PER]

Michigan
Emmet County:
1857-1890 Index of Early Prob Recs in
Emmet County, MI 1857-1890
(Detroit Soc for Geneal Res *Mag*
vol 33) [US/MI/PER]
Lapeer County:
1838-1899 Lapeer County Prob Index 1838-
1899 (Detroit Soc for Geneal Res
Mag vols 38 & 39) [US/MI/PER]

Mississippi

Lowndes County:
1830-1889 Lowndes County, MS Will Book
(*cal*) (Nat Geneal Soc Qtrly vol
55) [US/PER]

Missouri
1824-1858 Wills & Abst of Wills *In* "Lost
Links - New Recordings of Old
Data from Many States" [US/G
28]
Jackson County:
1850-1898 Will Abst, Jackson County, MO
(Kansas City Genealogist vol 27)
[US/MO/PER]

New Hampshire
1623-1660 *Abst of Wills, Admons & Invents
In* "Pioneers of ME & NH"
[US/ME/G 2]
Exeter:
1550-1639 Lincs Origins of Some Exeter, *NH*
Settlers (*will abst*) (NEHGR vol
68) [US/NE/PER]

New Jersey
1670-1730 Cal of New Jersey Wills, vol 1:
1670-1730 (*abst with invents*)
(Archives of the State of New
Jersey; 1st ser: vol 23) [Apply to
Staff]
Cumberland County:
1804-1825 *Abst of* Cumberland County, NJ
Wills (Nat Geneal Soc Qtrly vol
29) [US/PER]
Gloucester County:
1746-1748 Sealing Docket, Gloucester
County NJ beginning 1746
(*includes prob cases*) (Nat
Geneal Soc Qtrly vols 35 & 36)
[US/PER]
Sussex County:
1792-1859 Additional Sussex County Prob
Recs (*will & invent index*) (Geneal
Mag of NJ vol 46) [US/NJ/PER]

New York
1666-1775 *Index to NY Invents in NY Court
of Appeals* (Nat Geneal Soc Qtrly
vol 54) [US/PER]
1691-1815 Recs of the Chancery Court -
Province & State of NY; *Abst of
Guardnshps 1691-1815* (Holland
Soc of NY) [US/NY/G 21]
Herkimer County:
1780-1794 *Abst of* Herkimer County NY Wills
(RotaGene vol 12 no 6) [US/PER]

New York City:
1695-1742 *Index to the* Appointment of
Guardns *in NY City Mayor's
Court* (Nat Geneal Soc Qtrly vol
56) [US/PER]
1736-1775 *Index to* Wills of Colonial NY *in
Surrogate Court of NY City* (Nat
Geneal Soc Qtrly vol 54)
[US/PER]
1753-1799 Geneal Data from NY; *Abst of*
Admon Bonds 1753-1799 &
hitherto unpublished Letters of
Admon (Colls NY Geneal & Biog
Soc vol 10) [US/NY/L 13]
1776-1829 Index of Original Wills *in
Surrogate Court of NY City* (Nat
Geneal Soc Qtrly vol 55)
[US/PER]
Rensselaer County:
1792-1856 Some Abst of Wills in the
Surrogate's Office, Troy NY
(Geneal Forum of Portland Bull
vol 7) [US/OR/PER]
Westchester County:
1707 Westchester County Admons; list
of cases pending 1707 (NY
Geneal & Biog Rec vol 24)
[US/NY/PER]

North Carolina
1665-1900 NC Wills: A Testator Index,
1665-1900 [US/NC/G 10]
1680-1830 Directory of Scots in the
Carolinas 1680-1830 (*extr based
on prob sources*) [US/NC/G 9]
1686-1789 *Abst of* some Early NC & VA
Guardns' Bonds & *Civil Actions*
(NC Geneal Soc J vol 13)
[US/NC/PER]
1737-1849 Wills & Abst of Wills *In* "Lost
Links - New Recordings of Old
Data from Many States" [US/G
28]
1742-1786 Returns of Wills & Admons
granted in NC 1753-1790 (NC
Geneal Soc J vols 13-15)
[US/NC/PER] *COVERS the
counties of: Anson 1766-1772;
Beaufort 1753-1766; Bertie 1753-
1761; Bladen 1778-1779;
Brunswick 1764-1768; Camden
1777-1779; Carteret 1761-1768;
Caswell 1782-1786; Chowan
1763-1766; Currituck 1754 (also
Admon Bonds 1759-1772);
Dobbs 1763-1772; Duplin 1753-
1761; Edgecombe c1752-c1760;*

Granville 1763-1779; Greene
(now in Tennessee) 1783;
Hertford 1760-1773; Hyde 1766;
Johnston 1759-1768;
Mecklenburg 1765-1768;
Montgomery 1782; New Hanover
c1760-1768; Northampton 1760-
1767; Onslow 1765-1778;
Pasquotank 1752-1762;
Perquimans 1753-1762 (also
Admon Bonds 1742-c1755); Pitt
1761-1781

1816-1837 NC Court Recs; abst of prob
cases in the Supreme Court,
Raleigh, NC (Nat Geneal Soc
Qtrly vol 32) [US/PER]

Anson County:
1748-1783 Cal of Anson County Wills 1748-
1783 (A-LYN) (NC Hist & Geneal
Rec vols 1 & 2) [US/NC/PER]

Berkshire County:
1728-1744 Some Berkshire County, NC
Recs (admon & invents index)
(County Court Note-Book vol 7
no 2) [US & CAN GEN PER box]

Buncombe County:
1820-1850 Index of Wills - Buncombe
County, NC (Nat Geneal Soc
Qtrly vol 46) [US/PER]

Edgecombe County:
1764-1843 Abst of Wills in Edgecombe
County, NC (Nat Geneal Soc
Qtrly vol 33) [US/PER]

Hyde County:
1758-1763 Abst of Unpublished NC Wills
(County Court Note-Book vol 7
no 2) [US & CAN GEN PER box]

Sampson County:
1782-1831 Index to Unrecorded Wills,
Sampson County, NC (County
Court Note-Book vol 7 no 2) [US
& CAN GEN PER box]

Pasquotank County:
1753-1754 Pasquotank, NC List of Letters
Testmtry & of Admons 1 Oct
1753-23 Sep 1754 (NC Geneal
Soc J vol 13) [US/NC/PER]

Rockingham County:
1772-1832 List of Unrecorded Wills of
Rockingham County, NC (Nat
Geneal Soc Qtrly vol 46)
[US/PER]

Wake County:
1771-1802 Wake County, NC, Abst of Wills,
Invents & Settlements of Estates
1771-1802 [US/NC/L 1]

Ohio
Butler County:
1803-1825 Butler County, Ohio, Will Abst
Book 1 (Nat Geneal Soc Qtrly vol
32) [US/PER]

Delaware County:
1810-1814 Delaware County, Ohio, Prob
Recs (cal of wills) (American
Genealogist vol 34) [US/PER]

1812-1850 Early Wills, Delaware County,
Ohio (indexes: 1812-1814, 1835-
1850) (Nat Geneal Soc Qtrly vol
55) [US/PER]

Hamilton County:
1791-1809 Wills of Officers & Soldiers who
died at Fort Washington,
Cincinnati, OH (Nat Geneal Soc
Qtrly vol 57) [US/PER]

Trumbull County:
1803-1813 Prob Recs of Trumbull County,
Ohio (abst of estates A-HAY)
(Nat Geneal Soc Qtrly vols 34-
38) [US/PER]

Oregon
Columbia County:
1854-1907 Columbia County Prob Recs
(filed will & admon abst) (Geneal
Forum of Portland Bull vol 34)
[US/OR/PER]

Washington County:
1860-1910 Index to Book 1, Prob Recs of
Washington County, OR at the
Courthouse, Hillsboro, OR (wills
& guardnshps) (Geneal Forum of
Portland Bull vol 21)
[US/OR/PER]

Pennsylvania
1683-1799 Wills & Abst of Wills In "Lost
Links - New Recordings of Old
Data from Many States" [US/G
28]

1714-1726 Extr from Invents 1714-1726 In
"Immigration of the Irish Quakers
into PA 1682-1750 with their
Early Hist in Ireland" [US/PA/G
10]

Allegheny County:
1789-1813 Abst of Wills & Admons of
Allegheny County, registered at
Pittsburg, PA (Pubs Geneal Soc
of PA vol 7) [US/PA/PER]

Bedford County:
1771-1817 Abst of Wills & Admons of
Bedford County (1771-1782,
1798-1817) (Pubs Geneal Soc of

PA vols 10-12) [US/PA/PER]

Huntingdon County:

1787-1807 Guide to Decedents' Estates entered in *Huntingdon County* Will Book One: 1787-1807 (*cal*) (PA Geneal Mag vol 25) [US/PA/PER]

Northumberland County:

1772-1801 Abst of Wills & Admons of Northumberland County (Pubs Geneal Soc of PA vols 13 & 14) [US/PA/PER]

Philadelphia County:

1682-1692 *Abst of* Wills proved at Philadelphia 1682-1692 (Pubs Geneal Soc of PA rec ser no 1) [US/PA/PER]

1737-1743 *Abst of* Philadelphia County Admons; Book "D": 2 Jul 1737-8 Apr 1743 (PA Geneal Mag vol 28) [US/PA/PER]

1745-1817 Abst of Wills recorded in the Admon Books in the Regs Office, Philadelphia; Books "F", "G", "H", "K" & "L" (Pubs Geneal Soc of PA vol 5) [US/PA/PER]

Pittsburg: see Allegheny County

Washington County:

1781-1811 Abst of Wills of Washington County, registered at Little Washington, PA (Pubs Geneal Soc of PA vol 6) [US/PA/PER]

Westmoreland County:

1773-1799 Abst of Admons of Westmoreland County entered in Will Book No One (Pubs Geneal Soc of PA vol 6) [US/PA/PER]

1797-1817 Abst of Wills of Westmoreland County, registered at Greenburg (*1797-1812, 1815-1817*) (Pubs Geneal Soc of PA vols 6 & vol 11) [US/PA/PER]

Rhode Island

Middletown:

1744-1894 Abst of Wills & Prob Recs of the Town of Middletown, RI (NEHGR vol 122) [US/NE/PER]

South Carolina

1670-1740 Abst of the Wills of the State of SC - vol 1: 1670-1740 [US/SC/G 4]

1680-1830 Directory of Scots in the Carolinas 1680-1830 (*extr based on prob sources*) [US/NC/G 9]

1682-1768 Abst from the Recs of the Court of Ordinary of the Province of SC (*prob extr 1682-1698, 1768*) (SC Hist & Geneal Mag vols 11 & 27) [US/SC/PER]

1740-1836 Wills & Abst of Wills *In* "Lost Links - New Recordings of Old Data from Many States" [US/G 28]

Charleston:

1725-1779 Abst of Wills in the Probate Court, Charleston, SC from Will Books 1722-1784 (Nat Geneal Soc Qtrly vol 29) [US/PER]

Tennessee

1828-1857 Wills & Abst of Wills *In* "Lost Links - New Recordings of Old Data from Many States" [US/G 28]

Greene County: see North Carolina

Texas

1845 Wills & Abst of Wills *In* "Lost Links - New Recordings of Old Data from Many States" [US/G 28]

Denton County:

1876-1900 Index of Wills in the Office of the County Clerk, Denton County (*Dallas* Loc Hist & Geneal Soc vol 9 no 4) [US/TX/PER]

Montgomery County:

1838-1847 Montgomery County Prob Recs Index (Stirpes vol 12 no 3) [US/TX/PER]

Vermont

1691-1815 Recs of the Chancery Court - Province & State of NY; *Abst of* Guardnshps 1691-1815 (Holland Soc of NY) [US/NY/G 21]

Orleans County:

1797-1832 Abst from vol I of the Prob Recs of Orleans County, VT (*wills & admons*) (NEHGR vol 65 & 66) [US/NE/PER]

Virginia

including West Virginia

1484-1798 English Adventurers & VA Settlers - the co-ordinated use of 17th C British American recs by Genealogists - vols One & Two: Abst of Wills 1484-1798 (*in 2 pts*); vol 3: Prob Cases 1641-1722 *In* "Abst of Legal Proceedings 1566-1700"

[US/VA/G 6-8]
1632-1800 VA Wills & Admons 1632-1800; an index of wills recorded in local courts of VA, 1632-1800, & of admons on estates shown by invents of the estates of intestates recorded in will (& other) books of local courts, 1632-1800 [US/VA/G 10]

1686-1789 *Abst of* some Early NC & *VA* Guardns' Bonds & *Civil Actions* (NC Geneal Soc J vol 13 no 2) [US/NC/PER]

1686-1874 Wills & Abst of Wills *In* "Lost Links - New Recordings of Old Data from Many States" [US/G 28]

1794-1815 *Extr from some Virginian* Wills *In* "KY Pioneers & Their Descendants" [US/KY/G 1]

Accomack County:
1663-1800 *Abst of* Wills & Admons of Accomack County, VA 1663-1800 [US/VA/L 2]

Botetourt County:
1770-1773 Botetourt County Brief (*abst*) of Wills *In* "Annals of Southwest VA; pt 1 [US/VA/G 21a]

Cabell County:
1800-1900 Index to Cabell County, WV, Wills 1800-1900 [US/VA/L 7]

Elizabeth City County:
1730-1800 Index to Wills of Elizabeth *City* County, VA (Wm & Mary College Qtrly 2nd ser vol 13) [US/VA/PER]

Fairfax County:
1752-1782 *Abst of* Fairfax County, VA, Admon Bonds (Nat Geneal Soc Qtrly vol 74) [US/PER]

Fauquier County:
1761-1798 *Abst of* Fauquier County, VA Wills (Buried Treasures vol 17) [US/FL/PER]

Fincastle County:
1773-1776 Fincastle County Brief (*abst*) of Wills *In* "Annals of Southwest VA; pt 1" [US/VA/G 21a]

Fluvana County:
1777-1823 Index of Fluvana County, VA Wills, Admons, Invents & Divisions of Property 1777-1823 (*names only*) (Wm & Mary College Qtrly 2nd ser vol 9) [US/VA/PER]

Goochland County:
1728-1839 Index to Wills in Goochland

County, VA Court House (*with admons & invents*) (Wm & Mary College Qtrly 2nd ser vol 7) [US/VA/PER]

Hardy County:
1786-1800 *Index to* Early Wills of Hardy County, WV (Wm & Mary College Qtrly 1st ser vol 24 no 4) [US/VA/PER]

Isle of Wight County:
1644-1656 Early Wills & Deeds (*cal*) (VA Mag of Hist & Biog vols 5 & 6) [US/VA/PER]

King George County:
1726-1751 Probs & Admons from the Order Book of King George County, VA (*cals for 1726 & 1749-1751*) (County Court Note-Book vols 8 no 2 & 9 no 6) [US & CAN GEN PER box]

Montgomery County:
1776-1800 Montgomery County Brief (*abst*) of Wills *In* "Annals of Southwest VA; pt 1 [US/VA/G 21a]

Norfolk/Lower Norfolk Counties:
1637-1710 Brief Abstract of Lower Norfolk County & Norfolk County Wills 1637-1710 [US/VA/L 5]

Petersburg:
1784-1826 Abst of Will Book 1, Hustings Court, Petersburg, VA 1784-1805 & Will Book 1804-1826 (Nat Geneal Soc Qtrly vol 30) [US/PER]

Prince George County:
1759-1760 Abst to Prince George County, VA Rec Book (*includes wills & invents*) (Wm & Mary College Qtrly 2nd ser vol 11 no 1) [US/VA/PER]

Rappahannock County:
1656-1677 Abst of Wills in VA State Lib (VA Mag of Hist & Biog vol 5) [US/VA/PER]

Russell County:
1803-1857 Abst of Russell County, VA Wills 1803-1860 (VA Mag of Hist & Biog vols 35-37 & 39-40) [US/VA/PER]

Stafford County:
1729-1793 List of Wills which were in Will Books "M", "N" & "T" (*all now Lost*) of Stafford County, VA (*1729-1748, 1767-1783 & 1789-1793*) (County Court Note-Book vol 8 nos 5 & 6) [US & CAN GEN PER box]

Surry County:
1730-1739 Surry County, VA Will & Deed
Book 1730-1739 *(names only)*
(Wm & Mary College Qtrly 2nd
ser vol 12 no 4) [US/VA/PER]
Washington County:
1777-1800 Washington County Brief *(abst)*
of Wills *In* "Annals of Southwest
VA; pt 2" [US/VA/G 21b]
York County:
1716-1727 *Abst of* some York County Wills
(with invents & accounts) (Tyler's
Qtrly Hist & Geneal Mag vol 2 no
4) [US/VA/PER]

West Virginia *see Virginia*

WEST INDIES
*see also ANTIGUA, BARBADOS, JAMAICA,
NEVIS & ST CHRISTOPHER & UNITED
STATES*

*	= French WI
**	= Danish WI
***	= Dutch WI
****	= Spanish WI

1625-1799 List of Wills proved *in the* PCC
relating to the British WI)
(Caribbeana vol 2) [WI/G 2]
COVERS indexes to testators for:
*The Bahamas 1743-1799;
Bermuda 1625-1796; British
Guiana 1668-1799; British
Honduras & on the Mosquito
Shore 1765-1796; Dominica
1768-1799; Grenada 1765-1797;
Martinique* 1719-1799;
Montserrat 1664-1799; St Croix**
1772-1797; St Lucia 1788-1798;
St Thomas** 1780; St Vincent
1776-1799; Tobago 1766-1799;
Trinidad 1797; The Virgin Islands
1762-1798*
1625-1825 Directory of Scottish Settlers in N
America 1625-1825 - vol 4: *Abst
of N American Services of Heirs,
Testmts & Admons in Edinburgh
& the PCC;* vol 6: *Abst of N
American docs in the Edinburgh
Reg of Deeds including wills*
[US/MIG 20 & 87]

1631-1681 Admons *granted in the* PCC
relating to WI (Caribbeana vols 5
& 6) *(Admon Acts Book abst)*
[WI/G 5-6]
1632-1784 Extr from Wills relating to the WI
recorded in England *with admons*
*(Vernona Smith MSS in the Lib of
the Barbados Museum)*
(Barbados Museum & Hist Soc J
vols 11-14) [WI/PER]
1650-1900 Scottish American Wills
1650-1900; testmts & invents of
Scots in N America confirmed or
registered in Edinburgh with supp
data from the Index to Personal
Estates of Defuncts [US/G 147]
1766-1848 "Foreign" Wills proved at Carlisle
*(index to wills & admons of
persons who died in the WI)*
(Genealogists' Mag vol 15)
[PER/GEN]
1800-1816 List of Wills proved in the PCC
from 1800 to 1812 & from 1813-
1816 inclusive (relating mainly to
the British WI) (Caribbeana vols
3 & 5) [WI/G 3 & 5] *COVERS
indexes to testators for: Antigua
1813-1816; The Bahamas
1800-1810 & 1813-1816:
Barbados 1800-1816; Bermuda
1806-1811 & 1813-1816; British
Guiana 1801-1816; British
Honduras 1801-1816; Curacao***
1813-1816; Demerara
1813-1816; Dominica 1802-1816;
Grenada 1801-1816;
Guadeloupe* 1800-1812; Haiti*
1813-1816; Jamaica 1800-1816;
Martinique* 1800-1808 &
1813-1816; Montserrat
1803-1816; Nevis 1801-1807 &
1813-1816; Saint Christopher
1800-1816; Saint Croix**
1800-1816; Saint Lucia
1803-1806 & 1813-1816; Saint
Vincent 1801-1811 & 1813-1816;
Santo Domingo**** 1806-1812;
Tobago 1800-1816; Tortola
1813-1816; Trinidad 1801-1816;
The Virgin Islands 1800-1811*

PROBATE COURTS and REGISTRIES OF THE BRITISH ISLES
for which there is material in the Library of the Society of Genealogists

NATION-WIDE PROBATE JURISDICTIONS
before 1858, 'Court of Probate' or 'Somerset House' usually means the PCC
The Crown in Council: Privy Council
High Courts: Arches; Chancery; Delegates; Lancaster (Chancery of the Duchy); Man (Isle of); Wards & Liveries
Prerogative Courts: Armagh (PCA); Canterbury (PCC); York (PCY)
Commonwealth Period: *from 1646 ecclesiastical appointments were steadily abolished in England & Wales until 1653 when the* **Court of Civil Commission** *became the only Court of Probate; the ecclesiastical prob courts were restored in 1660 & the records of the Commission were merged with those of the PCC (qv)*
Principal Probate Registries: Dublin; London
District Registries: Birmingham; Lewes; Shrewsbury; Worcester; York
Other Courts, etc: Cambridge (University); Edinburgh (Commissariot); Estate Duty Office; Lambeth Palace Lib; Oxford (University); Treasury Solicitor

ABERDEEN, THE COMMISSARIOT OF
Superior Courts: Court of Session*; see also Edinburgh (Commissariot)*
1715-1800 Commissariot Rec of Aberdeen; Reg of Testmts 1715-1800 (Scottish Rec Soc vol 6) [SC/PER]
1801-1823 *Aberdeen Reg of Invents In* "Index to Regs of Testmts for various Commissariots 1801-1823" [Mf 2910]

ACHONRY *see Killala & Achonry*

ACOMB, THE COURT OF THE TESTAMENTARY JURISDICTION OF
formerly part of the Peculiar Jurisdiction of the Treasurer of York & later in lay hands
Superior Court: York (Dean & Chapter)
1456-1837 Prob Recs of the Peculiar Jurisdiction of Acomb (*index to wills, admons, invents, bonds, etc*) (Borthwick Inst Bull vol 2) [YK/PER]
1709-1837 York Registry; Peculiar Court of Acomb - Cal of Wills & Admons 1709-1837 [Mf 879]
1709-1837 Wills & Admons etc: listings taken from cals of the old

Diocese of York & the Diocese of Lincoln (with certain additions from Durham) (*index BUR-WRI*) (Fam Hist vols 2 & 3) [PER/FAM]

AGHADOE *see Ardfert*

ALDBOROUGH (in Stanwick St Johns), THE COURT OF THE MANOR OF
1610-1700 *Index to Wills, Invents, etc in* Aldborough Manor Court (pt of St John Stanwick) 1610-1700 (Yorks Archl Soc rec ser vol 60) [Apply to Staff]
1626-1700 *List of Aldborough Manorial Wills, Bonds & Invents (Hailstone Coll in York Minster Lib)* (Northern Genealogist vol 4) [PER/NOR]

ALNE and TOLLERTON, THE COURT OF THE TESTAMENTARY JURISDICTION OF
formerly part of the Peculiar Jurisdiction of the Treasurer of York & later in lay hands
Superior Courts: York (Dean & Chapter)
1601-1858 York Registry; Alne & Tollerton - Cal of Wills 1601-1858 [Mf 879]

ALRESFORD WITH NEW ALRESFORD and MEDSTEAD, THE TESTAMENTARY JURISDICTION OF THE PARISH OF OLD
Superior Court: Winchester (Archdeaconry)
1529-1775 Cal of Hants Wills proved in the Prerogative & Peculiar Courts of Winchester with other Prob Docs: *Old Arlesford including New Arlesford & Medstead - Index of "B" Wills 1529-1673, Invents 1545-1574, Enrolled Peculiar Wills 1728-1775 & Separate Peculiar Wills 1561-1775* [HA/G 62]

ALREWAS and WEEFORD, THE COURT OF THE PREBEND OF
Superior Court: Lichfield (Dean & Chapter)
1529-1652 Cal of Wills & Admons registered in the various Peculiar Courts now preserved at the Lichfield Registry 1529-1652 (BRS vol 7) [BRS]
1675-1858 Cal of Wills & Admons of Peculiar Jurisdictions in the Diocese of Lichfield; vols 1 & 2 *including:* Prebendal Courts of

Alrewas & Weeford & of Alrewas
1675-1858 [Mf 801]

ALTOFTS IN NORMANTON, THE COURT OF THE MANOR OF
1622-1677 Manor Court of Altofts in Normanton: *Index to* Wills, *Invents* & Admons (Northern Genealogist vol 1) [PER/NOR]

ALVERSTOKE, THE TESTAMENTARY JURISDICTION OF THE PARISH OF
Superior Court: Winchester (Archdeaconry)
1561-1845 Cal of Hants Wills proved in the Prerogative & Peculiar Courts of Winchester with other Prob Docs: *Alverstoke including Gosport - Separate Peculiar Wills* [HA/G 62]
1625-1637 Diocese of Winchester; Index to Registered Copies of Wills in the charge of the Diocesan Registrar (*including the Peculiar of Alverstoke*); Wills, Admons & Invents with the Winchester Diocesan Recs - *index to Registered Wills in the Peculiar Court of Alverstoke* [HA/G 67 & 40]

ALVESTON WITH WASPERTON, THE TESTAMENTARY JURISDICTION OF THE PARISH OF
Superior Courts: Worcester (Consistory); *see also Hampton Lucy*
1529-1652 Cal of Wills & Admons registered in the various Peculiar Courts now preserved at the Lichfield Registry 1529-1652 (BRS vol 7) [BRS]
1599-1858 Cal of Wills & Admons of Peculiar Jurisdictions in the Diocese of Lichfield; vols 1 & 2 *including:* Prebendal Court of Alveston & Wasperton 1599-1858 [Mf 801]

AMOUNDERNESS, THE DEANERY OF *see Richmond (Western Deaneries)*

AMPLEFORTH, THE COURT OF THE PREBEND OF
Superior Courts: York (Chancery); York (Dean & Chapter)
1661-1827 York Registry; Cal of Wills & Admons - Separate Peculiars & Dean & Chapter's General Peculiars: *Ampleforth Peculiar (in 3 pts) 1661-1706, 1661-1797,*

1738-1827; York Registry; Names of Peculiars wherein separate lists are kept of the wills etc proved therein *including Ampleforth with Heslington 1661-1706 & from 1738 to the present time*; York Registry; Cal of Vacancy & Prebendal Wills *including Ampleforth 1661-1827* [*all* Mf 879]

ARCHES, THE HIGH COURT OF THE
this was the court of appeal for the Province of Canterbury
Superior Courts: Delegates (High Court); *see also Lambeth Palace*
1660-1913 Index of Cases in the Recs of the Court of the Arches at Lambeth Palace Lib 1660-1913 (BRS vol 85) [BRS]
1726-1913 Lists of Depositions 1822-1854; of Exhibits 1726, 1735, 1743, 1747, 1751, 1757, 1766-1767, 1776 & 1782-1799; of Cause Papers 1826-1828 & 1869-1913 *In* "List of Recs of the Court of the Arches deposited for temporary safe keeping in the Bodleian Lib in 1941" [SP/ECC]

ARCHES, THE COURT OF THE PECULIAR JURISDICTION OF THE ARCHBISHOP OF CANTERBURY IN THE DEANERY OF THE
Superior Courts: Canterbury (PCC); *see also Croydon; Lambeth Palace; Shoreham*
1620-1845 Index to Testmtry Recs in the Archdeaconry Court of London & now preserved in the Guildhall Lib; vol 2: 1661-1700 (*wills, admons & invents*) & Index of Testmtry Recs of the Deanery of the Arches & now preserved in the Lambeth Court Lib 1620-1845 (BRS vol 98) [BRS]
1664-1738 Peculiars of the Arches of London, Shoreham, Kent & Croydon, Surrey - *Cal of* Invents & Admons 1664-1738 with a list of non-testmtry docs [KE/G 69]

ARDAGH, THE CONSISTORY COURT OF THE BISHOP OF
Superior Court: Armagh (PCA)
1695-1857 Index to Ardagh Wills (supp vol of Irish Ancestor for 1971) [IR/G 81]

ARDFERT and AGHADOE, THE CONSISTORY COURT OF THE BISHOP OF
Superior Court: Armagh (PCA)
1690-1800 *Phillimore's* Indexes to Irish Wills;
vol 2: Cal of Wills in the Dioceses
of Cashel & Emly, Killaloe &
Kilfenora, Waterford & Lismore,
Limerick, Ardfert & Aghadoe &
the Peculiar Jurisdiction of the
Dean of Lismore [IR/G 86]

ARGYLL, THE COMMISSARIOT OF
Superior Courts: Court of Session*; see also
Edinburgh (Commissariot)*
1674-1800 Commissariot Rec of Argyle; Reg
of Testmts 1674-1800 (Scottish
Rec Soc vol 9); Reg of Invents
1693-1702 (Scottish Rec Soc vol
33) [*both* SC/PER]
1801-1823 *Argyll Regs of Testmts & Invents
In* "Index to Regs of Testmts for
various Commissariots
1801-1823" [Mf 2910]

ARKENGARTHDALE WITH NEW FOREST and HOPE, THE COURT OF THE MANOR OF
1719-1811 Manor Court of Arkengarthdale:
Extr from Original Wills, *Admons,
Invents & Bonds (A-MIL)*
(Northern Genealogist vols 4-6)
[PER/NOR]
1726-1808 Manor Court of Arkengarthdale:
Index of Wills, *Admons, Invents &
Bonds* 1726-1808 [Mf 878]

ARMAGH, THE PREROGATIVE COURT OF ("the PCA")
*collections relating to locations, counties or
countries or for particular groups are shown
under the appropriate place or group; see also
the Public Record Office of Ireland, Dublin in
the IRELAND National section*
Superior Courts: Canterbury (PCC);
Delegates (High Court)
1536-1810 *Vicars's* Index to the Prerogative
Wills of Ireland 1536-1810 [IR/G
93 or IR/G 150 (*1989 reprint*)];
Errata to Vicars's Index to the
Prerogative Wills of Ireland
(Procs & Papers Royal Soc of
Antiquaries of Ireland vol 29)
[IR/PER]; Introduction to the
Prerogative Wills of Ireland 1536-
1810; a continuation of the "B"
series (*BOY-BRI, from the Irish
American Genealogist vol 9 no 1*)
(Augustan Soc Omnibus Book 7)

[PER/AUG]
16-19 C Betham's Geneal Abst of
Prerogative Wills (*partially
indexed*) [Mf 309-316]; Betham's
Geneal Abst of Prerogative
Admons (*partially indexed*) [Mf
317-323]; Betham's Geneal Abst
of Prerogative Letters of Tutelage
1595-1754 (*A-W*) [Mf 324]; A
'Missing' Betham MS Index to
Will Abst & Admons (*1662-1763*)
(Irish Genealogist vol 6) [IR/PER]
1612-1843 Index to Irish Wills in the
Carrigan MSS at St Kieran's
College, Kilkenny (Irish
Genealogist vol 4) [IR/PER]
1649-1834 List of Original Probs, etc &
Official Copies of Wills, Grants,
etc presented 1928: ... Wills in
salved Prerogative Will Books &
Wills & Grants of Admon in
salved Down & Connor Will &
Grant Books *In* appx 1A to "56th
Rep of Deputy Keeper of Public
Recs in Ireland" [IR/K]
1660-1845 Synopsis of the Davies Abst in
the State Lib at Melbourne,
*Australia (lists Irish will abst,
mainly PCA*) (Irish Genealogist
vol 4) [IR/PER]
1679-1738 Irwin's Abst of Irish Wills (*PCA
etc*) (Misc Gen et Her 5th ser vol
4) [PER/MIS]
1681-1846 Surname Index to the Swanzy
MSS (*these MSS include will abst
from the PRO, Dublin for the
PCA*) [IR/G 143]
1748-1751 Index to Prerogative Grant Book
for 1748-1751 *In* appx 1A to
"57th Rep of Deputy Keeper of
Public Recs in Ireland" [IR/K]
1748-1853 List Prerogative Wills that
survived the 1922 fire *In* "55th
Rep of Deputy Keeper of Public
Recs in Ireland" [IR/K]
1839 Index to Prerogative Grant Book
for 1839 *In* appx 1A to "57th Rep
of Deputy Keeper of Public Recs
in Ireland" [IR/K]

ARMITAGE *see Handsacre*

ASHFORD CARBONELL *see Hereford, Little*

ASHILL, THE COURT OF THE PREBEND OF
Superior Court: Wells (Dean)
1662-1845 Wells Wills; vol 13: Indexes to
Wells Registry Cals - Peculiar

Courts: *Ashill Wills, Admons & Tuit Bonds* (Mfc) [Apply to Staff]

ASHMANSWORTH *see Woodhay, East*

AYLESBURY, THE COURT OF THE PECULIAR JURISDICTION OF THE DEAN and CHAPTER OF LINCOLN IN
Superior Courts: Lincoln (Dean & Chapter) until 1834; Lincoln (Consistory) from 1834
1550-1858 *Index to* Berks, Bucks & Oxon Peculiars - Wills & Admons 1550-1858 *(also Invents & Bonds): Peculiar Court of Aylesbury* [Mf 913]

BADDESLEY, THE DONATIVE COURT OF THE PECULIAR JURISDICTION OF NORTH
Superior Court: Winchester (Archdeaconry)
1663-1681 Cal of Hants Wills proved in the Prerogative & Peculiar Courts of Winchester with other Prob Docs: *N Baddesley - Separate Peculiar Wills & Admons* [HA/G 62]

BADDESLEY CLINTON, THE COURT OF THE MANOR OF
1675-1790 Cal of Original Wills & Admon Papers transmitted *(to Birmingham Probate Registry)* from the registers of Barston, Bishops Itchington, Baddesley Clinton, Knowle, Packwood, Tachbrook & Temple Balsall from 1675-1790 inclusive (BRS vol 7) [BRS]
1773-1838 Cal of Original Wills & Admon Papers from the Regs of *Baddesley Clinton (with invents)* [Mf 802]

BANBURY, THE COURT OF THE PECULIAR JURISDICTION OF THE DEAN and CHAPTER OF LINCOLN IN
including the Peculiar Jurisdictions of the Dean & Chapter of Lincoln in Cropredy, Horley & Hornton & Kings Sutton; see also Sibford
Superior Courts: Lincoln (Dean & Chapter) until 1834; Lincoln (Consistory) from 1834
1542-1858 Index to Wills, *Admons, Invents & Bonds* proved in the Court of the Dean & Chapter of Lincoln in the Peculiar of Banbury 1542-1858 (Oxford Rec Soc vol 40 or Banbury Hist Soc no 1) [*both* OX/PER]
1550-1858 *Index to* Berks, Bucks & Oxon Peculiars - Wills & Admons 1550-

1858 *(also Invents & Bonds): Peculiar Courts of Banbury & Cropredy* [Mf 913]

BANGOR, THE CONSISTORY COURT OF THE BISHOP OF
Superior Court: Canterbury (PCC)
1635-1700 Index of the Prob Recs of the Bangor Consistory Court; vol 1: pre-1700 (National Lib of Wales Prob Indexes no 1) [WS/G 70]
1700-1857 Mynegai i Ewyllysiau Bangor/*Prob Index Bangor* 1700-1857 *(index to wills, admon bonds & invents in the National Lib of Wales)*; vol 1: 1700-1749; vols 2 & 3: 1750-1857 [WS/G 102-104]

BANWELL, THE COURT OF THE PECULIAR JURISDICTION OF
Superior Court: Wells (Episcopal Consistory)
1674-1857 Wells Wills; vol 13: Indexes to Wells Registry Cals - Peculiar Courts: *Banwell & Churchill (with Puxton) - Wills 1675-1857 & Admon Bonds 1674-1852 (in 2 pts)* (Mfc) [Apply to Staff]

BARMBY MOOR *see Barnby*

BARNBY, THE COURT OF THE PREBEND OF
Superior Courts: York (Chancery); York (Dean & Chapter)*; jurisdiction assumed by York (Dean) in 1736*
1661-1736 York Registry; Names of Peculiars wherein separate lists are kept of the wills etc proved therein *including Barmby Moor 1670-1736*; York Registry; Cal of Wills & Admons - Separate Peculiars & Dean & Chapter's General Peculiars: *Barnby 1661-1729* [both Mf 879]

BARNOLDSWICK, THE COURT OF THE MANOR OF
1660-1758 Some Docs of Barnoldswick Manor Court of Probate (*will & invent abst*) In "Miscellanea vol 6" (Yorks Archl Soc rec ser vol 118) [YK/PER]
1660-1794 Manor Court of Barnoldswick: Index of Wills [Mf 878]; *Indexes to* Wills &c in the Peculiar Courts at Wakefield: *Barnoldswick Manor Court* (Northern

Genealogist vol 1) [PER/NOR]

BARNSTAPLE, THE CONSISTORIAL COURT OF THE ARCHDEACON OF
Superior Court: Exeter (Episcopal Principal Registry)
1529-1812 Index to copies of Lost Prob Recs of the Diocese of Exeter in the Library of the Society of Genealogists, London & other sources outside Devon, up to 1812 (*wills, admons, invents, etc*) [DE/G 25]
1570-1579 *Extr from* Testmtry Depositions *In* "Of chirche-reves & of testmts; the Church, Sex & Scandal in Elizabethan N Devon" [DE/G 69]

BARSTON, THE COURT OF THE MANOR OF
1675-1790 Cal of Original Wills & Admon Papers transmitted (*to Birmingham Probate Registry*) from the registers of Barston, Bishops Itchington, Baddesley Clinton, Knowle, Packwood, Tachbrook & Temple Balsall from 1675-1790 inclusive (BRS vol 7) [BRS]
1675-1857 Cal of Original Wills & Admon Papers from the Regs of *Barston* (with invents) [Mf 802]

BASWICH see *Whittington*

BATH and WELLS see *Wells*

BATH, THE ARCHDEACONRY OF
not a probate jurisdiction: see Wells (Episcopal Consistory)

BATLEY, THE COURT OF THE MANOR OF
1615-1694 Batley Manor Court *Abst of* Wills etc *In* "Miscellanea vol 2" (Yorks Archl Soc rec ser vol 74) [YK/PER]
1615-1753 Alphabetical List of Testmtry docs of the Manorial Peculiar of Batley 1651-1753 & References to Wills etc recovered from the Batley Court Rolls 1615-1652 both *In* "Miscellanea vol 2" (Yorks Archl Soc rec ser vol 74) [YK/PER]

BATTLE, THE COURT OF THE EXEMPT JURISDICTION OF THE DEANERY OF
Superior Court: Lewes (Archdeaconry)
1426-1557 Sussex Prob Recs 1: The Exempt Deanery of Battle (*pt 1: List of Wills*) (Sussex Geneal & Loc Hn vol 1) [SX/PER]
1530-1547 Cal of Wills at Lewes 1543-1548 *with abst of Deanery of Battle Wills & Admons 1530-1547* (Sussex Archl Colls vol 32) [SX/PER]
1530-1617 Cals of Wills & Admons in the Archdeaconry Court of Lewes in the Bishopric of Chichester together with those in the Archbishop of Canterbury's Peculiar Jurisdiction of S Malling & the Peculiar of the Deanery of Battle comprising together the whole of the Eastern division of the County of Sussex & the parish of Edburton in W Sussex, from the earliest extant instruments in the reign of Henry VIII to the Commonwealth (BRS vol 24) [BRS]
1610-1857 Sussex Prob Recs 1: Exempt Deanery of Battle (*pt 2: List of Admon Bonds 1610-1851; pt 3: Cal of Wills, Admons, Bonds & Invents 1657-1857*) (Sussex Geneal & Loc Hn vol 1) [SX/PER]

BAUGHURST, THE TESTAMENTARY JURISDICTION OF THE PARISH OF
Superior Court: Winchester (Archdeaconry)
1583-1720 Cal of Hants Wills proved in the Prerogative & Peculiar Courts of Winchester with other Prob Docs: *Baughurst including Inhurst - Separate Peculiar Wills* [HA/G 62]

BAWTRY see *Gringley-on-the-Hill*

BEAMINSTER see *Netherbury*

BEDFORD, THE COURTS OF THE ARCHDEACONRY OF
ie the Court of the Commissary of the Bishop of Lincoln for the Archdeaconry of Bedford (dissolved 1837) & the Court of the Archdeacon of Bedford; the recs of these Courts were combined
Superior Courts: Lincoln (Consistory) until 1837; Ely (Consistory) from 1837
1480-1519 *Abst of* Beds Wills 1480-1519; Latin wills from the first surviving register in the Court of the Archdeacon of Bedford (Beds Hist Rec Soc Pubs vol 45)

[BE/PER]
1484-1858 Index of Beds Prob Recs 1484-1858 (*wills, admons, invents, guardnshp & other bonds, etc in the Courts of the Archdeaconry of Bedford - Wills: 1484-1858, Admon Caveats: 1558-1662 & Admons: 1670-1692 & 1700-1857*); pts 1 & 2 (BRS vols 104 & 105) [*both* BRS]

1496-1560 Archdeaconry Court of Bedford Indexes to Wills; vols 12 (pt 1): 1496-1560, 1 (Liber 1): 1546-1514, 2 (Liber 2): 1515-1528, 3 (Liber 3): 1529-1533, 4: 1537-1539, 5: 1537-1543, 6: 1539-1540 & 7: 1540-1541 [Mf 709]

1498-1526 *Abst of* English Wills 1498-1526 contained in the first surviving register of wills in the Court of the Archdeacon of Bedford (Beds Hist Rec Soc Pubs vol 37) [BE/PER]

1536-1700 Archdeaconry Court of Bedford Indexes to Wills & Admons; vols 11: 1536-1700 (*cal, admons from 1669*), 8 (Liber 15): 1565-1568, 9 (Liber 31): 1638-1640 & 10: 1653-1654 [Mf 709]

1562-1591 *Abst of Beds* Elizabethan Invents *1562, 1575, 1587-1591* (Beds Hist Rec Soc Pubs vol 32) [BE/PER]

1578-1616 Archdeacon of Bedford's Admon Act Books (Beds N&Q vol 3) [BE/PER]

1630-1631 *Abst of* Beds Wills; a summary of wills proved in the Bedford Archdeaconry Court for the cal year 1630-31 [BE/G 31]

1701-1857 Archdeaconry Court of Bedford Indexes to Wills & Admons; vol 12 (pt 2): 1701-1857 (*cal*) [Mf 709]

BEEFORD, THE COURT OF THE MANOR OF

1586-1768 Index of Wills, Admon & Prob Acts in the York Registry ... *including* the Peculiar of Beeford (Yorks Archl Soc rec ser vol 68) [YK/PER]

BERKSHIRE, THE COURT OF THE ARCHDEACON OF

Superior Courts: Sarum (Consistory) until 1836; Oxford (Archdeaconry) from 1836
   Note: *see the note on the Snell Geneal*

Coll under BERKSHIRE
1508-1652 Index of the Prob Recs of the Court of the Archdeacon of Berkshire; vol 1: *Wills & Admons* 1508-1652 (BRS vol 8 or Oxford Hist Soc vol 23) [Mf 710 (*with many ms amendments*), BK/G 77, BRS or OX/PER]

1525-1710 Cal of the Unregistered Wills 1525-1710 [Mf 713]

1540-1767 Cal of Admon Acts 1540-1767 [Mf 711]

1653-1710 Index of the Prob Recs of the Court of the Archdeacon of Berkshire; vol 2: *Registered Wills, Admons & Invents* 1653-1710 (BRS vol 87) [BRS]; Index of Registered Wills, 1653-1710, deposited in the Bodleian Lib [Mf 712 or Apply to Staff]

1711-1768 Cal of Registered Wills 1711-1768 [Mf 713]

1768-1857 Cal of Wills & Admons 1768-1857 [Mf 714]

BEVERLEY, THE COURT OF THE PECULIAR JURISDICTION OF THE PROVOST OF THE COLLEGIATE CHURCH OF ST JOHN AT

Superior Courts: York (Exchequer)*; court dissolved by 1560*
1286-1347 *Abst of Prob Cases In* "Memorials of Beverley Minster - the Chapter Act Book of the Collegiate Church of St John of Beverley; vol 1" (Surtees Soc vol 98) [DU/PER]

1539-1552 *Index to* Beverley Wills (Peculiar of the Provost of the Collegiate Church of St John) (Yorks Archl Soc rec ser vol 60) [Apply to Staff]

BIBURY, THE COURT OF THE PECULIAR JURISDICTION OF

Superior Court: Gloucester (Consistory)
1590-1649 Cal of Wills proved in the Consistory Court of the Bishop Gloucester; vol 1: 1541-1650 with an appx of Dispersed Wills & *of* Wills proved in the Peculiar Courts of Bibury (*with invents*) & Bishops Cleeve (BRS vol 12) [BRS]; *Index to* 17th C Bibury & Bishop's Cleeve Wills now in the Gloucester City Lib *In* "*Index to* Berks, Bucks & Oxon Peculiars - Wills & Admons 1550-1858" [Mf

913]

1590-1833 *Index to* Bibury Wills & Invents 1590-1833 *In* "Wills & Admons proved in Glos Peculiar Courts" (Gloucester City Libs Loc Hist Pamphlet no 2) [GL/G 31 or GL Tracts]

BIERTON, THE COURT OF THE PECULIAR JURISDICTION OF THE DEAN and CHAPTER OF LINCOLN IN
Superior Courts: Lincoln (Dean & Chapter) until 1834; Lincoln (Consistory) from 1834: *see also Aylesbury; Banbury; Buckingham (Archdeaconry)*

1550-1858 *Index to* Berks, Bucks & Oxon Peculiars - Wills & Admons 1550-1858 (*also Invents & Bonds*): *Peculiar Court of Bierton* [Mf 913]

BIGGLESWADE, THE COURT OF THE PREBEND OF
Superior Courts: Lincoln (Dean & Chapter) until 1834; Lincoln (Consistory) from 1834; *see also Bedford (Archdeaconry)*

1540-1857 Index of Beds Prob Recs 1484-1858 (*wills, admons, invents, guardnshp & other bonds, etc in the Court of Biggleswade Peculiar - Wills: 1540-1559, 1575, 1639 & 1713-1857 & Admons: 1712-1755*); pts 1 & 2 (BRS vols 104 & 105) [*both* BRS]

1639-1740 Lincoln Wills; vol 4: Cal of Wills & Admons at Lincoln; Archdeaconry of Stow, Peculiar Courts & Misc Courts - *including the Court of the Prebend of Biggleswade (1639, 1730-1740 with bonds & invents)* (BRS vol 57) [BRS]; Index to Lincoln Peculiar Courts: Wills & Admons of persons dying at Biggleswade in the county of Bedford [Mf 759]

BINGLEY, THE COURT OF THE MANOR OF
see Crossley

BINSTEAD, THE TESTAMENTARY JURISDICTION OF THE PARISH OF
Superior Court: Winchester (Archdeaconry)
1612-1713 Cal of Hants Wills proved in the Prerogative & Peculiar Courts of Winchester with other Prob Docs: *Binstead (IoW) - Separate Peculiar Wills* [HA/G 62]

BIRMINGHAM, THE DISTRICT PROBATE REGISTRY IN
Superior Registry: London (Principal Probate Registry)
1858-1860 Birmingham Probate Court - Cal of Wills & Admons; vol 10: 1858-1860 [Mf 808 or Mf 809]
Note: *this is a continuation from the series beginning in 1472: see Lichfield (Consistory)*

BISHOP NORTON, THE COURT OF THE PREBEND OF
also called Norton Episcopi
Superior Court: Lincoln (Dean & Chapter) *until merged with Lincoln (Consistory) in 1834*
1613-1814 Lincoln Wills; vol 4: Cal of Wills & Admons at Lincoln; Archdeaconry of Stow, Peculiar Courts & Misc Courts - *including the Court of the Prebend of Bishop Norton (with invents)* (BRS vol 57) [BRS]; Index to Lincoln Peculiar Courts: Prebendal Court of Bishop Norton Wills & Admons [Mf 759]

BISHOP WILTON, THE COURT OF THE TESTAMENTARY JURISDICTION OF
formerly part of the Peculiar Jurisdiction of the Treasurer of York & later in lay hands
Superior Court: York (Dean & Chapter)
1616-1842 Peculiar Court of Bishop Wilton - Cal & Index of Wills & Admons 1616-1858 [Mf 878]

BISHOPS CLEEVE, THE COURT OF THE PECULIAR JURISDICTION OF
Superior Court: Gloucester (Consistory); *until 1796 when merged with Gloucester (Consistory)*
1590-1649 *Index to* 17th C Bibury & Bishop's Cleeve Wills now in the Gloucester City Lib *In* "*Index to Berks, Bucks & Oxon Peculiars - Wills & Admons 1550-1858*" [Mf 913]
1611-1796 *Index to* Bishop's Cleeve Wills & Invents 1611-1796 *In* "Wills & Admons proved in Glos Peculiar Courts" (Gloucester City Libs Loc Hist Pamphlet no 2) [GL/G 31 or GL Tracts]
1635-1796 Cal of Wills proved in the Consistory Court of the Bishop of Gloucester; vol 1: 1541-1650 with an appx of Dispersed Wills & *of* Wills proved in the Peculiar

Courts of Bibury & Bishops
Cleeve (BRS vol 12) [BRS]

**BISHOPS ITCHINGTON, THE COURT OF
THE PREBEND OF**
Superior Court: Lichfield (Dean & Chapter):
see also Colwich
1675-1790 Cals of Original Wills & Admon
Papers transmitted (*to
Birmingham Probate Registry*)
from the registers of Barston,
Bishops Itchington, Baddesley
Clinton, Knowle, Packwood,
Tachbrook & Temple Balsall from
1675-1790 inclusive (BRS vol 7)
[BRS]
1701-1858 Cal of Original Wills & Admon
Papers from the Regs of *Bishops
Itchington (wills only)* [Mf 802]

BISHOPS LYNN *see King's Lynn*

**BISHOPS TACHBROOK, THE COURT OF
THE PREBEND OF**
Superior Court: Lichfield (Dean & Chapter)
1675-1790 Cals of Original Wills & Admon
Papers transmitted (*to
Birmingham Probate Registry*)
from the registers of Barston,
Bishops Itchington, Baddesley
Clinton, Knowle, Packwood,
Tachbrook & Temple Balsall from
1675 to 1790 inclusive (BRS vol
7) [BRS]
1731-1858 Cal of Original Wills & Admon
Papers from the Regs of *Bishops
Tachbrook (wills only)* [Mf 802]

**BISHOPS WALTHAM, THE TESTAMENTARY
JURISDICTION OF THE PARISH OF**
Superior Court: Winchester (Archdeaconry)
1625-1832 Cal of Hants Wills proved in the
Prerogative & Peculiar Courts of
Winchester with other Prob Docs:
*Bishops Waltham including
Hamble & Bursledon - Index of
Peculiar Court Wills* [HA/G 62]

**BISHOPSTOKE, THE TESTAMENTARY
JURISDICTION OF THE PARISH OF**
Superior Court: Winchester (Archdeaconry)
1569-1845 Cal of Hants Wills proved in the
Prerogative & Peculiar Courts of
Winchester with other Prob Docs:
*Bishopstoke - Separate Peculiar
Wills* [HA/G 62]
1625-1638 Diocese of Winchester; Index to
Registered Copies of Wills in the

charge of the Diocesan Registrar
*including the Peculiar of
Bishopstoke*; Wills, Admons &
Invents with the Winchester
Diocesan Recs - *index to
Registered Wills in the Peculiar
Court of Alverstoke* [HA/G 67 &
40]

**BISHOPSTONE, THE COURT OF THE
PREBEND OF**
Superior Court: Sarum (Dean)
1627-1799 Peculiar & Prebendal Courts of
the Diocese of Sarum - Indexes
to Wills & Admons 1462-1810:
*Prebendal Court of Bishopstone
(with invents)* [Mf 836]
1800-1848 Wilts Wills Beneficiaries Index
1800-1858: Name Abst; vol 4:
Bishopstone 1800-1848, Wilsford
& Woodford 1800-1854, Chute &
Chisenbury 1800-1855, Coombe
& Harnham 1800-1856 (Peculiar
Court docs 398-507) [WL/G 67]
1800-1858 Sarum Courts, Deanery &
Archdeaconry of Wilts; vol "A":
Index for Wills & *Admons* 1800-
1858 with names beginning A-B
only [Mf 838]

**BOCKING, THE COURT OF THE PECULIAR
JURISDICTION OF THE ARCHBISHOP OF
CANTERBURY IN THE DEANERY OF**
Superior Courts: Canterbury (PCC); *see also
Lambeth Palace & London (Commissary -
Essex & Herts)*
1627-1857 *Abst of* Wills, Admons, Bonds &
Invents in the Peculiar of the
Deanery of Bocking, County
Essex 1627-1857 [ES/G 62]
1627-1858 Wills at Chelmsford; Index to
Wills now preserved in the Essex
RO at Chelmsford *including the
Peculiar Court of the Deanery of
Bocking from 1627*; vols 2: 1620-
1720 & 3: 1721-1858 (BRS vols
79 & 84) [*both* BRS]

BOROUGHBRIDGE, THE DEANERY OF *see
Richmond (Eastern Deaneries)*

BOURTON *see Gillingham*

**BRAMPTON, THE COURT OF THE
PECULIAR JURISDICTION OF**
Superior Court: Huntingdon (Archdeaconry)
1549-1659 Cal of Wills & Admons in the Act
Books of the Archdeaconry of

Huntingdon relating to the counties of Beds, Herts & Hunts & to the Peculiar Court of Brampton (*wills only*) previous to 1660; now preserved in the Probate Registry of Peterborough (BRS vol 42) [Apply to Staff]

BRATTON see Sarum (Precentor)

BRAUNTON see Exeter (Dean)

BRECHIN, THE COMMISSARIOT OF
Superior Courts: Court of Session; see also Edinburgh (Commissariot)
1576-1800 Commissariot Rec of Brechin; Reg of Testmts 1576-1800 (Scottish Rec Soc vol 13) [SC/PER]
1801-1823 *Brechin Regs of Testmts & Invents In* "Index to Regs of Testmts for various Commissariots 1801-1823" [Mf 2910]

BRECON, THE CONSISTORIAL COURT OF THE ARCHDEACON OF
Superior Court: St David's (Episcopal Consistory)
1750-1857 Mynegai i Ewyllysiau Aberhonddy/*Prob Index Brecon 1750-1857 (index to wills, admon bonds & invents in the National Lib of Wales)* [WS/G 110]

BRIDGNORTH, THE COURT OF THE ROYAL PECULIAR and EXEMPT JURISDICTION OF THE DEANERY OF
Superior Court: Delegates (High Court)
1635-1858 Cal of Salop Wills & Admons (*with invents*) deposited in Shrewsbury District Probate Registry *including: Peculiar Court of Bridgnorth* (supp to Trans Salop Archl & Nat Hist Soc 4th ser vols 12 *now 45* & 46) [Mf 800 or SH/PER]
1727-1843 Royal Peculiar & Exempt Jurisdiction of the Deanery of Bridgnorth: Act Book 1727-1843 [Mf 800]

BRIDGWATER, THE COURT OF THE MAYOR OF THE BOROUGH OF
1200-1485 Abst of Wills etc enrolled *In* "Bridgwater Borough Archives 1200-1485; vols 1-5" (Somerset Rec Soc vols 48, 53, 58, 60, 70)

[SO/PER]
1310-1415 *Extr from* Prob Copies of Wills at Bridgwater *In* "3rd HMC Rep" [SP/HMC]

BRIDPORT, THE COURT OF THE MAYOR OF THE BOROUGH OF
1269-1460 Cal of Wills & Admons relating to Dorset in the Courts of Sarum; *from Borough of Bridport recs* (BRS vol 53) [BRS]

BRIGHSTONE, THE TESTAMENTARY JURISDICTION OF THE PARISH OF
Superior Court: Winchester (Archdeaconry)
1563-1668 Cal of Hants Wills proved in the Prerogative & Peculiar Courts of Winchester with other Prob Docs: *Brighstone (IoW) - Separate Peculiar Wills* [HA/G 62]

BRISTOL (CITY and DEANERY DIVISION), THE CONSISTORY COURT OF THE BISHOP OF
Superior Courts: Wells (Episcopal Consistory) until 1542; Worcester (Consistory) until 1542; Canterbury (PCC) from 1542; see also Bristol (Dean & Chapter); Gloucester (Consistory)
1542-1804 Guide to the Prob Invents of the Bristol Deanery 1542-1804 (*an index*) [GL/G 33 or GL/G 36]
1546-1593 *Abst of* Bristol Wills 1546-1593 [GL/G 39 or GL/G 47]
1546-1603 *Abst of* Tudor Wills proved in Bristol 1546-1603 (Bristol Rec Soc Pubs vol 44) [GL/PER]
1570-1857 Consistory Court of Bristol Cal of Wills 1570-1857 [Mf 905]
1572-1792 Cal of Wills proved in the Consistory Court (City & Deanery of Bristol Div) of the Bishop of Bristol 1572-1792 (*with Admons granted 1770-1792*) & also cal of the Wills contained in the Great Orphan Books, preserved in the Council House, Bristol 1379-1674 (BRS vol 17) [BRS]
1597-1598 *Abst of* Bristol Wills 1597-1598 [GL/G 40]
1611-1643 *Index of* Invents from the Consistory Court, Bristol [Apply to Staff]
1770-1858 Consistory Court of Bristol Cal of Admons 1770-1858 [Mf 734]
1793-1858 Index to Bristol Wills 1793-1858 (*continuation of BRS vol 17*) [Apply to Staff]

BRISTOL, THE COURT OF THE DEAN and CHAPTER OF

Superior Court: Bristol (Consistory - City & Deanery)

1546-1603 Abst of Tudor Wills proved in Bristol 1546-1603 (Bristol Rec Soc Pubs vol 44) [GL/PER]

1559-1594 Cal of Wills in the Dean & Chapter of Bristol Cathedral (*1559, 1567-1572, 1593-1594*) (Somerset & Dorset N&Q vol 13) [SO/PER]; *Abst of* Bristol Wills & Docs & *proved at the Bishop's Visitation of 1559* (Trans Bristol & Glos Rec Soc vol 64) [GL/PER]; Cal of Wills in the Archives of the Dean & Chapter of the Cathedral of Bristol (*1559, 1567, 1572 & 1593*) (*In* Addenda to BRS vol 22) [BRS]

1567-1593 *Index to* Dorset Wills in the Archives of the Dean & Chapter of the Cathedral of Bristol (BRS vol 53) [BRS]; *Abst of* Dorset Wills in the Dean & Chapter of Bristol Cathedral & *proved at the Bishop's Visitations of 1567 & 1572* (Somerset & Dorset N&Q vol 24) [SO/PER]

BRISTOL (DORSET DIVISION), THE CONSISTORY COURT OF THE BISHOP OF

Superior Courts: Sarum (Consistory) until 1542; Bristol (Consistory - City & Deanery) from 1542*; see also Dorset (Archdeaconry)*

1681-1792 Cals of Wills & Admons relating to the County of Dorset, proved in the Consistory Court (Dorset Div) of the late Diocese of Bristol 1681-1792, in the Archdeaconry Court of Dorset 1568-1792 & in the several peculiars 1660-1799 (BRS vol 22) [BRS]

1727-1729 Cals of Dorset Wills, Admons, etc in the Probate Registry at Blandford; pt 2: Cal of Admons for the years 1727, 1728 & 1729 in the Consistory Court of Dorset at Blandford (BRS vol 53) [BRS]

1793-1855 Cal of Wills & Admons relating to the County of Dorset preserved in the Probate Registry at Blandford & among the Ecclesiastical Recs of Wimborne Minster to 1857 (*including the Consistory Court*) (*Fry MSS*) [Apply to Staff]

1820-1855 List of wills proved in the Bishop's Court during Inhibitions *of the Archdeacon's Court in 1820, 1831, 1835, 1839, 1842, 1845, 1848, 1851 & 1855 (at the end of vol 1 of Archdeaconry Indexes)* [Mf 730]

BRISTOL, THE ORPHAN'S COURT OF THE CITY OF

1379-1674 Cal of Wills proved in the Consistory Court (City & Deanery of Bristol Div) of the Bishop of Bristol 1572-1792 (*& Admons granted 1770-1792*) & also cal of the Wills contained in the Great Orphan Books, preserved in the Council House, Bristol 1379-1674 (BRS vol 17) [BRS]

1382-1605 Notes or Abst of the Wills contained in the vol entitled 'The Great Orphan Book & Book of Wills' in the Council House at Bristol (*1382-1595, 1605*) [GL/G 41]

BUCKDEN, THE COURT OF THE PREBEND OF

Superior Courts: Lincoln (Dean & Chapter) until 1834; Lincoln (Consistory) from 1834*; see also Huntingdon (Archdeaconry)*

1691-1749 Lincoln Wills; vol 4: Cal of Wills & Admons at Lincoln; Archdeaconry of Stow, Peculiar Courts & Misc Courts - *including wills proved in the Court of the Prebendary of Buckden* (BRS vol 57) [BRS]

BUCKINGHAM, THE COURTS OF THE ARCHDEACONRY OF

ie the Court of the Commissary of the Chancellor of Lincoln for the Archdeaconry of Buckingham (dissolved in 1845) & the Court of the Archdeacon of Buckingham; the records of the Courts were combined

Superior Courts: Lincoln (Consistory - until 1845); Oxford (Consistory - from 1845)

1483-1523 Courts of the Archdeaconry of Buckingham 1483-1523 (*will abst*) (Bucks Rec Soc vol 19) [BU/PER]

1483-1601 Archdeaconry Court of Buckingham; Cal of Wills & Admons - vol 1: Wills 1483-1601 [Mf 715]

1491-1495 A Fragment of Folios of a MS of the Archdeaconry of Buckingham (*abst of wills & admons 1491-*

1495 not in the cal for 1483-1523) (Recs of Bucks vol 10 pt 5) [BU/PER]

1598-1708 Archdeaconry Court of Buckingham; Cal of Wills & Admons - vols 2 (pt 1): Wills 1602-1708 & 3: Admons 1598, 1632-1708; Index to Admon Bonds 1639-1708 *(at the end of vol 4)* [Mf 715]

1686-1695 Abst of Registered Wills proved in the Archdeaconry Court of Buckingham 1686-1695 *(also Mfc)* [BU/G 32 or Apply to Staff]

1709-1857 Archdeaconry Court of Buckingham; Cal of Wills & Admons - vols 2 (pt 2): Wills 1709-1837, 4: Admons 1709-1857 & 5: Wills 1800-1853 [Mf 715]

BUCKINGHAM, THE COURT OF THE PECULIAR JURISDICTION OF THE DEAN and CHAPTER OF LINCOLN IN THE PREBEND OF
Superior Courts: Lincoln (Dean & Chapter) until 1834; Lincoln (Consistory) from 1834; *see also Aylesbury & Buckingham (Archdeaconry)*

1550-1856 *Index to* Berks, Bucks & Oxon Peculiars - Wills & Admons 1550-1858 *(also Invents & Bonds)*: *Peculiar Court of Buckingham* [Mf 913]

BUCKLAND DINHAM, THE COURT OF THE PREBEND OF
Superior Court: Wells (Dean)

1637-1857 Wells Wills; vol 13: Indexes to Wells Registry Cals - Peculiar Courts: *Buckland Dinham Wills, Admons, Invents & Tuit Bonds* (Mfc) [Apply to Staff]

BUGTHORPE, THE COURT OF THE PREBEND OF
Superior Courts: York (Chancery); York (Dean & Chapter)

1669-1831 York Registry; Names of Peculiars wherein Separate Lists are kept of Wills etc proved therein: *Bugthorpe with Stockton 1669-1831*; York Registry; Calendar of Wills & Administrations - Separate Peculiars & Dean & Chapter's General Peculiars: *Bugthorpe 1669-1739* [*both* Mf 879]

BUILDWAS, THE COURT OF THE PECULIAR JURISDICTION OF
formerly the Peculiar Jurisdiction of Buildwas Abbey
Superior Court: Lichfield (Consistory)

1799-1819 Cal of Salop Wills & Admons *(with invents)* deposited in Shrewsbury District Probate Registry *including: Manor of Buildwas* (supps to Trans Salop Archl & Nat Hist Soc 4th ser vols 12 *now 45* & 46) [Mf 800 or SH/PER]

BULLINGHAM, UPPER *see Bullinghope, Upper*

BULLINGHOPE, THE COURT OF THE PREBEND OF UPPER
Superior Court: Hereford (Dean)

1675-1858 Upper Bullingham Index of Wills & Admons together with registered copies of Wills proved in the Peculiar Prebendal Court of Upper Bullingham or Bullinghope May 1675-1858 [Mf 2591]

BURBAGE *see Hurstbourne*

BURGHCLERE, THE TESTAMENTARY JURISDICTION OF THE PARISH OF
Superior Court: Winchester (Archdeaconry)

1661-1834 Cal of Hants Wills proved in the Prerogative & Peculiar Courts of Winchester with other Prob Docs: *Burghclere with Newton - Separate Peculiar Wills* [HA/G 62]

BURSLEDON *see Bishops Waltham*

BURTON-ON-TRENT, THE COURT OF THE MANOR OF
see also Lichfield (Consistory)

1529-1652 Cal of Wills & Admons registered in the various Peculiar Courts now preserved at the Lichfield Registry 1529-1652 (BRS vol 7) [BRS]

1671-1858 Cal of Wills & Admons of Peculiar Jurisdictions in the Diocese of Lichfield; vols 1 & 2 *including the* Manorial Court of Burton on Trent 1671-1858 [Mf 801]

BURY ST EDMUNDS *see Sudbury*

CAISTOR, THE COURT OF THE PREBEND OF
Superior Court: Lincoln (Dean & Chapter)
until merged with Lincoln (Consistory) in 1834
1636-1833 Lincoln Wills; vol 4: Cal of Wills & Admons at Lincoln; Archdeaconry of Stow, Peculiar Courts & Misc Courts - *including the Court of the Prebend of Caistor (with invents)* (BRS vol 57) [BRS]; *Indexes of Wills & Admons in the Peculiar Courts at Lincoln: Caistor Prebendal Court (Northern Genealogist vol 1)* [PER/NOR]; Index to Lincoln Peculiar Courts: Prebendal Court of Caistor [Mf 759]
1772-1819 Wills & Admons etc: listings taken from cals of the old Diocese of York & the Diocese of Lincoln (with certain additions from Durham) *(index BUR-WRI)* (Fam Hist vols 2 & 3) [PER/FAM]

CAITHNESS, THE COMMISSARIOT OF
Superior Courts: Court of Session; *see also Edinburgh (Commissariot)*
1661-1664 Commissariot Rec of Caithness; Reg of Testmts 1661-1664 (Scottish Rec Soc vol 10) [SC/PER]
1801-1823 *Caithness Regs of Deeds, Testmts & Invents In* "Index to Regs of Testmts for various Commissariots 1801-1823" [Mf 2910]

CALDECOTT, THE COURT OF THE PREBEND OF
Superior Courts: Lincoln (Dean & Chapter) until 1834; Lincoln (Consistory) from 1834; *see also Liddington*
1669-1820 Index to Wills & Admons proved & granted in the Archdeaconry Court of Leicester 1660-1750 & in the Peculiars of St Margaret Leicester & Rothley & in the Rutland Peculiars of Caldecott, Ketton & Tixover & Liddington prior to 1821; now preserved in the Probate Registry at Leicester (BRS vol 51) [Apply to Staff]

CALNE, THE COURT OF THE PREBEND OF
see Sarum (Treasurer)

CAMBRIDGE, THE EPISCOPAL CONSISTORY COURT OF ELY and *see Ely (Consistory)*

CAMBRIDGE, THE COURT OF THE CHANCELLOR, MASTERS and SCHOLARS OF THE UNIVERSITY OF
often called the Court of the Vice-Chancellor
Superior Courts: Delegates (High Court); *see also Canterbury (PCC)*
1501-1765 Cal of Wills proved in the Court of the Vice-Chancellor of the University of Cambridge 1501-1765 [CA/G 26]

CAMBRIDGE, THE COURT OF THE MAYOR OF THE BOROUGH OF
1419-1589 Extr from Wills *In* "Cambridge Borough Docs vol 1" [CA/L 3]

CAMBRIDGE, THE PECULIAR JURISDICTION OF TRINITY COLLEGE AT
see Masham; see also Cambridge (University)

CANFORD and POOLE, THE COURT OF THE PECULIAR JURISDICTION OF GREAT
also called Canford Magna & Poole
Superior Courts: Bristol (Consistory - Dorset); *see also Dorset (Archdeaconry)*
1650-1857 Alphabetical Reg of Wills lodged in the Registry of Great Canford & Poole 1650-1857 [Mf 732]
1667-1820 Cal of Wills & Admons relating to the County of Dorset, proved in the Consistory Court (Dorset Div) of the late Diocese of Bristol 1681-1792, in the Archdeaconry Court of Dorset 1568-1792 & in the several peculiars 1660-1799 - *including* wills of the Peculiar of Canford Magna & Poole from 1650-*1820* & admons from 1680-*1799* (BRS vol 22) [BRS]
1680-1857 Peculiar Court of Great Canford & Poole; Index of Admons 1680-1857 with a few original wills [Mf 729]
1781-1857 Cal of Wills & Admons relating to the County of Dorset preserved in the Probate Registry at Blandford & among the Ecclesiastical Recs of Wimborne Minster to 1857 *including the Peculiar Court of Great Canford & Poole (Fry MSS)* [Apply to Staff]

CANTERBURY, THE PREROGATIVE COURT OF THE ARCHBISHOP OF ("the PCC")

collections relating to locations, counties or countries or for particular groups are shown under the appropriate place or group; the records of the Court of Civil Commission (1653-1660) are included with this Court **Superior Courts:** Arches (High Court); Canterbury (Dean & Chapter - during vacancies); Delegates (High Court); *see Lambeth Palace for the Archiepiscopal Registers, etc; see also other courts in Canterbury for mis-filed papers, sede vacante probates, etc*

PCC Administrations

1559-1580 *Indexes of* Admons in the PCC; vols 1: 1559-1571 & 2: 1572-1580 (*Glencross*) (supp to The Genealogist new ser vols 26-34) [WILLS/PCC]

1581-1582 PCC Admons - Cal of Admons 1581-1582 (*Glencross MSS*) [WILLS/PCC]

1581-1619 Index to Admons granted in the PCC & now preserved in the Principal Probate Registry; vols 3: 1581-1595, 4: 1596-1608 & 5: 1609-1619 (BRS vols 76, 81 & 83) [*all* BRS]

1620-1630 PCC Letters of Admons 1620-1630; abst, translated from the original Latin, arranged & numbered in alphabetical order of intestates, with separate indexes of stray names & places (*Morrison*) [WILLS/PCC or Apply to Staff]

1631-1660 Index to Admons granted in the PCC & now preserved in the Principal Probate Registry; vols 1: 1631-1648, 2: 1649-1654 & 3: 1655-1660 (*in 3 pts*) (BRS vols 100, 68, 72, 74 & 75 [*all* BRS]

1680 Admons - 1679/1680 Jan & Feb - PCC [Apply to Staff]

1700-1704 Index to Wills & Admons 1700-1704 for surnames beginning with the letter "B" [WILLS/PCC]

1721 A *partial* Index to Wills & Admons in Reg "Buckingham" *In* the Bernau Index (Mf) [Lower Library: Bernau Index drawers]

1751-1760 Index to Wills & Admons 1751-1760 for surnames beginning with the letter "A" (*Glencross MSS*) [WILLS/PCC]

1801-1804 PCC Admons & Prob Acts letter "B" (*BAB-BEL*) 1801-1804 (supp to Blackmansbury vols 1 nos 1-3 & 5-6, 5 nos 5-6, 6 nos 5-6 & 7 no 5) [PER/BLA]

1853-1857 Cal of the Grants of Prob & Letters of Admon made in the PCC 1 Jan 1853-31 Dec 1857 inclusive (*in 15 pts*) [*all* WILLS/PCC] **Note:** *these vols do NOT cover the period 1-10 Jan 1858*

American Probates in the PCC

ie material in the PCC associated with N America; see also WEST INDIES

1610-1699 English Estates of American Colonists; American Wills & Admons in the PCC vol 1: 1610-1699 [US/G 78]

1610-1857 American Wills & Admons in the PCC 1610-1857 (*list with extr*) [US/G 81]

1611-1775 *Abst of* American Wills Proved in London 1611-1775 [WILLS/PCC & US/G 126]

1641-1736 Lord Mayor's Court of London Depositions relating to Americans 1641-1736 *with* PCC testmtry cases [US/G 76]

1642-1809 American Wills contested in the PCC (*abst of Depositions 1657-1809 & Cause Papers 1642-1722*) (Nat Geneal Soc Qtrly vol 66) [US/PER]

1671-1689 Some Early Invents in the PCC (*index to American testators*) (Nat Geneal Soc Qtrly vol 67) [US/PER]

1680-1830 Directory of Scots in the Carolinas 1680-1830 (*prob extr*) [US/NC/G 9]

1700-1780 *Cal of* American Admons & Prob Acts in the PCC; pt 1: 1700-1710 (*A-HAS*) (Nat Geneal Soc Qtrly vol 61); pts 2: 1711-1715, 3: 1716-1720 & 4: 1721-1725 (Nat Geneal Soc Qtrly vol 62); pts 5: 1726-1730 & 6: 1731-1740 (Nat Geneal Soc Qtrly vol 64); pts 7: 1741-1750 & 8: 1751-1760 (Nat Geneal Soc Qtrly vol 65); pts 9: 1761-1770 & 10: 1771-1780 (Nat Geneal Soc Qtrly vol 66) [*all* US/PER]

1700-1799 English Estates of American Colonists; American Wills & Admons in the PCC; vol 2:

1700-1799 [US/G 79]

1772-1858 *Index to* American Invents in the PCC (Nat Geneal Soc Qtrly vol 69) [US/PER]

1791-1799 *Cal of* American Admons & Prob Acts in the PCC; pt 12: 1791-1799 (Nat Geneal Soc Qtrly vol 68) [US/PER]

1828-1849 *Abst about* Americans in Litigation Papers in the PCC (Nat Geneal Soc Qtrly vol 80) [US/PER]

PCC Inventories

1653-1660 Cal of Invents 1653-1660 being Lists of Invents exhibited in the PCC for the Commonwealth period, for the following counties: *Beds, Cambs, Cornwall, Devon, Dorset, Glos, Hants, Hunts, Kent, Norfolk, Somerset, Suffolk & Wilts; also (for 1660 only) Bucks, Essex, Herts, Lancs, Middx & Overseas* [WILLS/PCC]

1660-1720 PCC Parchment Invents post 1600 (*index to PRO Class PROB 4*) (List & Index Soc vol 221) [SP/PER]

1661-1725 PCC Paper Invents 1661-c1725 (*index to PRO Class PROB 5*) (List & Index Soc vol 149) [SP/PER]

1662-1720 PCC Filed Exhibits with Invents (*index to PRO Class PROB 32*) (List & Index Soc vol 204) [SP/PER]

1702-1783 *Cal of* PCC Invents (ser 2); pts 1: 1702, 1718-1733 & 2: 1734-1783 (List & Index Soc vols 85 & 86) [*both* SP/PER]

PCC Wills

1383-1619 Wills proved in the PCC; vol 1: 1383-1558 (*in 2 pts*) (BRS vols 10 & 11) [*both* BRS or *both* WILLS/PCC]; Index of Wills proved in the PCC & now preserved in the Principal Probate Registry; vol 2: 1558-1583 (BRS vol 18) [BRS]; vol 3: 1584-1604 (BRS vol 25) [Apply to Staff]; vol 4: 1605-1619 (BRS vol 43) [BRS]

1620 Abst of Wills in Reg "Soame" (*Lea*) [WILLS/PCC]

1620-1624 Year Books of Probs; Abst of Probs & Sentences in the PCC - *1st ser* vol 1: 1620-1624

[WILLS/PCC]

1620-1629 Wills proved in the PCC; vol 5: 1620-1629 (BRS vol 44) [BRS]

1630 Abst of Wills in Reg "Scroope" (*Morrison*) [WILLS/PCC]

1630-1652 Year Books of Probs; Abst of Probs & Sentences in the PCC - *2nd ser* vol 1: 1630-1634; Abst of Prob Acts in the PCC - *2nd ser* vol 2: 1635-1639; extra vol: Sentences & Complete Index Nominum (Probs & Sentences) for the years 1630-1639; *Boyd's* Index to Testators in vols 1 & 2 (*1630-1639*) of "Year Books of Prob, being abst of Prob Acts in the PCC"; Abst of Prob Acts in the PCC - *2nd ser* vol 3: 1640-1644; Abst of Prob Acts in the PCC - *2nd ser* vol 4: 1645-1649; Abst of Prob Acts in the PCC - vol 5: *Commonwealth Probs vol 1*: 1650-1651 [*all* WILLS/PCC]; *Boyd's* Index to Testators 1640-1652 [Apply to Staff]

1650-1651 Abst of Wills in Reg "Grey" (*vols 1-15: 1650-1651; Rowan MSS, in 6 pts*) [Apply to Staff]

1652-1655 Year Books of Probs; Abst of Prob Acts in the PCC - vol 6: Commonwealth Probs vol 2: 1652-1653; Abst of Prob Acts in the PCC - *vol 7:* Commonwealth Probs vol 3: 1654-1655; Abst of Prob Acts in the PCC - *vol 8:* Commonwealth Probs vol 4: 1655 (*A-M*) [*all* WILLS/PCC]

1653-1660 Wills proved in the PCC; vols 6: 1653-1656 & 7: 1657-1660 (BRS vol 54 & 61) [*both* BRS]

1658 Geneal Abst of Wills proved in the PCC in Reg "Wootton"; vols 1-7: 1658 (*Brigg, in 3 pts*) [*all* WILLS/PCC]

1661-1670 Wills, Sentences & Prob Acts 1661-1670, arranged & numbered in alphabetical order of testators with separate indexes of places, ships, stray names & trades & conditions (*Morrison*) [WILLS/PCC]

1671-1693 Wills proved in the PCC; vols 8: 1671-1675, 9: 1676-1685 & 10: 1686-1693 (BRS vols 67, 71 & 77) [*all* BRS]

1680-1682 Index to Wills 1680-1682 (*Wenban*) [WILLS/PCC]

1694-1700 Wills proved in the PCC; vol 11:

1694-1700 (BRS vol 80) [BRS]

1700-1704 Index to Wills & Admons 1700-1704 for surnames beginning with the letter "B" (*Fothergill MSS*) [WILLS/PCC]

1721 A *partial* Index to Wills & Admons in Reg "Buckingham" *In* the Bernau Index (Mf) [Lower Library: Bernau Index drawers]

1721-1727 PCC Wills - Card Index: 1721-1725 (*A-WAY*) & 1726-1727 (*incomplete*) [Lower Library: Index drawers 161-169 & 189]

1746-1747 Index to Wills in Regs "Edmonds" & "Potter", 1746-1747, including indexes of testators, places & collateral & incidental names (*Snell MSS*) [WILLS/PCC]

1750 List of Persons named in Wills in Reg "Greenly" 1750; Groups 1-8 (*Sherwood MSS, in 3 pts*) [WILLS/PCC]; *also indexed in* The Bernau Index (Mf) [Lower Library: Bernau Index drawers]

1750-1800 Index to Wills 1750-1800; vols 1-6 (vol 4 also Mfc) [WILLS/PCC or Apply to Staff]

1751-1760 Index to Wills & Admons 1751-1760 for surnames beginning with the letter "A" (*Glencross MSS*) [WILLS/PCC]

1801-1804 PCC Admons & Prob Acts letter "B" (*BAB-BEL*) 1801-1804 (supp to Blackmansbury vols 1 nos 1-3 & 5-6, 5 nos 5-6, 6 nos 5-6 & 7 no 5) [PER/BLA]

1853-1857 Cal of the Grants of Prob & Letters of Admon made in the PCC 1 Jan 1853-31 Dec 1857 inclusive (*in 15 pts*) [*all* WILLS/PCC] **Note:** *these vols do NOT cover the period 1-10 Jan 1858*

Other PCC Papers
see also Lambeth Palace for Archiepiscopal Registers

1387-1454 Fifty Earliest English Wills in the Court of Probate 1387-1454 [WILLS/PCC]

15-16 C Index of Wills; an arbitrary coll of 15th & 16th C wills (*mostly PCC wills*) (*Soper*) [WILLS/GEN]

1495-1695 Wills from Doctors' Commons; a selection from the wills of eminent persons, proved in the PCC 1495-1695 (Camden Soc old ser vol 83) [WILLS/PCC or

PER/CS]

16-17 C Notes on unpublished wills at Somerset House (*extr*) (The Genealogist new ser vol 4) [PER/GEN]

1526-1858 Prob Act Books (*partial index to PRO Class PROB 8*) *In* the Bernau Index (Mf) [Lower Library: Bernau Index drawers]

1642-1722 PCC Cause Papers, Early ser 1642-1722 (*index to PRO Class PROB 28*) (List & Index Soc vol 161) [SP/PER]

1662-1720 PCC Filed Exhibits with Invents (*index to PRO Class PROB 32*) (List & Index Soc vol 204) [SP/PER]

CANTERBURY, THE CONSISTORY COURT OF THE ARCHBISHOP OF
including, from 1547, the Court of the Provost of the Collegiate Court at Wingham; few Kent probates are to be found in the PCC as prerogative probate jurisdiction for the Archdiocese of Canterbury was normally delegated to the Archbishop's Commissary-General

Superior Courts: Canterbury (Commissary); Canterbury (Dean & Chapter); Canterbury (PCC)

1396-1558 Index of Wills & Admons; vol 1: 1396-1558 (BRS vol 50 or Kent Recs vol 6) [BRS, KE/PER & KE/G 67]; Index of Wills - an arbitrary coll of 15th & 16th C wills (*including some from Canterbury Consistory Court*) (*Soper*) [WILLS/GEN]

1396-1731 Consistory Court of Canterbury; Cals of Wills 1396-1731 [Mf 743]

1498-1596 Kentish Wills; Geneal Extr from 16th C Wills in the Consistory Court at Canterbury (reprinted from Misc Gen et Her with additions) [KE/G 68]; *also* (Misc Gen et Her 5th ser vols 2-5) [PER/MIS]

1539-1577 Index of Wills & Admons; vol 2: Wills 1558-1577 & Admons 1539-1545 (BRS vol 65) [BRS]

1557-1637 Stray Wills at Canterbury (*index to Cause Papers 1557 & 1595-1637*) (Genealogists' Mag vol 17) [PER/GEN]

1569-1735 Archdeaconry & Consistory Courts of Canterbury, County of Kent: Index of Prob Accounts (*1569-1650, 1660-1728 & 1735*)

(Kent FHS Rec Pub no 1682)
(Mfc) [Apply to Staff]

1596-1679 Consistory Court of Canterbury, County of Kent: *Index of* Invents; pt 1: 1596-1679 (Kent FHS Rec Pub no 714) (Mfc) [Apply to Staff]

1600-1857 Consistory Court of Canterbury; Indexes of Wills 1600-1640, 1638-1857 [Mf 744]

1640-1650 Index of Wills & Admons; vol 3: 1640-1650 (BRS vol 50 or Kent Recs vol 6) [BRS, KE/PER & KE/G 67]

1680-1679 Consistory Court of Canterbury, County of Kent: *Index of* Invents; pt 2: 1680-1748 (Kent FHS Rec Pub no 715) (Mfc) [Apply to Staff]

CANTERBURY, THE COURT OF THE COMMISSARY-GENERAL OF THE ARCHBISHOP OF
Superior Courts: Canterbury (Consistory); Canterbury (Dean & Chapter); Canterbury (PCC)

997-1655 Sede Vacante Wills; Cal of Wills proved before the Commissary of Canterbury during vacancies in the Primacy with an appx of transcripts of Archiepiscopal wills & wills of importance (*abst of wills 997-1559, 1655 & admons 1500-1559*) (Kent Recs vol 3) [KE/PER]

1446-1541 Extr from the Regs of the several Wills & Testmts proved in the Court of the Archbishop's Commissary for the Diocese & City of Canterbury beginning with the reign of King Edward IV; vols 1: 1444-1493 & 2: 1494-1541 [KE/G 60-61]; Index to vol 1 [KE/G 60A];

1500-1503 *List of* Wills proved before the Commissary of the Prior of Canterbury 'sede Cantuar vacante' *In* "8th HMC Rep" [SP/HMC]

1541-1731 Extr from the Regs of the several Wills & Testmts proved in the Court of the Archbishop's Commissary for the Diocese & City of Canterbury beginning with the reign of King Edward IV; vols 3: 1541-1596, 4: 1596-1618, 5: 1618-1640 & 6-7: 1640/*1660*-1712 & 1721-1731 [KE/G 62-65]

CANTERBURY, THE COURT OF THE ARCHDEACON OF
Superior Court: Canterbury (Consistory)

1396-1650 Cal of Wills & Admons now preserved in the Probate Registry at Canterbury; vols 1: 1396-1558, 1640-1650 & 2: Admons 1558-1577, Wills 1539-1545 (BRS vols 50 & 65) [*both* BRS]

1442-1467 *Abst from the Archidiaconal Reg; vol 1:* Early Kentish Wills 1442-1467 (Archaeologica Cantiana vol 11) [KE/PER]

1449-1583 Archdeaconry Court of Canterbury Prob Recs: Index to Wills; vol 1: 1449-1583 [Mf 738]

1449-1712 Archdeaconry Court of Canterbury, County of Kent: Indexes of Wills by name & by Parish; vol 1: 1449-1712 listed alphabetically by name & by parish (Kent FHS Rec Pub nos 1041 & 1042) (Mfc) [Apply to Staff]

1449-1858 Archdeaconry Court of Canterbury, County of Kent: Index of Wills 1449-1858 listed alphabetically by name & by parish (containing only those Original Wills not registered) (Kent FHS Rec Pub no 1607) (Mfc) [Apply to Staff]

1550-1582 Archdeaconry Court of Canterbury Prob Recs; Index to Act Books 1550-1582 [Mf 739]

1564-1638 Archdeaconry Court of Canterbury Prob Recs: Index to Invents 1564-1638 [Mf 740]

1558-1699 Archdeaconry & Consistory Courts of Canterbury Prob Recs: Index to Prob Accounts 1558-1621 & 1620-1699 [Mf 739]

1569-1735 Archdeaconry Court of Canterbury, County of Kent: Index of Prob Accounts (*1569-1650, 1660-1728 & 1735*) (Kent FHS Rec Pub no 1682) (Mfc) [Apply to Staff]

1584-1858 Archdeaconry Court of Canterbury Prob Recs: Index to Wills; vol 2 (pt 1): 1584-1711 & (pt 2): 1712-1858 [Mf 741-742]

1713-1857 Archdeaconry Court of Canterbury, County of Kent: Indexes of Registered Wills by name & by Parish; vol 2: 1449-1712 listed alphabetically by name & by parish (Kent FHS Rec

Pub nos 1603-1606) (Mfc) [Apply to Staff]

1685-1842 Archdeaconry Court of Canterbury, County of Kent: *Index of* Invents; pts 1: 1685-1709 & 2: 1710-1842 (Kent FHS Rec Pub nos 712 & 713) (*both* Mfc) [Apply to Staff]

CANTERBURY, THE COURT OF THE DEAN and CHAPTER OF

until 1559 this was the Court of the Prior & Chapter of Christ Church at Canterbury
Superior Courts: Canterbury (PCC); *see also* Canterbury (Commissary)

997-1655 *Extr from* Wills in the *Dean & Chapter's* MSS in Canterbury Cathedral (*997-1655*) *In* "5th HMC Rep" [SP/HMC]; Sede Vacante Wills; Cal of Wills proved before the Commissary of Canterbury during vacancies in the Primacy with an appx of transcripts of Archiepiscopal wills & wills of importance (*abst of wills 997-1559, 1655 & admons 1500-1559*) (Kent Recs vol 3) [KE/PER]; *addenda* (The Genealogist vol 6) [PER/GEN]

1500-1503 *List of* Wills proved before the Commissary of the Prior of Canterbury sede Cantuar vacante *In* "8th HMC Rep" [SP/HMC]

1557-1646 Stray Wills at Canterbury (*Cathedral Lib index 1557, 1595-1646*) (Genealogists' Mag vol 17) [PER/GEN]

CARDIGAN, THE CONSISTORIAL COURT OF THE ARCHDEACON OF

Superior Court: St David's (Episcopal Consistory)

1600-1858 Cals of Wills & Admons including the Archdeaconries of Cardigan, Carmarthen & St David's (*in 9 pts*); vols 1: 1600-1700 & 8: 1837-1858; vols 2: 1700-1747, 3: 1746-1798, 4: 1799-1836 & 9: 1700-1740 (*Admons only*) [Mf 881-882]

CARLISLE, THE CONSISTORY COURT OF THE BISHOP OF

Superior Court: York (PCY)

1353-1386 Testamenta Karleolensia: *abst of* the series of Wills from the Pre-Reformation Regs of the Bishop

of Carlisle 1353-1386 (Trans Cumberland & Westmorland Antqn & Archl Soc extra ser vol 9) [CU/G 18]

1355-1385 Names of Testators whose Wills are copied in the Ancient Regs of the Diocese of Carlisle 1355-1385 *In* "HMC Rep on the Hist MSS of the See of Carlisle" (appx to "9th HMC Rep") [SP/HMC]

16-17 C Extr from 16th & 17th C Invents *In* "Prelates & People of the Lake Counties: a history of the Diocese of Carlisle 1133-1933" [CU/G 16]

1558-1564 Box 6 of Wills & Invents at the District Probate Registry, Carlisle (*facsimiles*) [Mf 723]

1564-1800 Consistory Court of Carlisle: Cals of Wills & Admons; vols 1: 1564-1599 (*with invents*) & 2: 1600-1644, 1661-1699 (*with invents*); vols 3 & 4: 1700-1800 [Mf 724 & 726]

1736-1857 "Foreign" Wills proved at Carlisle (*will & admon index to persons who died outside England, at sea or in the armed forces*) (Genealogists' Mag vol 15) [PER/GEN]

1800-1858 Consistory Court of Carlisle: Cals of Wills & Admons; vols 5 & 6: 1800-1858 [Mf 727]

CARLISLE, THE ARCHDEACONRY OF

not a probate jurisdiction: see Carlisle (Consistory)

CARMARTHEN, THE CONSISTORIAL COURT OF THE ARCHDEACON OF

Superior Court: St David's (Episcopal Consistory)

1576-1768 List of Welsh Wills in the Carmarthen Registry; abst & scraps of pedigrees 1576-1768 [WS/G 58]

1600-1858 Cals of Wills & Admons including the Archdeaconries of Cardigan, Carmarthen & St David's (*in 9 pts*); vols 1: 1600-1704, 5: 1705-1779, 6: 1780-1816, 7: 1817-1836 & 8: 1837-1858; vol 9: 1700-1733 (*Admons only*) [Mf 881-882]

CASHEL and EMLY, THE CONSISTORY COURT OF THE ARCHBISHOP OF
after 1834 the Diocese of Cashel was under an Bishop
Superior Court: Armagh (PCA)
1618-1706 Extr from Original Wills formerly preserved in the Consistorial Office, Cashel but now removed to the Court of Probate, Waterford (Kilkenny & SE Ireland Archl Soc J vol 2) [Apply to Staff]
1618-1800 *Phillimore's* Indexes to Irish Wills; vol 2: Cal of Wills in the Dioceses of Cashel & Emly, Killaloe & Kilfenora, Waterford & Lismore, Limerick, Ardfert & Aghadoe & the Peculiar Jurisdiction of the Dean of Lismore [IR/G 86]

CASTLE COMBE, THE COURT OF THE PECULIAR JURISDICTION OF
Superior Court: Sarum (Consistory) *until 1786 when merged into Wiltshire (Archdeaconry)*
1669-1786 Peculiar & Prebendal Courts of the Diocese of Sarum - Indexes to Wills & Admons 1462-1810: *Peculiar Court of Castle Combe* [Mf 836]

CASTLE RISING, THE COURT OF THE PECULIAR JURISDICTION OF
Superior Court: Norwich (Archdeaconry)
1624-1724 Norfolk Peculiar Jurisdictions; *index of* wills & other prob recs: the Peculiar of the Dean & Chapter of Norwich 1416-1857; Prob Invents *(in the Dean & Chapter Archives)* 1688-1782; the Peculiar of Great Cressingham 1675-1754; the Peculiar of Castle Rising 1624-1724 (Norfolk Genealogy vol 16) [NF/PER]

CATTERICK, THE DEANERY OF *see Richmond (Eastern Deaneries)*

CAVE, THE COURT OF THE TESTAMENTARY JURISDICTION OF SOUTH
formerly a prebend & later in lay hands
Superior Courts: York (Dean & Chapter); *see also York (Chancery); York (St Leonard's Hospital)*
1687-1858 S Cave Index of Wills & *Admons* 1687-1858 [Mf 878]

CHANCERY, THE HIGH COURT OF
collections relating to locations, counties or countries or for particular groups are shown under the appropriate place or group; see also Next of Kin Tracing & Other Monetary Records in the NATIONAL section
Superior Court: The Privy Council
Note: *many of the items listed below are indexed in the Burnau Index (Mf)* [Lower Library: Bernau Index drawers]; *full info on this Index is given in the Society's publication "How to Use the Bernau Index"* [TB Quick Reference]
1240-1885 List of Wills, Admons, etc in the PRO, London, England from 12-19th C *(prob items in court & departmental recs)* [WILLS/GEN]
1385-1467 Index to Persons named in Early Chancery Proceedings Richard II to Edward IV *(in 2 pts)* (Harleian Soc vols 78 & 79) *[both HS]*
1386-1529 List of Early Chancery Proceedings preserved in the PRO - *ser 1*; vols 1: 1386-1468, 2: 1468-1485, 3: 1485-1500, 1504-1515, 1515-1529 & 4: 1500-1515 (PRO Lists & Indexes nos 12, 16, 20 & 29) *[all SP/LST]*
1508-1714 *Selection of Abst from* Early Chancery Proceedings *(Fairbrother MMS)*; vol 1: 1508-1714 [SP/LST]
1538-1544 List of Chancery Proceedings preserved in the PRO - *ser 2*; vol 8: 1538-1544 (PRO Lists & Indexes no 51) [SP/LST]
1539-1841 Dramatis Personae *(Sherwood's abst of prob cases in Chancery, etc)* [FH/MISC]
1553-1579 List of Chancery Proceedings preserved in the PRO - *ser 2*; vol 10: 1553-1555, 1556-1558 (PRO Lists & Indexes no 55); Index to vol 10; vol 1: 1558-1579 (PRO Lists & Indexes no 7) *[all SP/LST]*
1575-1714 Index to Disputed Estates in Chancery *(PRO Class* C 8) 1575-1714: Mitford Div [SP/CHA]
1579-1621 List of Chancery Proceedings preserved in the PRO - *ser 2; v*ol 2: 1579-1621 (PRO Lists & Indexes no 24) [SP/LST]
1598-1724 *Cal of* Chancery Depositions before 1714 - *(Snell's abst for plaintiffs beginning with the letter "A" including the Attorney-General)* (supp to British

Archivist) [SP/LST (*with index to parties*) or PER/BRI]; Rough Index (*Snell MSS*) [SP/LST]

17 C-1714 *Cal of* Chancery Proceedings before 1714: Collins Div (*A-C*) (*Dwelly MMS*) [SP/LST]

1613-1714 Index to Chancery Proceedings preserved in the PRO: Bridges Div 1613-1714; vols 2-4 (PRO Lists & Indexes nos 42-44) [*all* SP/LST]

1614-1714 Index to Disputed Estates: Bridges Div of Chancery (*PRO Class C 5*) [SP/CHA]

1621-1660 List of Chancery Proceedings preserved in the PRO - *ser 2*; vol 3: 1621-1660 (PRO Lists & Indexes no 30) [SP/LST]

1622-1714 Index to Disputed Estates in Chancery: Hamilton Div (*PRO Class C 7*) 1622-1714 [SP/CHA]

1625-1649 Cal of Chancery Proceedings: Bills & Answers filed in the reign of King Charles I; vols 1-4 (BRS vols 2, 5, 6 & 14) [*all* BRS]

1625-1649 A Genealogists' Kalendar of Chancery Suits of the time of Charles I (*extr A-MAY*) (Ancestor nos 1-4) [PER/ANC]

1649-1714 Index to Chancery proceedings (Reynardson's Div) preserved in the PRO (*PRO Class C 9*); vol 1 & 2 (BRS vols 29 & 32) [*both* BRS]

1649-1714 Index to Disputed Estates in Chancery 1649-1714 (*PRO Class C 10*): Whittington Div [SP/CHA]

1650-1714 Index to Disputed Estates in Chancery Proceedings before 1714: Collins Div (*PRO Class C 6*) [SP/CHA]

1714-1800 *Selection of Abst from* Early Chancery Proceedings (*Fairbrother MMS*); vol 2: 1714-1800 [SP/LST]; *indexed in vol 1 (1508-1714)*

CHANCERY COURT OF DUCHY OF LANCASTER (THE) *see Lancaster (Chancery)*

CHANCERY COURT OF DURHAM (THE) *see Durham (Chancery)*

CHANCERY COURT OF YORK (THE) *see York (Chancery)*

CHARDSTOCK, THE COURT OF THE PREBEND OF
Superior Court: Sarum (Dean)

1639-1799 Cal of Wills & Admons relating to Dorset in the Courts of Sarum: *Prebendal Court of Chardstock including Wambrook* (BRS vol 53) [BRS]; The Peculiar & Prebendal Courts of the Diocese of Sarum - Indexes to Wills & Admons 1462-1810: *Prebendal Court of Chardstock (with invents)* [Mf 836]

1800-1858 Sarum Courts, Deanery & Archdeaconry of Wiltshire; vol "A": Index for Wills & *Admons* 1800-1858 with names beginning A-B only [Mf 838]

CHERITON WITH KILMESTON and TICHBORNE, THE TESTAMENTARY JURISDICTION OF THE PARISH OF
Superior Court: Winchester (Archdeaconry)

1612-1841 Cal of Hants Wills proved in the Prerogative & Peculiar Courts of Winchester with other Prob Docs: *Cheriton including Kilmeston & Tichborne - Enrolled Peculiar Wills 1681-1674, Index of Peculiar Courts 1613-1763 & Separate Peculiar Wills 1612-1841* [HA/G 62]

CHESTER, THE CONSISTORY COURT OF THE BISHOP OF
Superior Courts: Lichfield (Consistory) until 1541; York (PCY) from 1541
Note: *at Chester, undisputed wills for estates of less than £40 were called "infra" wills & were processed by the Rural Deans (clergy & esquires excepted), other undisputed wills were called "supra" wills & all disputed wills were called "diocesan" wills*

1301-1752 Coll of Lancs & Cheshire Wills & *Invents* not now to be found in any prob registry 1301-1752 (*Earwaker's abst from the Bishop's Enrolment Books; includes Wales*) (Lancs & Cheshire Rec Soc Procs vol 30) [LA/PER]

1477-1807 Lancs & Cheshire Wills, *Admons* & Invents from the Ecclesiastical Court, Chester (*abst in the Piccope MSS*); pt 1: The First Portion (*1525-1563*) (Chetham Soc *original ser* vol 33); pt 2: The Second Portion (*1521-1641*)

(Chetham Soc *original ser* vol 51); pt 3: The Third Portion (*1536-1644*) (Chetham Soc *original ser* vol 54); pt 4: (*Rylands's additions 1477-1746*) (Chetham Soc new ser vol 3); pt 6: *Earwaker's additions 1563-1807* (Chetham Soc new ser vol 37); List of wills & invents printed by the Chetham Soc vols 33, 51 & 54 (*1521-1644*) (Lancs & Cheshire Rec Soc Procs vols 2 & 4) [*all* LA/PER]

1487-1620 Index to the Wills, Invents, Admon Bonds, Citations, Accounts & Depositions in Testmtry Suits now preserved in the Court of Probate at Chester; vols 1: 1487-1620 (*"diocesan"* wills) *In* "Miscellanies relating to Lancs & Cheshire vol 3" [*also* CH/G 43] & 2: 1545-1620 (*"supra"* wills) (Lancs & Cheshire Rec Soc Procs vols 33 & 2) [*both* LA/PER]

1512-1720 List of Wills Transcribed in vols 1-3 of the Enrolment Books in the Bishop's Reg, Chester (*Piccope MSS*); pts 1: 1512-1618, 2: 1625-1635, 3: 1660-1680, 4: 1681-1700 & 5: 1701-1720 (Lancs & Cheshire Rec Soc Procs vols 2, 4, 15, 18 & 20); List of wills, etc examined by the Revs J & CJ Piccope & since lost or destroyed; pts A: 1523-1620 & B: 1621-1650 (Lancs & Cheshire Rec Soc Procs vols 2 & 4) [*all* LA/PER]

1545-1650 *List of* Wills not now to be found in the Probate Court, Chester 1545-1650 (Chetham Soc new ser vol 3) [LA/PER]

1545-1858 Welsh Wills proved at Chester 1545-1858 (*will, admon, invent, bond, etc index*) [WS/G 127]

1568-1650 Wills, admons & invents of persons belonging to places outside the Diocese of Chester 1568-1650 & now preserved at Chester (Lancs & Cheshire Rec Soc Procs vol 4) [LA/PER]

1590-1665 Index to the Wills, Invents, Admon Bonds, Citations, Accounts & Depositions in Testmtry Suits now preserved in the Court of Probate at Chester; vol 3: 1590-1665 (*"infra"* wills) *In*

"Miscellanies relating to Lancs & Cheshire vol 5" (Lancs & Cheshire Rec Soc Procs vol 52) [LA/PER or CH/G 43]

1621-1800 Index to the Wills, Invents, Admon Bonds & Depositions in Testmtry Suits now preserved in the Diocesan Registry, Chester; pt 2: 1621-1700 (*offprint of* Lancs & Cheshire Rec Soc Procs vol 43); pt 3: 1701-1800 (*offprint of* Lancs & Cheshire Rec Soc Procs vol 52) [CH/G 43]

1621-1820 Index to the Wills, Invents, Admon Bonds, Citations, Accounts & Depositions in Testmtry Suits now preserved in the Court of Probate at Chester; vols 4: 1621-1700 (*"diocesan"* wills) *In* "Miscellanies relating to Lancs & Cheshire vol 4" [*also* CH/G 43], 5: 1621-1650 (*"supra"* wills), 6: 1660-1680 (*"supra"* & *"infra"* wills), 7: 1681-1700 (*"supra"* & *"infra"* wills), 8: 1701-1800 (*"diocesan"* wills) *In* "Miscellanies relating to Lancs & Cheshire vol 5", 9: 1701-1720 (*"supra"* & *"infra"* wills), 10: 1721-1740 (*"supra"* & *"infra"* wills), 11: 1741-1760 (*"supra"* & *"infra"* wills), 12: 1761-1780 (*"supra"* wills A-M), 13: 1761-1780 (*"supra"* wills N-Z & *"infra"* wills), 14: 1781-1790 (*"supra"* & *"infra"* wills), 15: 1791-1800 (*"supra"* & *"infra"* wills), 16-17: 1801-1810 (*all wills*), 18-19: 1811-1820 (*all wills*) (Lancs & Cheshire Rec Soc Procs vols 42, 4, 15, 18, 52, 20, 22, 25, 37, 38, 44, 45, 62-63 & 78-79); supp indexes *for 1670 (A-C) & 1693 (*"infra"* wills) (*both* Lancs & Cheshire Rec Soc Procs vol 63) [*all* LA/PER]

1815-1830 Episcopal Consistory Court of Chester; Cal of Wills & Admons; 1815-1830 (*all wills*) [Mf 718]

1821-1837 Index to the Wills, Invents, Admon Bonds, Citations, Accounts & Depositions in Testmtry Suits now preserved in the Court of Probate at Chester; vols 20: 1821-1825 (*all wills*), 21: 1826-1830 (*all wills*), 22: 1831-1833 (*all wills*) & 23: 1834-1837 (*all wills*) (Lancs & Cheshire Rec Soc Procs vols 107, 113, 118 &

120) [all LA/PER]

1831-1858 Episcopal Consistory Court of Chester; Cal of Wills & Admons; vol 2: 1831-1844 (*all wills*); vol 3: 1845-1858 (*all wills*) [Mf 719-720]

CHESTER, THE ARCHDEACONRY OF
ie the Court of the Rural Deans of the Twelve Deaneries of the Ancient Archdeaconry of Chester; the deaneries were Bangor, Blackburn, Chester, Frodsham, Leyland, Macclesfield, Malpas, Manchester, Middlewich, Nantwich, Warrington & the Wirral; separate records do not seem to have survived but see Lichfield (Consistory) until 1541 or Chester (Consistory) from 1541

CHETNOLE *see Yetminster*

CHICHESTER, THE CONSISTORY COURT OF THE BISHOP OF
not a probate jurisdiction: see Chichester (Archdeaconry) for Western Deaneries & Lewes (Archdeaconry) for Eastern Deaneries

CHICHESTER, THE CONSISTORIAL COURT OF THE BISHOP OF CHICHESTER FOR THE ARCHDEACONRY OF
Superior Courts: Canterbury (PCC); Pagham & Tarring (during vacancies)

1482-1800 Cal of Wills in the Consistory Court of the Bishop of Chichester 1482-1800 now preserved in the Probate Registry at Chichester (BRS vol 49) [BRS]

1511-1554 Consistory Court of Chichester Copies of Registered Wills; vols 1: 1511-1550, 2: 1518-1543 & 3: 1518-1554 [Mf 831]

1511-1670 Consistory Court for the Archdeaconry of Chichester Cals to Wills; vols 1: 1518-1574, 2: 1575-1613, 3: 1630-1670 & 4: 1511-1571 [Mf 829]

1555-1800 Cal of Admons granted in the Consistory Court of the Bishop of Chichester 1555-1800; Cal of Wills & Admons in the Peculiar Court of the Archbishop of Canterbury 1520-1670; Cal of Wills & Admons for the Peculiar Court of the Dean of Chichester 1577-1800 (BRS vol 64) [BRS]

1577-1857 Consistory Court for the Archdeaconry of Chichester Cals to Admons; vols 8: 1577-1599, 9: 1600-1609, 10: 1592-1857, 11: 1556-1839 & 12: 1595-1857 [Mf

830]

1642-1668 Some 17th C Chichester Wills (*cal of wills & admons in Consistory Court vol "21b", not in BRS vol 49 & cross-referred with PCC recs*) [SX Tracts]

1644-1857 Consistory Court for the Archdeaconry of Chichester Cals to Wills; vol 5 & 6: 1644-1857 [Mf 833]

1675-1676 A Chichester Court Diary of 1675; Index of Admons of Intestates granted by the Chichester Consistory Court 8 Oct 1675-11 Jan 1676 (Sussex N&Q vol 12) [SX/PER]

CHICHESTER, THE COURT OF THE DEAN OF
Superior Court: Chichester (Archdeaconry)

1197-1284 Testmtry matters enrolled *In* "Chartulary of the High Church of Chichester" (Sussex Rec Soc vol 46) [SX/PER]

1483-1504 Some Chichester Wills (*abst from the Peculiar Court of the Dean*) (Sussex Archl Colls vol 87) [SX/PER]

1577-1800 Cal of Admons granted in the Consistory Court of the Bishop of Chichester 1555-1800; Cal of Wills & Admons in the Peculiar Court of the Archbishop of Canterbury 1520-1670; Cal of Wills & Admons for the Peculiar Court of the Dean of Chichester 1577-1800 *with ms supp index to Dean's Court Wills & Admons 1678-1685, 1718-1728, 1731-1769* (BRS vol 64) [BRS]

1577-1668 Consistory Court for the Archdeaconry of Chichester Cals; vol 14: Dean's Peculiar Wills & Admons 1578-1668 [Mf 832]

1781-1857 Consistory Court for the Archdeaconry of Chichester Cals; vol 13: Archbishop's Peculiar *of Pagham* & Dean's Peculiar Admons 1781-1857 [Mf 834]

CHILBOLTON, THE TESTAMENTARY JURISDICTION OF THE PARISH OF
Superior Court: Winchester (Archdeaconry)

1568-1804 Cal of Hants Wills proved in the Prerogative & Peculiar Courts of Winchester with other Prob Docs: *Chilbolton - Separate Peculiar Wills* [HA/G 62]

CHILCOMB, THE TESTAMENTARY JURISDICTION OF THE PARISH OF
Superior Court: Winchester (Archdeaconry)
1566-1665   Cal of Hants Wills proved in the Prerogative & Peculiar Courts of Winchester with other Prob Docs - *Chilcombe: Separate Peculiar Wills* [HA/G 62]

CHISENBURY *see Chute*

CHURCHILL *see Banwell*

CHURCH FENTON *see Fenton*

CHUTE and CHISENBURY, THE COURT OF THE PREBEND OF
Superior Court: Sarum (Dean)
1608-1798   Peculiar & Prebendal Courts of the Diocese of Sarum - Indexes to Wills & Admons 1462-1810: *Prebendal Court of Chute & Chisenbury (with invents)* [Mf 836]
1800-1855   Wilts Wills Beneficiaries Index 1800-1858: Name Abst; vol 4: Bishopstone 1800-1848, Wilsford & Woodford 1800-1854, Chute & Chisenbury 1800-1855, Coombe & Harnham 1800-1856 (Peculiar Court docs 398-507) [WL/G 67]
1800-1858   Sarum Courts, Deanery & Archdeaconry of Wiltshire; vol "A": Index for Wills & *Admons* 1800-1858 with names beginning A-B only [Mf 838]

CIVIL COMMISSION, THE COURT OF *see Canterbury (PCC)*

CLEEVE, BISHOPS *see Bishops Cleeve*

CLEVELAND, THE ARCHDEACONRY OF
not a probate jurisdiction: see York (Chancery); York (Exchequer)

CLOGHER, THE CONSISTORY COURT OF THE BISHOP OF
Superior Court: Armagh (PCA)
1712-1750   Surname Index to the Swanzy MSS *(these MSS include will abst from the PRO, Dublin for the Diocese of Clogher)* [IR/G 143]

CLONFERT, THE CONSISTORY COURT OF THE BISHOP OF
Superior Court: Armagh (PCA)
1663-1857   Indexes to Clonfert Marriage

Licence Bonds, Wills (*1663-1837*) & Admon Bonds (*1738-1857*) (supp vol of Irish Ancestor for 1970) [IR/R 4]
1664-1838   Index to Clonfert & Kilmacduagh Wills [IR/G 139 or IR Tracts]

CLOYNE, THE CONSISTORY COURT OF THE BISHOP OF
Superior Court: Armagh (PCA)
1569-1628   *Index of Wills proved in* the Diocesan Court of Cloyne, 16th C (Cork Hist & Archl Soc J 2nd ser vol 1) [IR/PER]
1621-1800   *Phillimore's* Indexes to Irish Wills; vol 2: Cal of Wills in the Dioceses of Cork & Ross & Cloyne [IR/G 85]
1630-1857   Index to Admon Bonds: Diocese of Cloyne, County Cork 1630-1857 *In* "O'Kief, Coshe Mang, Slieve Lougher & Upper Blackwater in Ireland; vol 6: Hist & Geneal Items relating to N Cork & E Kerry" [IR/G 196]

COCKINGTON, THE COURT OF THE MANOR OF
1540-1694   *Extr from some* Cockington Manor Wills (Devon & Cornwall N&Q vol 33) [DE/PER]

COLCHESTER, THE COURT OF THE ARCHDEACON OF
Superior Courts: London (Consistory): *see also London (Commissary - Essex & Herts)*
1500-1619   Wills at Chelmsford *including the Archdeaconry Court of Colchester from 1500*; Index to Wills now preserved in the Essex RO at Chelmsford; vol 1: 1400-1619 (BRS vol 78) [BRS]
1558-1603   *Abst of* Essex Wills 1558-1603; pt 1: Wills proved in the Archdeaconry of Essex, the Archdeaconry of Colchester & the Archdeaconry of Middlesex (Essex Div); vol 1: 1558-1565 (Nat Geneal Soc Spec Pub no 51); vol 2: 1565-1571 (NEHG Soc *Spec Pub*); vol 3: 1571-1577 *(with additions for 1559-1571)* (NEHG Soc *Spec Pub*); vol 4: 1577-1584 (*with unregistered wills 1581-1588*) (Essex RO Pub no 96); vol 5: 1583-1592 (Essex RO Pub no 101); vol 6: 1591-1597 (Essex RO Pub no 114); vol

7: 1597-1603 (Essex RO Pub no 107) [*all* ES/PER]

1620-1858 Wills at Chelmsford *including the Archdeaconry Court of Colchester*, Index to Wills now preserved in the Essex RO at Chelmsford; vols 2: 1620-1720 & 3: 1721-1858 (BRS vols 79 & 84) [*both* BRS]

COLEMERE *see Hampton*

COLWAY *see Lyme Regis*

COLWICH, THE COURT OF THE PREBEND OF
Superior Court: Lichfield (Dean & Chapter); *see also Bishops Itchington*
1529-1652 Cal of Wills & Admons registered in the various Peculiar Courts now preserved at the Lichfield Registry 1529-1652 (BRS vol 7) [BRS]
1614-1857 Colwich Peculiar Court: Index of Wills & Admons [Apply to Staff]
1684-1858 Cal of Wills & Admons of Peculiar Jurisdictions in the Diocese of Lichfield; vols 1 & 2 *including*: Prebendal Court of Colwich 1684-1858 [Mf 801]

COMPTON, THE TESTAMENTARY JURISDICTION OF THE PARISH OF
Superior Court: Winchester (Archdeaconry)
1616-1670 Cal of Hants Wills proved in the Prerogative & Peculiar Courts of Winchester with other Prob Docs: *Compton - Separate Peculiar Wills* [HA/G 62]

COMPTON BISHOP, THE COURT OF THE PREBEND OF
Superior Court: Wells (Dean)
1647-1851 Wells Wills; vol 13: Indexes to Wells Registry Cals - Peculiar Courts: *Compton Bishop Wills, Admons & Tuit Bonds* (Mfc) [Apply to Staff]

COMPTON DUNDON, THE COURT OF THE PREBEND OF
Superior Court: Wells (Dean)
1678-1857 Wells Wills; vol 13: Indexes to Wells Registry Cals - Peculiar Courts: *Compton Dundon Wills, Admons (to 1745) & Tuit Bonds (in 2 pts)* (Mfc) [Apply to Staff]

CONNOR, THE CONSISTORY COURT OF THE BISHOP OF
Superior Court: Armagh (PCA)
17-19 C Surname Index to the Swanzy MSS (*these MSS include will abst from the PRO, Dublin for the Diocese of Connor*) [IR/G 143]; *indexed in Analecta Hibernica no 17* [IR/PER]
1818-1820 Index to Will & Grant Book for 1818-1820 *In* appx 1A to "56th Rep of Deputy Keeper of Public Recs in Ireland" [IR/K]
1853-1858 Index to Will & Grant Book for 1853-1858 *In* appx 1A to "56th Rep of Deputy Keeper of Public Recs in Ireland" [IR/K]

COOMBE and HARNHAM, THE COURT OF THE PREBEND OF
Superior Court: Sarum (Dean)
1648-1796 Peculiar & Prebendal Courts of the Diocese of Sarum - Indexes to Wills & Admons 1462-1810: *Prebendal Court of Combe & Harnham (1648, 1687-1796)* [Mf 836]
1800-1856 Wilts Wills Beneficiaries Index 1800-1858: Name Abst; vol 4: Bishopstone 1800-1848, Wilsford & Woodford 1800-1854, Chute & Chisenbury 1800-1855, Coombe & Harnham 1800-1856 (Peculiar Court docs 398-507) [WL/G 67]
1800-1858 Sarum Courts, Deanery & Archdeaconry of Wiltshire; vol "A": Index for Wills & *Admons* 1800-1858 with names beginning A-B only [Mf 838]

COPELAND, THE DEANERY OF *see Richmond (Western Deaneries)*

CORFE CASTLE, THE COURT OF THE ROYAL PECULIAR JURISDICTION OF
Superior Courts: Delegates (High Court); *see also Canterbury (PCC); Dorset (Archdeaconry)*
1576-1849 Peculiar Court of Corfe Castle - Index to Wills, Admons & Invents 1576-1849 (with a number of original wills & invents) [Mf 728]
1577-1801 Cal of Wills & Admons relating to the County of Dorset, proved in the Consistory Court (Dorset Div) of the late Diocese of Bristol 1681-1792, in the Archdeaconry Court of Dorset 1568-1792 & in

the several peculiars 1660-1799 - *including* wills & admons of the Peculiar of Corfe Castle (*wills 1732-1801 & admons 1770-1799*) together with additional wills proved & admons granted in the Royal Peculiar of Corfe Castle, Dorset, formerly preserved at Corfe Castle & not deposited at the Probate Registry, Blandford (*1577-1587, 1602-1651, 1663-1771 with invents & prob accounts*) (BRS vol 22) [BRS]

1623-1766 Royal Peculiar of Corfe Castle - List of Wills & Admons (*1623-1624 with a List of Prob Acts 1727-1766*) (Somerset & Dorset N&Q vol 6) [SO/PER]

CORHAMPTON *see Droxford*

CORK and ROSS, THE CONSISTORY COURT OF THE BISHOP OF
Superior Court: Armagh (PCA)
1454-1800 *Phillimore's* Indexes to Irish Wills; vol 2: Cal of Wills in the Dioceses of Cork & Ross (*1454-1479, 1548-1800*) & Cloyne [IR/G 85]
1571-1587 Extr from a book of Wills & Invents preserved in the Diocesan Registry, Cork, temp Elizabeth (N&Q 2nd ser vol 7) [N&Q]
1600-1833 Index Testamentorum olim Registro Corcagiae (*Index of Wills formerly in the Registry at Cork 1600-1802 with cal for 1611-1803 & supp for 1802-1833*) (Cork Hist & Archl Soc J 2nd ser vols 1 & 2, 3rd ser vols 2 & 4) [IR/PER]
1612-1858 Index to Admon Bonds: Diocese of Cork 1612-1858 *In* "O'Kief, Coshe Mang, Slieve Lougher & Upper Blackwater in Ireland; vol 6: Hist & Geneal Items relating to N Cork & E Kerry" [IR/G 196]

CORNWALL, THE CONSISTORIAL COURT OF THE ARCHDEACON OF
Superior Court: Exeter (Episcopal Principal Registry)
1529-1812 Index to copies of Lost Prob Recs of the Diocese of Exeter in the Library of the Society of Genealogists, London & other sources outside Devon, up to 1812 (*wills, admons, invents, etc*) [DE/G 25]; Index to Copies of Prob Recs relating to Cornwall in the Library of the Society of Genealogists from the Lost Prob Recs of the Diocese of Exeter (*1559-1807*) [Apply to Staff]
1569-1799 Cal of Wills, Admons & Accounts relating to the counties of Devon & Cornwall in the Consistorial Archidiaconal Court of Cornwall (with which are included the recs of the Royal Peculiar of St Buryan) now preserved in the District Probate Registry at Bodmin; pts 1: 1569-1699 & 2: 1700-1799 (BRS vols 56 & 59) [*both* BRS]
1660-1858 Cal of Wills for parishes in Cornwall proved in the Archdeaconry; pts 1: 1660-1773 & 2: 1773-1858 [Mf 721-722]
1687-1856 Unproved Wills of Cornwall; an index to Archdeaconry recs (Cornwall FH J no 27) [CO/PER or CO/G 16]

CORRINGHAM, THE COURT OF THE PREBEND OF
Superior Court: Lincoln (Dean & Chapter) *until merged with Lincoln (Consistory) in 1834*
1632-1833 Lincoln Wills; vol 4: Cal of Wills & Admons at Lincoln; Archdeaconry of Stow, Peculiar Courts & Misc Courts - *including the Court of the Prebend of Corringham (with invents)* (BRS vol 57) [BRS]; Index to Lincoln Peculiar Courts: Prebendal Court of Corringham Wills & Admons [Mf 759]

CORSHAM, THE COURT OF THE PECULIAR JURISDICTION OF
Superior Courts: Sarum (Consistory); Wiltshire (Archdeaconry)
1462-1802 Peculiar & Prebendal Courts of the Diocese of Sarum - Indexes to Wills & Admons 1462-1810: *Peculiar Court of the Perpetual Vicar of Corsham 1462-1799* [Mf 836]; *Wills* in the Principal Probate Registry, London - Peculiar Court of the Perpetual Vicar of Corsham 1462-1799 (Complete List *to 1802*) [WL/G 54]; Wilts Wills & other Geneal Evidences *including* Wills in the

Peculiar Court of the Perpetual
Vicar of Corsham (*list 1462-1799*)
& Misc items (*Sherwood MSS*)
[Apply to Staff]
1800-1857 Wilts Wills Beneficiaries Index
1800-1858: Name Abst; vol 1:
Corsham & Highworth 1800-1857
(Peculiar Court docs 1-137)
[WL/G 67]
1800-1858 Sarum Courts, Deanery &
Archdeaconry of Wiltshire; vol
"A": Index for Wills & *Admons*
1800-1858 with names beginning
A-B only [Mf 838]

**COTTINGLEY, THE COURT OF THE MANOR
OF** see Crossley

COVENTRY see Lichfield

CRAIKE see Crayke

**CRAWLEY and HUNTON, THE
TESTAMENTARY JURISDICTION OF THE
PARISH OF**
Superior Court: Winchester (Archdeaconry)
1598-1761 Cal of Hants Wills proved in the
Prerogative & Peculiar Courts of
Winchester with other Prob Docs:
*Crawley including Hunton -
Separate Peculiar Wills* [HA/G
62]

**CRAYKE or CRAIKE, THE COURT OF THE
PECULIAR JURISDICTION OF** see Durham
(*Consistory*) *until 1837 when the jurisdiction
ceased*

**CRESHALL, THE COURT OF THE
PECULIAR JURISDICTION OF THE BISHOP
OF LONDON IN**
*prior to the Reformation this was the Court of
the Commissary of the Royal Collegiate
Church of St Martin le Grand for the Prebend
of Creshall: see Westminster (Abbot/Dean &
Chapter) until 1540 & London (Consistory)
from 1540*

**CRESSINGHAM, THE COURT OF THE
ROYAL PECULIAR JURISDICTION OF
GREAT**
Superior Courts: Delegates (High Court); *see
also Norwich (Archdeaconry)*
1675-1754 Norfolk Peculiar Jurisdictions;
index of wills & other prob recs:
the Peculiar of the Dean &
Chapter of Norwich 1416-1857;
Prob Invents (*in the Dean &*

Chapter's Archives) 1688-1782;
the Peculiar of Great
Cressingham 1675-1754; the
Peculiar of Castle Rising 1624-
1724 (Norfolk Genealogy vol 16)
[NF/PER]

**CROPREDY, THE COURT OF THE
PECULIAR JURISDICTION OF THE DEAN
and CHAPTER OF LINCOLN IN** see Banbury

**CROSSLEY, BINGLEY, COTTINGLEY and
PUDSEY, THE COURT OF THE KNIGHTS
OF ST JOHN OF JERUSALEM IN THE
MANORS OF**
1580-1676 Indexes to Wills &c in the
Peculiar Courts at Wakefield:
*Crossley, Bingley & Pudsey
Court of the Knights of St John of
Jerusalem* (Northern Genealogist
vol 1) [PER/NOR]
1585-1804 Manorial Court of the Knights of
St John of Jerusalem in Crossley,
Bingley, Cottingley & Pudsey -
Indexes of Wills & *Admons 1599-
1804 & of Wills, Admons, Invents
& Bonds 1585-1700* [Mf 878]
1599-1646 Abst of Wills proved in the Court
of the Manor of Crossley,
Bingley, Cottingley & Pudsey in
County York with invents & abst
of the same (Bradford Hist &
Antqn Soc Loc Recs ser vol 1)
[YK/PER]

**CROYDON, THE COURT OF THE PECULIAR
JURISDICTION OF THE ARCHBISHOP OF
CANTERBURY IN THE DEANERY OF**
Superior Courts: Canterbury (PCC); *see also
Arches (Deanery); Lambeth Palace;
Shoreham*
1614-1813 Middx Wills in the Deanery of
Croydon 1614-1813 (*Act Book
transcripts*) [MX/G 247]
1614-1825 Index to Surrey Wills, Admons &
Invents in the Deanery of
Croydon [SR/G 47]
1660-1751 Index to Wills, Admons & Invents
in the Peculiar Court of the
Deanery of Croydon 1660-1751
[SR/G 53]
1664-1738 Peculiars of the Arches of
London, Shoreham, Kent &
Croydon, Surrey - *Cal of* Invents
& Admons 1664-1738 with a list
of non-testmtry docs [KE/G 69]
1752-1858 Commissary Court of the Bishop
of Winchester; Index to the

Original Wills (collated with the Act Books & Will Regs, etc; also Peculiar Court of the Archbishop of Canterbury in the Deanery of Croydon; Index to Wills 1752-1858 (W Surrey FHS rec ser no 3; 2nd ed) *with Invents List 1752-1754* [SR/PER]; (W Surrey FHS rec ser no 3; 1st ed) [Apply to Staff]

CUDWORTH, THE COURT OF THE PREBEND OF
Superior Court: Wells (Dean)
1626-1855 Wells Wills; vol 13: Indexes to Wells Registry Cals - Peculiar Courts*: Cudworth Wills, Admons & Tuit Bonds 1626-1831 & Knowle St Giles Wills 1722-1855* (Mfc) [Apply to Staff]

DALE ABBEY, THE COURT OF THE PECULIAR JURISDICTION IN THE MANOR OF
Superior Courts: Lichfield (Consistory)*: see also Nottingham (Archdeaconry)*
1753-1790 Cal of Original Wills transmitted to *Derby Probate Registry* from the Peculiar Court of Dale Abbey 1753-1790 inclusive (BRS vol 7) [BRS]

DEATH DUTY REGISTRY *see Estate Duty Office*

DELEGATES, THE HIGH COURT OF
originally final appeal in disputed probate cases lay to Rome; after the Reformation this court replaced that route from 1533 until 1832 when its powers were assumed by the Privy Council; collections relating to locations, counties or countries or for particular groups are shown under the appropriate place or group
Superior Court: The Privy Council
1603-1857 *Index to* Wills & Admons in the Court of Delegates (The Genealogist new ser vols 11 & 12) [PER/GEN]
1634-1707 Dramatis Personae (*Sherwood's abst of prob cases in the Delegates' Examination Papers, etc*) [FH/MISC]
1640-1737 *List of* Deeds & other docs in the Court of Delegates (The Genealogist new ser vol 17) [PER/GEN]

DERBY, THE ARCHDEACONRY OF
not a probate jurisdiction: see Lichfield (Consistory)

DERRY, THE CONSISTORY COURT OF THE BISHOP OF
Superior Court: Armagh (PCA)
1679-1738 *Irwin's Abst of* Irish Wills (*in the Consistory Court of Derry etc*) (Misc Gen et Her 5th ser vol 4) [PER/MIS]
1612-1858 *Phillimore's* Indexes to Irish Wills; vol 5: Cal of Wills in the Dioceses of Derry & Raphoe [IR/G 88]

DILTON *see Sarum (Precentor)*

DISTRICT PROBATE REGISTRIES *see under Birmingham; Lewes; Shrewsbury; Worcester; York*

DORCHESTER (Dorset), THE COURT OF THE MAYOR OF THE BOROUGH OF
1394-1866 Cal of Wills & Admons relating to Dorset in the Courts of Sarum; *including Dorset wills enrolled in the Dorchester Domesday Book & preserved in Borough of Dorchester records (1394-1547, 1620, 1738); also, wills & admons owned by the Dorset Field Club (1618-1866) & now preserved in the County Museum, Dorchester* (BRS vol 53) [BRS]
1395-1547 List of Enrolled Wills *In* "Municipal Recs of the Borough of Dorchester" [DO/L 8]

DORCHESTER (Oxon), THE COURT OF THE PECULIAR JURISDICTION OF
formerly the Peculiar Jurisdiction of Dorchester Abbey
Superior Courts: Lincoln (Consistory) until 1541; Oxford (Consistory) from 1541
1550-1856 *Index to* Berks, Bucks & Oxon Peculiars - Wills & Admons 1550-1858 (*also Invents & Bonds*)*: Peculiar Court & Exempt Jurisdiction of Dorchester* [Mf 913]

DORSET, THE COURT OF THE ARCHDEACON OF
Superior Courts: Sarum until 1542; Bristol (Consistory - Dorset) from 1542
1568-1792 Cals of Wills & Admons relating to the County of Dorset, proved

in the Consistory Court (Dorset Div) of the late Diocese of Bristol 1681-1792, in the Archdeaconry Court of Dorset 1568-1792 & in the several peculiars 1660-1799 (BRS vol 22) [BRS]

1568-1857 Archdeaconry Court of Dorset; vol 1: Index of Wills & Admons (*1568, 1638, 1659 & 1660-1857*); *List of* Original Wills not proved *1702-1837*; Lists of Wills where the Original Wills are not in the *Blandford* Registry *1649-1762* & of Admons *1750 & 1784*; List of Probs proved in other courts *1693-1842*; List of wills proved in the Bishop's Court during Inhibitions *in 1820, 1831, 1835, 1839, 1842, 1845, 1848, 1851 & 1855*; List of Probs & Acts *1800-1837 (at the end of vol 1)*; vol 2: Search Book of Wills, Admons & Invents 1568-1857 *with* Extr of Admons (*1620, 1660-1857*) [*all* Mf 730]

1568-1857 Archdeaconry Court of Dorset; vols 3: Index of Wills 1568-1851 & 4: Index of Admons 1660-1857 *followed by* cal of Testmts *1568, 1638, 1659 & 1660-1848 (with invents 1761-1820) & Cal of* Invents 1685-1730 [Mf 731]

1649-1837 Cals of Dorset Wills, Admons, etc in the Probate Registry at Blandford; pts 3: Cal of Invents in the Archdeacon's Court at Blandford 1686-1790, 4: Cal of Bonds of Guardnshp preserved in the Archdeacon's Court at Blandford (*1683-1803*), 5: Cal of Original Unproved Wills preserved in the Archdeacon's Court at Blandford (*1680-1837*), 6: Cal of Probs of Wills & Admons granted, whereof the Originals are not in the Archdeacon's Court at Blandford (*1649-1784*), 7: Cal of Copies of Wills the originals of which are elsewhere than in the Archdeacon's Court at Blandford (*1663-1817*) & 8: Cal of Copies of Wills proved in courts other than the Archdeacon's Court at Blandford (*1708-1788*) (BRS vol 53) [BRS]

1793-1857 Cal of Wills & Admons relating to the County of Dorset preserved in the Probate Registry at

Blandford & among the Ecclesiastical Recs of Wimborne Minster to 1857 (*including the Archdeaconry Court*) (*Fry MSS*) [Apply to Staff]

(DORSET DIVISION), THE CONSISTORY COURT OF THE BISHOP OF BRISTOL *see Bristol (Consistory - Dorset)*

DOWN, THE CONSISTORY COURT OF THE BISHOP OF
Superior Court: Armagh (PCA)
17-19 C Surname Index to the Swanzy MSS (*these MSS include will abst from the PRO, Dublin relating to the Diocese of Down*) [IR/G 143]; *indexed in Analecta Hibernica no 17* [IR/PER]
1850-1858 Index to Will & Grant Books for 1850-1858 *In* appx 1A to "56th Rep of Deputy Keeper of Public Recs in Ireland" [IR/K]

DROMORE, THE CONSISTORY COURT OF THE BISHOP OF
Superior Court: Armagh (PCA)
17-19 C Surname Index to the Swanzy MSS (*these MSS include will abst from the PRO, Dublin relating to the Diocese of Dromore*) [IR/G 143]; *indexed in Analecta Hibernica no 17* [IR/PER]
1678-1858 *Phillimore's* Indexes to Irish Wills; vol 4: Cal of Wills in the Diocese of Dromore & the Exempt Jurisdiction of Newry & Mourne [IR/G 87]

DROXFORD, THE TESTAMENTARY JURISDICTION OF THE PARISH OF
Superior Court: Winchester (Archdeaconry)
1580-1838 Cal of Hants Wills proved in the Prerogative & Peculiar Courts of Winchester with other Prob Docs: *Droxford including Corhampton - Separate Peculiar Wills* [HA/G 62]

DUBLIN, THE CONSISTORY COURT OF THE ARCHBISHOP OF
Superior Court: Armagh (PCA)
1270-1799 Index to the Act or Grant Books & to the Original Wills & *Admons* of the Diocese of Dublin to the Year 1800) (appx to "26th Rep of the

Deputy Keeper of Public Recs in Ireland") [IR/K]

1457-1483 Reg of Wills & Invents of the Diocese of Dublin in the time of Archbishops Tregury & Walton 1457-1483 (*abst*) (Procs & Papers Royal Soc of Antiquaries of Ireland extra vol for the Years 1896-1897) [IR/PER]

1721-1848 Index to Dublin Consistorial Cause Papers (*GOUGH-GREEN 1721-1846 plus one Appeal Case for 1848*) *In* appx 1A to "57th Rep of Deputy Keeper of Public Recs in Ireland") [IR/K]

1800-1858 Index to the Act or Grant Books & to the Original Wills & *Admons* of the Diocese of Dublin 1800-1858 (appx to "30th Rep of the Deputy Keeper of Public Recs in Ireland") [IR/K]

DUBLIN, THE COURT OF THE LORD MAYOR OF THE CITY OF

1270-1799 Index to the Act or Grant Books & to the Original Wills & *Admons* of the Diocese of Dublin to the Year 1800 (*including wills amongst the Archives of the Corp of the City of Dublin*) (appx to "26th Rep of the Deputy Keeper of Public Recs in Ireland") [IR/K]

DUBLIN, THE PRINCIPAL PROBATE REGISTRY IN

1885 Irish Wills & **WHEN** to look for them ... pre-1858 Wills noted in the Irish Will Cal for 1885 (*extr from Letters of Admon for late probs for people who died 1828-1857*) (All-Ireland Heritage vol 1 no 2) [IR/PER]

DUDDINGTON, THE COURT OF THE PECULIAR JURISDICTION OF

Superior Courts: Lincoln (Dean & Chapter) until 1834; Lincoln (Consistory) from 1834

1740-1830 Index to Lincoln Peculiar Courts: Wills proved & Admons granted in the exempt jurisdiction of Duddington in the County of Northampton [Mf 759]

DUMFRIES, THE COMMISSARIOT OF

Superior Court: Court of Session; *see also Edinburgh (Commissariot)*

1624-1800 Commissariot Rec of Dumfries; Reg of Testmts 1624-1800

(Scottish Rec Soc vol 14) [SC/PER]

1781-1788 *Cal of* Testmts for the Commissariot of Dumfries (Dumfries & Galloway FHS N/L no 14) [SC/PER]

1801-1823 *Dumfries Regs of Testmts & Invents In* "Index to Regs of Testmts for various Commissariots 1801-1823" [Mf 2910]

DUNBLANE, THE COMMISSARIOT OF

Superior Court: Court of Session; *see also Edinburgh (Commissariot)*

1539-1800 Commissariot Rec of Dunblane; Reg of Testmts 1539-1800 (Scottish Rec Soc vol 15) [SC/PER]

DUNKELD, THE COMMISSARIOT OF

Superior Court: Court of Session; *see also Edinburgh (Commissariot)*

1682-1800 Commissariot Rec of Dunkeld; Reg of Testmts 1682-1800 (Scottish Rec Soc vol 16) [SC/PER]

1801-1823 *Dunkeld Regs of Testmts & Invents In* "Index to Regs of Testmts for various Commissariots 1801-1823" [Mf 2910]

DURHAM, THE PALATINE and CONSISTORY COURT OF THE BISHOP OF

including the records of the Court of the Peculiar Jurisdiction of Crayke or Craike until 1837

Superior Court: York (PCY)

1095-1649 Wills & Invents illustrating the history, manners, language, statistics, &c of the Northern Counties of England from the Registry at Durham (*selected abst mainly from the Consistory Court at Durham*); vols 1: 1095-1580, 2: 1580-1599, 3: 1543-1603 & 4: 1603-1649 (Surtees Soc vols 2, 38, 112 & 142) [*all* DU/PER]

1311-1837 Newcastle Public Reference Lib; Index of *Consistory Court of Durham Wills & Admons c1540-1837* with an index of wills related to Durham but proved in other courts (*Robinson MSS, wills, admons & invents 1372-1812*) & *with a list of Durham* *wills proved from 1311* [Mf 907 or Apply to Staff]

1540-1599 Index of Wills, etc in the Probate Registry, Durham & from other sources (Newcastle Rec Committee Pubs vol 8) [DU/G 27]

1540-1599 Palatine & Episcopal Court of Durham - Indexes to Wills & Admons; vol 1: c1540-1599 (*Wills only*) [Mf 909]

1542-1808 List of Durham Testmts, *Admons & Invents (Dodds MSS)* (Durham & Northumberland Notes vol 20) [DU/G 19]

1553-1810 Index to Durham Wills, *Admons & Invents*; Neasham's Coll (*2 vols*) [Apply to Staff]

1555-1729 *Abst of* Wills from the MSS of Sir Cuthbert Sharp (Northern N&Q for 1906-1907) [PER/NOR]

1595-1597 Some Durham Admons (*index to Visitation Books in the Bishop's Reg*) (Misc Gen et Her 5th ser vol 7) [PER/MIS]

1600-1786 Palatine & Episcopal Court of Durham - Indexes to Wills & Admons; vols 2: 1600-1660 (*Wills, Tuit Bonds & Invents only*) & 3: 1661-1786 [Mf 909-910]

1699-1857 Wills & Admons etc: listings taken from cals of the old Diocese of York & the Diocese of Lincoln (with certain additions from Durham) (*index BUR-WRI*) (Fam Hist vols 2 & 3) [PER/FAM]

1787-1790 *Index to* Disputed Wills in the Consistory Court of Durham (Northumberland & Durham FHS J vol 19 no 3) [NU/PER]

1787-1797 Personal Names in Wills Proved at Durham (*extr*); pts 1: 1787-1791, 2: 1792-1794 & 3: 1795-1797 (*all* Mfc) [Apply to Staff]

1787-1858 Palatine & Episcopal Court of Durham - Indexes to Wills & Admons; vols 4: 1787-1831, 5: 1832-1839 & 6: 1832-1858 [Mf 911]

DURHAM, THE CHANCERY COURT OF THE BISHOP OF

Superior Court: Durham (Consistory)

1618-1682 County of Durham - Diocesan Chancery Suits 1618-1620 & 1681-1682 (*Dale MSS*) [Apply to Staff]

DURHAM, THE COURT OF THE DEAN and CHAPTER OF

Superior Court: Durham (Consistory)

1555-1729 *Abst of* Wills from the MSS of Sir Cuthbert Sharp (Northern N&Q for 1906-1907) [PER/NOR]

DURLEY *see Upham*

DURNFORD, THE COURT OF THE PREBEND OF

Superior Court: Sarum (Dean)

1634-1799 Peculiar & Prebendal Courts of the Diocese of Sarum - Indexes to Wills & Admons 1462-1810: *Prebendal Court of Durnford (with Admon Bonds)* [Mf 836]

1800-1857 Wilts Wills Beneficiaries Index 1800-1858: Name Abst; vol 5: Durnford 1800-1857, Fordington & Writhlington 1800-1855, Hurstbourne & Burbage 1800-1856, Netheravon 1800-1854 (Peculiar Court docs 508-632) [WL/G 67]

1800-1858 Sarum Courts, Deanery & Archdeaconry of Wiltshire; vol "A": Index for Wills & *Admons* 1800-1858 with names beginning A-B only [Mf 838]

EAST RIDING OF YORKSHIRE, THE ARCHDEACONRY OF THE

not a probate jurisdiction: see York (Exchequer); York (Chancery); see also Mappleton

EASTON, THE TESTAMENTARY JURISDICTION OF THE PARISH OF

Superior Court: Winchester (Archdeaconry)

1594-1835 Cal of Hants Wills proved in the Prerogative & Peculiar Courts of Winchester with other Prob Docs: *Easton - Separate Peculiar Wills* [HA/G 62]

EASTON-IN-GORDANO, THE COURT OF THE PREBEND OF

Superior Court: Wells (Dean)

1661-1856 Wells Wills; vol 13: Indexes to Wells Registry Cals - Peculiar Courts: *Easton-in-Gordano Wills 1661-1856 & Index to Admon Bonds, etc 1662-1854 (in 2 pts)* (Mfc) [Apply to Staff]

ECCLESHALL, THE COURT OF THE PREBEND OF
Superior Court: Lichfield (Dean & Chapter): *see also Stafford (Commissary)*
1529-1652 Cal of Wills & Admons registered in the various Peculiar Courts now preserved at the Lichfield Registry 1529-1652 (BRS vol 7) [BRS]
1681-1858 Cal of Wills & Admons of Peculiar Jurisdictions in the Diocese of Lichfield; vols 1 & 2 *including*: Prebendal Court of Eccleshall 1681-1858 [Mf 801]

EDBURTON *see Malling, South*

EDINBURGH, THE COMMISSARIOT OF
Superior Court: Court of Session
1514-1600 Commissariot Rec of Edinburgh; Reg of Testmts; pt 1: vols 1-35 for 1514-1600 (Scottish Rec Soc vol 1 or BRS vol 16) [SC/PER or BRS]
1562-1675 Commissariot Rec of Edinburgh; Haddington Reg of Testmts 1652-1657 (Scottish Rec Soc vol 2 - *entries marked "H"*) [SC/PER]
1569-1812 Edinburgh Commissariot Testmts - Abst (*Macleod MSS*) [SC/G 118A]
1573-1838 Edinburgh Commissariot Testmts - Abst (*Macleod MSS*) [SC/G 117]
1601-1700 Commissariot Rec of Edinburgh; Reg of Testmts; pt 2: vols 36-81 for 1601-1700 (Scottish Rec Soc vol 2) [SC/PER]
1625-1825 Directory of Scottish Settlers in N America 1625-1825; vol 4: *Abst of N American Services of Heirs, Testmts & Admons in Edinburgh & the PCC* [US/MIG 20]
1658-1800 Consistorial Processes & Decreets 1658-1800 (Scottish Rec Soc vol 34) [SC/PER]
1701-1800 Commissariot Rec of Edinburgh; Reg of Testmts; pt 3: vols 81-131 for 1701-1800 (Scottish Rec Soc vol 3) [Apply to Staff]
1801-1829 Index to Reg of Testmts of the Commissariot of Edinburgh 1801-1829 [Mf 2907]

EDWINSTOWE, THE COURT OF THE MANOR OF
1521-1801 Manor Court of Edwinstowe, County Notts - *Index of* Wills,

Admons & Invents (Northern Genealogist vol 1) [PER/NOR]

ELLESMERE, THE COURTS OF THE MANOR OF
ie the Court of the Manor of Ellesmere with Welshampton & the Court of the Town & Liberties of Ellesmere; see also Hampton & Colemere; see also Lyneal
1630-1857 Cal of Salop Wills & Admons *(with invents)* deposited in Shrewsbury District Probate Registry *including: Manor, Town & Liberties of Ellesmere* (supps to Trans Salop Archl & Nat Hist Soc 4th ser vols 12 *now 45 & 46*) [Mf 800 or SH/PER]
1734-1845 Manorial Court of Ellesmere: Copies of Wills [Mf 800]

ELPHIN, THE CONSISTORY COURT OF THE BISHOP OF
Superior Court: Armagh (PCA)
1679-1738 Irwin's Abst of Irish Wills (*in the Consistory Court of Elphin etc*) (*Misc Gen et Her 5th ser vol 4*) [PER/MIS]

ELY, THE CONSISTORY COURT OF THE BISHOP OF
also called the Episcopal Consistory Court of Ely & Cambridge & including the Audience Court of the Bishop of Ely
Superior Court: Canterbury (PCC)
1382-1526 List of Wills & Admons entered in the Bishop's Reg, *with some abst In* "Ely Episcopal Recs" [CA/G 12]
15-16 C Testmtry Extr from Ely Episcopal Reg (pages from the "Ely Episcopal Remembrancer") [CA/G 11]
1449-1486 Consistory Court of Ely Wills; Reg A: 1449-1460; Reg B: 1459-1485 & Reg C: 1478-1486 (*Matthews MSS*) [Apply to Staff]
1449-1858 Episcopal Consistory Court of Ely - Cal of Wills 1449-1858 [Mf 884]
1449-1858 Index of Prob Recs of the Consistory Court of Ely 1449-1858 (*wills, admons, invents, guardnship & other bonds, etc*); pts 1 & 2: A-P (BRS vols 103 & 106) [*both* BRS]; *series in progress & on order*
1449-1618 Episcopal Consistory Court of Ely - Wills Index; vol 1: 1449-1618 [Mf 952]

1449-1763 Episcopal Consistory Court of Ely - Wills Index; vol 2: 1619-1763 [Mf 952]
1489-1640 List of a Bundle of Wills *In* "Ely Episcopal Recs" [CA/G 12]
1562-1582 Reg of Admons *In* "Ely Episcopal Recs" [CA/G 12]
1662-1858 Episcopal Consistory Court of Ely - Cal of Admons 1662-1858 [Mf 716]
1752-1755 Episcopal Consistory Court of Ely - Cal of Unregistered Admons 1752-1755 [Mf 717]
1764-1858 Episcopal Consistory Court of Ely - Wills Index; vol 3: 1764-1858 & Thorney Peculiars [Mf 952]
1800-1844 List of a Parcel of Wills & Letters of Admon *In* "Ely Episcopal Recs" [CA/G 12]

ELY, THE COURT OF THE ARCHDEACON OF
Superior Court: Ely (Consistory)
1513-1857 Index of the Prob Recs of the Court of the Archdeacon of Ely 1513-1857 (*wills & admons*) (BRS vol 88) [BRS]

EMLY *see Cashel & Emly*

EMPINGHAM, THE COURT OF THE PREBEND OF
Superior Courts: Lincoln (Dean & Chapter) until 1834; Lincoln (Consistory) from 1834*: see also Huntingdon (Archdeaconry); Stow (Archdeaconry)*
1669-1744 Lincoln Wills; vol 4: Cal of Wills & Admons at Lincoln; Archdeaconry of Stow, Peculiar Courts & Misc Courts - *including the Court of the Prebend of Empingham (with invents)* (BRS vol 57) [BRS]; Index to Lincoln Peculiar Courts: Wills proved & Admons granted in the exempt jurisdiction of Empingham in the county of Rutland [Mf 759]

(ESSEX and HERTFORDSHIRE DIVISION), THE COURT OF THE COMMISSARY OF LONDON
ie the Court of the Commissary of the Bishop of London for the Parts of Essex & Herts: see London (Commissary - Essex & Herts); also called the "(Essex Division)"

ESSEX, THE COURT OF THE ARCHDEACON OF
Superior Court: London (Consistory)*; see also London (Commissary - Essex & Herts)*
1400-1603 Archdeaconry Court of Essex - Cal of Wills & Admons; vol 1: 1400-1603 (*wills only*) [Mf 733]
1400-1619 Wills at Chelmsford *including the Archdeaconry Court of Essex from 1400*; Index to Wills now preserved in the Essex RO at Chelmsford; vol 1: 1400-1619 (BRS vol 78) [BRS]
1558-1603 *Abst of* Essex Wills 1558-1603; pt 1: Wills proved in the Archdeaconry of Essex, the Archdeaconry of Colchester & the Archdeaconry of Middlesex (Essex Div); vol 1: 1558-1565 (Nat Geneal Soc Spec Pub no 51); vol 2: 1565-1571 (NEHG Soc *Spec Pub*); vol 3: 1571-1577 (*with additions for 1559-1571*) (NEHG Soc *Spec Pub*); vol 4: 1577-1584 (*with unregistered wills 1581-1588*) (Essex RO Pub no 96); vol 5: 1583-1592 (Essex RO Pub no 101); vol 6: 1591-1597 (Essex RO Pub no 114); vol 7: 1597-1603 (Essex RO Pub no 107) [*all* ES/PER]
1604-1725 Archdeaconry Court of Essex - Cal of Wills & Admons; vol 2: 1604-1725 (*admons from 1647*) [Mf 733]
1620-1858 Wills at Chelmsford *including the Archdeaconry Court of Essex*; Index to Wills now preserved in the Essex RO at Chelmsford; vols 2: 1620-1720 & 3: 1721-1858 (BRS vols 79 & 84) [*both* BRS]
1726-1858 Archdeaconry Court of Essex - Cal of Wills & Admons; vols 3: 1726-1794 & 4: 1795-1858 [*both* Mf 733]

(ESSEX and HERTFORDSHIRE DIVISION), THE COURT OF THE ARCHDEACON OF
MIDDLESEX *see Middlesex (Archdeaconry - Essex & Herts)*

ESTATE DUTY OFFICE
Collections relating to locations, counties or countries or for particular groups are shown under the appropriate place or group
1796-1801 Death Duty Recs (*PCC will extr*) (QL FHn vol 7 no 5)

1796-1857 Indexes to Regs of Death Duty
Returns (*PRO Class IR 27/1-323*)
(Mf) [Lower Library: Estate Duty
Will Indexes cabinet]

EVINGTON, THE COURT OF THE COMMISSARY OF THE BISHOP OF LINCOLN FOR THE MANOR OF
Superior Court: Lincoln (Consistory)
1557-1819 Evington Prob Invents *In* "Leics
Prob Invents" 1557-1819 [LE/G
31]
1581-1800 Cal of Wills & Admons relating to
the County of Leicester, proved
in the Archdeaconry Court of
Leicester 1495-1649 & in the
Peculiars of St Margaret
Leicester, Rothley, Groby,
Evington & unproved Wills
previous to 1801; all now
preserved in the Probate Registry
at Luckiest (BRS vol 27) [BRS]

EXBURY *see Fawley*

EXCHEQUER COURT OF YORK (THE) *see*
York (Exchequer)

EXETER, THE EPISCOPAL CONSISTORY COURT OF THE BISHOP OF
this Court had probate jurisdiction in the
Diocese of Exeter over vacancies in, &
inhibitions of, peculiars & over probates not
involving 'bona notabilia' (ie goods worth less
than £5) in more than one subordinate
jurisdiction
Superior Court: Canterbury (PCC); *see also*
Exeter (Episcopal Principal Registry)
1424-1455 Wills proved in the Bishop's Court
In "Reg of Edmund Lacy, Bishop
of Exeter, 1420-1455; vol 4" &
index (Devon & Cornwall Rec
Soc new ser vols 16 & 18) [*both*
DE/PER]
1487-1493 Reg of John Morton, Archbishop
of Canterbury 1486-1500; vol 2:
Abst from the Reg of Testmts
pertaining to the Prerogative
Jurisdiction of the Archbishop
proved in the Diocese of Exeter
from the Feast of St Peter ad
Vincula (Canterbury & York Soc
vol 78) [CE/GEN]
1529-1812 Index to copies of Lost Prob
Recs of the Diocese of Exeter in
the Library of the Society of
Genealogists, London & other

sources outside Devon, up to
1812 (*wills, admons, invents, etc*)
[DE/G 25]; Index to Copies of
Prob Recs relating to Cornwall in
the Library of the Society of
Genealogists from the Lost Prob
Recs of the Diocese of Exeter
(*1559-1807*) [Apply to Staff]
1532-1800 Cal of Wills & Admons relating to
the counties of Devon &
Cornwall, proved in the
Consistory Court of the Bishop of
Exeter 1532-1800; now
preserved in the Probate Registry
at Exeter (Trans Devon Assn
extra vol for *Wills*: pt 10 or BRS
vol 46) [DE/G 57 or BRS]

EXETER, THE EPISCOPAL PRINCIPAL REGISTRY OF THE BISHOP OF
this Registry had probate jurisdiction in the
Diocese of Exeter over all clergy, vacancies
in, & inhibitions of, Archdeaconries & probates
involving 'bona notabilia' (ie goods worth more
than £5) in more than one subordinate
jurisdiction
Superior Court: Exeter (Consistory)
1529-1812 Index to copies of Lost Prob
Recs of the Diocese of Exeter in
the Library of the Society of
Genealogists, London & other
sources outside Devon, up to
1812 (*wills, admons, invents, etc*)
[DE/G 25]; Index to Copies of
Prob Recs relating to Cornwall in
the Library of the Society of
Genealogists from the Lost Prob
Recs of the Diocese of Exeter
(*1559-1807*) [Apply to Staff]
1553-1799 Cals of Wills & Admons relating
to the counties of Devon &
Cornwall, proved in the Court of
the Principal Registry of the
Bishop of Exeter 1559-1799; & of
Devon only, proved in the Court
of the Archdeaconry of Exeter
1540-1799; all now preserved in
the Probate Registry at Exeter;
with Archdeaconry Wills 1653-
1660 previously uncalendared
(Trans Devon Assn extra vol for
Wills; pts 1-4 or BRS vol 35)
[DE/G 55 or BRS]; Cals of Wills
& Admons relating to the
counties of Devon & Cornwall,
proved in the Court of the
Principal Registry of the Bishop
of Exeter 1559-1799; & of Devon
only, proved in the Court of the

Archdeaconry of Exeter 1540-1799; all now preserved in the Probate Registry at Exeter; vols 1 & 2 (*H from 1608*) (Trans Devon Assn extra vol for *Wills*) [DE/G 56 & DE/G 53]; *Corrigenda* (Devon & Cornwall N&Q vol 9) [DE/PER]

EXETER, THE CONSISTORIAL COURT OF THE ARCHDEACON OF
Superior Court: Exeter (Episcopal Principal Registry)
1529-1812 Index to copies of Lost Prob Recs of the Diocese of Exeter in the Library of the Society of Genealogists, London & other sources outside Devon, up to 1812 (*wills, admons, invents, etc*) [DE/G 25]
1540-1799 Cals of Wills & Admons relating to the counties of Devon & Cornwall, proved in the Court of the Principal Registry of the Bishop of Exeter 1559-1799; & of Devon only, proved in the Court of the Archdeaconry of Exeter 1540-1799; all now preserved in the Probate Registry at Exeter; with Archdeaconry Wills 1653-1660 previously uncalendared (Trans Devon Assn extra vol for *Wills*; pts 1-4 or BRS vol 35) [DE/G 55 or BRS]; Cals of Wills & Admons relating to the counties of Devon & Cornwall, proved in the Court of the Principal Registry of the Bishop of Exeter 1559-1799; & of Devon only, proved in the Court of the Archdeaconry of Exeter 1540-1799; all now preserved in the Probate Registry at Exeter; vols 1 & 2 (*H from 1608*) (Trans Devon Assn extra vol for *Wills*) [DE/G 56 & DE/G 53]; *Corrigenda* (Devon & Cornwall N&Q vol 9) [DE/PER]

EXETER, THE COURT OF THE DEAN OF
Superior Court: Exeter (Dean & Chapter)
1529-1812 Index to copies of Lost Prob Recs of the Diocese of Exeter in the Library of the Society of Genealogists, London & other sources outside Devon, up to 1812 (*wills, admons, invents, etc*) [DE/G 25]
1632-1858 Peculiar Court of the Custos & College of Vicars Choral,

Woodbury 1633-1858 (Cal of Wills & Admons) *with cal* of Wills proved & Admons granted in the Peculiar Jurisdiction of the Dean of Exeter within the Close of Exeter & the parish of Braunton, Devon 1632-1857 [DE/G 72]

EXETER, THE COURT OF THE DEAN and CHAPTER OF
Superior Court: Exeter (Consistory)
1529-1812 Index to copies of Lost Prob Recs of the Diocese of Exeter in the Library of the Society of Genealogists, London & other sources outside Devon, up to 1812 (*wills, admons, invents, etc*) [DE/G 25]

EXETER, THE PECULIAR JURISDICTION OF THE BISHOP OF
probate jurisdiction in the Peculiars of the Bishop of Exeter was undertaken by the Consistory Court of Exeter (qv)

EXETER IN WOODBURY, THE COURT OF THE PECULIAR JURISDICTION OF THE CUSTOS and COLLEGE OF VICARS CHORAL OF see *Woodbury*

EXETER, THE CUSTOMARY COURT OF THE MAYOR OF THE CITY OF
1286-1400 Index to Early Exeter Wills 1286-1400 from Hooker's Commonplace Book & preserved in the Court Rolls of the Mayors of Exeter [Apply to Staff]
1555-1511 *Extr from* Early Wills with Misc Deeds in the City Archives *In* "HMC Rep on the Recs of the City of Exeter" [Apply to Staff]

EXETER, THE ORPHAN'S COURT OF THE CITY OF
1555-1765 Orphan's Court of City of Exeter; List of a bundle of Wills the City Archives *In* "HMC Rep on the Recs of the City of Exeter" [Apply to Staff]

EXTON, THE TESTAMENTARY JURISDICTION OF THE PARISH OF
Superior Court: Winchester (Archdeaconry)
1667-1758 Cal of Hants Wills proved in the Prerogative & Peculiar Courts of Winchester with other Prob Docs: *Exton - Separate Peculiar Wills* [HA/G 62]

FAREHAM, THE TESTAMENTARY JURISDICTION OF THE PARISH OF
Superior Court: Winchester (Archdeaconry)
1561-1845 Cal of Hants Wills proved in the Prerogative & Peculiar Courts of Winchester with other Prob Docs: *Fareham - Separate Peculiar Wills* [HA/G 62]

FARINGDON, THE COURT OF THE PREBEND OF
Superior Court: Sarum (Dean)
1547-1854 Indexes of Faringdon Wills 1547-1799 & of Wills & Bonds 1800-1854 [Apply to Staff]
1580-1636 Schedule of Wills proved in Faringdon Peculiar (*cal*) ("Berks J" new ser vol 41) [BK/PER]
1550-1856 *Index to Berks, Bucks & Oxon Peculiars - Wills & Admons 1550-1858 (also Invents & Bonds): Prebendal Court of Faringdon* [Mf 913]

FAWLEY WITH EXBURY, THE TESTAMENTARY JURISDICTION OF THE PARISH OF
Superior Court: Winchester (Archdeaconry)
1593-1841 Cal of Hants Wills proved in the Prerogative & Peculiar Courts of Winchester with other Prob Docs: *Fawley including Hythe & Exbury - Separate Peculiar Wills* [HA/G 62]

FENTON, THE COURT OF THE PREBEND OF
also known as Church Fenton; see also Riccall
Superior Courts: York (Chancery; York (Dean & Chapter)
1617-1854 York Registry; Names of Peculiars wherein separate lists are kept of the wills etc proved therein *including Fenton with Sherburn from an early period to the present time*; York Registry; Cal of Vacancy & Prebendal Wills *including Fenton* [both Mf 879]

FERNS, THE CONSISTORY COURT THE BISHOP OF
Superior Court: Armagh (PCA)
1601-1800 *Phillimore's Indexes to Irish Wills; vol 1: Cal of Wills in the Dioceses of Ossory, Leighlin, Ferns & Kildare* [IR/G 84]

FITZHEAD *see Wivelscombe*

FLIXTON *see Offley, High*

FORDINGTON and WRITHLINGTON, THE COURT OF THE PREBEND OF
Superior Court: Sarum (Dean)
1660-1788 List of Wills, *Admons & Invents* proved in Fordington Peculiar Court 1660-1788 *In* "Hist of Fordington" [DO/L 9]
1660-1799 Peculiar & Prebendal Courts of the Diocese of Sarum - Indexes to Wills & Admons 1462-1810: *Prebendal Court of Forthington & Writhlington (with invents)* [Mf 836]; Cal of Wills & Admons relating to Dorset in the Courts of Sarum & *elsewhere (including Fordington & Writhlington)* (BRS vol 53) [BRS]
1800-1855 Wilts Wills Beneficiaries Index 1800-1858: Name Abst; vol 5: Durnford 1800-1857, Fordington & Writhlington (*Fordington only*) 1800-1855, Hurstbourne & Burbage 1800-1856, Netheravon 1800-1854 (Peculiar Court docs 508-632) [WL/G 67]
1800-1858 Sarum Courts, Deanery & Archdeaconry of Wiltshire; vol "A": Index for Wills & *Admons* 1800-1858 with names beginning A-B only [Mf 838]

FOREST, NEW in Kirkby Ravensworth: *see Arkengarthdale*

FORTHINGTON *see Fordington*

FRAMPTON, THE COURT OF THE MANOR and LIBERTY OF
1678-1755 Cal of Frampton Wills, *Invents* & Admons (Somerset & Dorset N&Q vol 27) [SO/PER]

FRECKENHAM *see Isleham*

FREEFOLK *see Whitchurch*

FRIDAYTHORPE, THE COURT OF THE PREBEND OF
Superior Courts: York (Chancery); York (Dean & Chapter); *jurisdiction assumed by Wetwang after 1730*
1593-1730 Prob Recs Index (*wills, admons, invents, tuit & other bonds*) (Banyan Tree no 13) [YK/PER]

FROXFIELD *see Meon, East*

FURNESS, THE DEANERY OF *see Richmond (Western Deaneries)*

GATE HELMSLEY *see Osbaldwick*

GILLINGHAM, THE COURT OF THE ROYAL PECULIAR JURISDICTION OF
Superior Court: Delegates (High Court)*; see also Canterbury (PCC)*
1559-1584   Cal of Wills proved in Gillingham Peculiar Prob Court (Somerset & Dorset N&Q vol 19) [SO/PER]
1658-1799   Peculiar & Prebendal Courts of the Diocese of Sarum - Indexes to Wills & Admons 1462-1810*: Royal Peculiar Court of Gillingham (with invents)* [Mf 836]; Cal of Wills & Admons relating to Dorset in the Courts of Sarum & *elsewhere (including Gillingham with Bourton, Motcombe & E & W Stour)* (BRS vol 53) [BRS]
1800-1858   Wilts Wills Beneficiaries Index 1800-1858: Name Abst; vols 6 & 7: Gillingham (*pts 1-2*) 1800-1858 (Peculiar Court docs 633-843) [WL/G 67]
1800-1858   Sarum Courts, Deanery & Archdeaconry of Wiltshire; vol "A": Index for Wills & *Admons* 1800-1858 with names beginning A-B only [Mf 838]

GIVENDALE, THE COURT OF THE PREBEND OF
except for 1661-1669 the records of this court are with York (Dean) (qv)

GLASGOW, THE COMMISSARIOT OF
Superior Court: Court of Session*; see also Edinburgh (Commissariot)*
1547-1800   Commissariot Rec of Glasgow; Reg of Testmts 1547-1800 (Scottish Rec Soc vol 7) [SC/PER]
1801-1823   Index to Reg of Testmts of the Commissariot of Glasgow 1801-1823 [Mf 2908]

GLOUCESTER, THE CONSISTORY COURT OF THE BISHOP OF
Superior Courts: Worcester (Consistory) until 1541; Canterbury (PCC) from 1541*; see also Bristol (Consistory - City & Deanery)*
1508-1858   Cal of Wills proved in the Consistory Court of the Bishop Gloucester; vol 1: 1541-1650 with an appx of Dispersed Wills *1508-1701* & wills proved in the Peculiar Courts of Bibury & Bishops Cleeve (BRS vol 12) [BRS]; vol 2: 1660-1800 (BRS vol 34) [Apply to Staff]; Glos Wills & Admons; Cal of Wills Proved & Letters of Admons granted in the Diocese of Gloucester 1801-1858 (Mfc: BRS Mfc ser 3) [Apply to Staff]

GLOUCESTER, THE ARCHDEACONRY OF
not a probate jurisdiction: see Gloucester (Consistory)

GLOUCESTER, THE COURT OF THE MAYOR OF THE CITY OF
1334-1578   Index of Early Gloucester Wills in the recs of the City of Gloucester 1334-1578 (Trans Bristol & Glos Rec Soc vol 60) [GL/PER]

GNOSALL, THE COURT OF THE PREBEND OF
also called the Court of the Peculiar Jurisdiction of the Bishop of Lichfield in the Manor of Gnosall
Superior Court: Lichfield (Dean & Chapter)*; see also Stafford (Commissary)*
1529-1652   Cal of Wills & Admons registered in the various Peculiar Courts now preserved at the Lichfield Registry 1529-1652 (BRS vol 7) [BRS]
1627-1858   Cal of Wills & Admons of Peculiar Jurisdictions in the Diocese of Lichfield; vols 1 & 2 *including*: Peculiar & Manorial Court of Gnosall 1627-1858 [Mf 801]

GOOD EASTER, THE COURT OF THE PECULIAR JURISDICTION OF THE BISHOP OF LONDON IN
prior to the Reformation this was the Court of the Commissary of the Royal Collegiate Church of St Martin le Grand for the Prebend of Good Easter
Superior Courts: Westminster (Abbot/Dean & Chapter) until 1540; London (Consistory) from 1540*; see also Middlesex (Archdeaconry - Essex & Herts)*
1613-1847   *Abst of* Wills, Admons, Bonds & Invents of the Peculiar Court of Good Easter, County Essex

[ES/G 64]

1613-1858 Wills at Chelmsford *including the Peculiar Court of Good Easter from*; Index to Wills now preserved in the Essex RO at Chelmsford *1613*; vols 1: 1400-1619, 2: 1620-1720 & 3: 1721-1858 (BRS vols 78, 79 & 84) [*all BRS*]

GOSPORT *see Alverstoke*

GRETTON, THE COURT OF THE PREBEND OF
Superior Courts: Lincoln (Dean & Chapter) until 1834; Lincoln (Consistory) from 1834
1657-1832 Lincoln Wills; vol 4: Cal of Wills & Admons at Lincoln; Archdeaconry of Stow, Peculiar Courts & Misc Courts - *including the Court of the Prebend of Gretton (with invents)* (BRS vol 57) [BRS]
1684-1832 Index to Lincoln Peculiar Courts: Wills & Admons granted in the exempt jurisdiction of Gretton [Mf 759]

GRIMSTON *see Yetminster*

GRINGLEY-ON-THE-HILL, THE COURT OF THE MANOR OF
including the Manor of Bawtry
1739-1855 Manor of Bawtry - Peculiar Court of Gringley on the Hill: Schedule of Wills 1739-1855 & Schedule of Admon Bonds 1805-1855 [Mf 796]

GROBY, THE COURT OF THE COMMISSARY OF THE BISHOP OF LINCOLN FOR THE MANOR OF
Superior Court: Lincoln (Consistory)
1580-1800 Cal of Wills & Admons relating to the County of Leicester, proved in the Archdeaconry Court of Leicester 1495-1649 & in the Peculiars of St Margaret Leicester, Rothley, Groby, Evington & unproved Wills previous to 1801; all now preserved in the Probate Registry at Leicester (BRS vol 27) [BRS]
1621-1844 Abst of Ratby Prob Invents 1621-1844 *In* "Leics Prob Invents" [LE/G 31]

GUERNSEY, THE COURT OF THE COMMISSARY OF THE BISHOP OF WINCHESTER FOR THE BAILIWICK OF
called the Ecclesiastical Court of the Dean of Guernsey from 1841
Superior Courts: Winchester (Archdeaconry) until 1858; Guernsey (Royal Court) from 1858
1664-1751 Royal Court of Guernsey Act Books; vols 1: Wills 1664-1698 & 1729-1751, 2: 1704-1730 (*in 2 pts*) & 3: 1730-1737 [Mf 624]

HADDINGTON *see Edinburgh (Commissariot)*

HALSTOCK *see Lyme Regis*

HALTON (Bucks), THE COURT OF THE PECULIAR JURISDICTION OF *see Monks Risborough*

HALTON (Lancs), THE COURT OF THE MANOR OF
1615-1815 List of Wills, *Admons, Invents & Bonds* proved within the Peculiar of the Manor of Halton; pts 1: 1615-1792 & 2 (*in 2 pts*): 1793-1815 (Lancs & Cheshire Rec Soc Procs vols 23, 66 & 99) [*both* LA/PER]

HAMBLE *see Bishops Waltham*

HAMBLEDON, THE TESTAMENTARY JURISDICTION OF THE PARISH OF
Superior Court: Winchester (Archdeaconry)
1572-1845 Cal of Hants Wills proved in the Prerogative & Peculiar Courts of Winchester with other Prob Docs: *Hambledon - Separate Peculiar Wills* [HA/G 62]

HAMILTON and CAMPSIE, THE COMMISSARIOT OF
Superior Court: Court of Session*; see also Edinburgh (Commissariot)*
1564-1800 Commissariot Rec of Hamilton & Campsie; Reg of Testmts 1564-1800 (Scottish Rec Soc vol 5 or BRS vol 20) [SC/PER or BRS]
1801-1823 *Hamilton & Campsie Regs of Settlements, Testmts & Invents In* "Index to Regs of Testmts for various Commissariots 1801-1823" [Mf 2910]

HAMPTON and COLEMERE, THE COURT OF THE MANOR OF
see also Ellesmere
1734-1845 Cal of Salop Wills & Admons *(with Invents)* deposited in Shrewsbury District Probate Registry *including: Manor of Hampton & Colemere* (supps to the Trans Salop Archl & Nat Hist Soc 4th ser vols 12 *now 45* & 46) [Mf 800 or SH/PER]

HAMPTON LUCY, THE TESTAMENTARY JURISDICTION OF THE PARISH OF
Superior Court: Worcester (Consistory); *see also Lichfield (Consistory); Alveston & Wasperton*
1529-1652 Cal of Wills & Admons registered in the various Peculiar Courts now preserved at the Lichfield Registry 1529-1652 (BRS vol 7) [BRS]
1593-1858 Cal of Wills & Admons of Peculiar Jurisdictions in the Diocese of Lichfield; vols 1 & 2 *including*: Peculiar Court of Hampton Lucy 1593-1858 [Mf 801]

HANDSACRE and ARMITAGE, THE COURT OF THE PREBEND OF
Superior Court: Lichfield (Dean & Chapter)
1529-1652 Cal of Wills & Admons registered in the various Peculiar Courts now preserved at the Lichfield Registry 1529-1652 (BRS vol 7) [BRS]
1677-1858 Cal of Wills & Admons of Peculiar Jurisdictions in the Diocese of Lichfield; vols 1 & 2 *including*: Prebendal Court of Handsacre & Armitage 1677-1858 [Mf 801]

HARBRIDGE *see Ringwood*

HARNHAM *see Coombe*

HARPTREE, THE COURT OF THE PREBEND OF EAST
Superior Court: Wells (Dean)
1657-1854 Wells Wills; vol 13: Indexes to Wells Registry Cals - Peculiar Courts: *E Harptree Wills, Admons & Tuit Bonds* (Mfc) [Apply to Staff]

HARTINGTON, THE COURT OF THE EXEMPT JURISDICTION OF THE DEANERY OF

Superior Court: Lichfield (Consistory)
1529-1652 Cal of Wills & Admons registered in the various Peculiar Courts now preserved at the Lichfield Registry 1529-1652 (BRS vol 7) [BRS]
1680-1858 Cal of Wills & Admons of Peculiar Jurisdictions in the Diocese of Lichfield; vols 1 & 2 *including*: Deanery Court of Hartington 1680-1858 [Mf 801]

HASLEBURY PLUCKNETT *see Hazlebere*

HAVANT, THE TESTAMENTARY JURISDICTION OF THE PARISH OF
Superior Court: Winchester (Archdeaconry)
1593-1700 Cal of Hants Wills proved in the Prerogative & Peculiar Courts of Winchester with other Prob Docs: *Havant - Separate Peculiar Wills* [HA/G 62]

HAVERING-ATTE-BOWER *see Hornchurch*

HAWARDEN, THE COURT OF THE PECULIAR JURISDICTION OF
Superior Courts: Lichfield (Consistory) before 1541 & Chester (Consistory) after 1541
1554-1800 Index to the Wills proved at the Peculiar Court of Hawarden & also to Misc Papers relating to the same Court (now preserved at the St Asaph Court of Probate) 1554-1800 (Flints Hist Soc *Paper no 4*) [WS/G 84]; *also In* "Flints Miscellany" [WS/L 21]

HAWKESBURY, THE COURT OF THE MANOR OF
1508-1548 *Abst of* Hawkesbury Wills 1508-1548 *In* "Off the Beaten Track: The Church & Manor of Hawkesbury" [GL Tracts]

HAZLEBERE, THE COURT OF THE PREBEND OF
also known as Haslebury Plucknett
Superior Court: Wells (Dean)
1676-1856 Wells Wills; vol 13: Indexes to Wells Registry Cals - Peculiar Courts: *Hazlebere Wills 1676-1855 & Admon Bonds 1679-1856 (in 2 pts)* (Mfc) [Apply to Staff]

HEATH *see Warmfield*

HENSTRIDGE, THE COURT OF THE PREBEND OF
Superior Court: Wells (Dean)
1665-1856   Wells Wills; vol 13: Indexes to
            Wells Registry Cals - Peculiar
            Courts: Henstridge Wills 1677-
            1856 & Admon Bonds 1665-1856
            (in 2 pts) (Mfc) [Apply to Staff]

HEREFORD, THE EPISCOPAL CONSISTORY COURT OF THE BISHOP OF
Superior Court: Canterbury (PCC)
1407-1581   Cal of Prob & Admon Acts
            1407-1541 & abst of Wills
            1541-1581 in the Court Books of
            the Bishop of Hereford (Mfc: BRS
            Mfc ser no 2) [Apply to Staff]
1435-1697   Early Hereford Wills 1435-1697
            (Bloom's extr) [HR/G 20]
1444-1446   Abst of 15th C wills in the
            Consistory Court books of the
            Diocese of Hereford (Misc Gen et
            Her 5th ser vols 6 & 7) [PER/MIS]
1444-1578   List of Wills Registered in the
            Cause Books of the Bishop of
            Hereford (Misc Gen et Her 5th
            ser vol 4) [PER/MIS]
1542-1543   Wills in the Act Books of the
            Episcopal Consistory Court of the
            Bishop of Hereford (Faraday's
            abst) [HR/G 21]
1662-1830   Hereford Diocesan Prob Regs;
            pts 1: 1662-1723, 2: 1723-1774
            & 3: 1775-1830 [Mf 2588-2590]
1781-1793   Hereford Deanery Wills 1670-
            1858 & Diocesan Wills 1781-
            1793 [Mf 2592]
1831-1858   Hereford Diocesan Prob Regs; pt
            4: 1831-1858 [Mf 2591]

HEREFORD, THE ARCHDEACONRY OF
not a probate jurisdiction: see Hereford
(Episcopal Consistory)

HEREFORD, THE CONSISTORIAL COURT OF THE DEAN OF
Superior Court: Hereford (Episcopal
Consistory)
1670-1858   Hereford Deanery Wills 1670-
            1858 & Diocesan Wills 1781-
            1793 [Mf 2592]

HEREFORD, THE COURT OF THE MAYOR OF THE CITY OF
1433-1558   Extr from Wills in Misc Docs &
            Papers 1433-1558 In "HMC Rep
            on the MSS of the Corp of
            Hereford" [Apply to Staff]

HEREFORD WITH ASHFORD CARBONELL, THE COURT OF THE PECULIAR JURISDICTION OF THE CHANCELLOR OF THE CHOIR OF THE CATHEDRAL CHURCH OF HEREFORD IN LITTLE
also called Hereford Parva & Ashford
Carbonell
Superior Court: Hereford (Dean)
1662-1858   Index of Wills & Admons together
            with Registered Copies of Wills -
            Little Hereford & Ashford
            Carbonell Peculiar: Wills 1662-
            1858 [Mf 2591]

HERTFORDSHIRE DIVISION), THE COURT OF THE COMMISSARY OF LONDON (ESSEX and
ie the Court of the Commissary of the Bishop
of London for the Parts of Essex & Herts: see
London (Commissary - Essex & Herts)

HERTFORDSHIRE DIVISION), THE COURT OF THE ARCHDEACON OF MIDDLESEX (ESSEX and see Middlesex (Archdeaconry -
Essex & Herts)

HESLINGTON see Ampleforth

HEXHAM and HEXHAMSHIRE, THE COURT OF THE PECULIAR JURISDICTION OF THE ARCHBISHOP OF YORK IN
Superior Court: York (PCY); Durham
(Consistory) from 1837
1593-1602   Peculiar of the Archbishop of
            York in Hexham & Hexhamshire:
            Index to the Act Book for 1593-
            1602 in the Probate Registry at
            York (Yorks Archl Soc rec ser vol
            60) [Apply to Staff]
1685-1705   Index to Wills & Invents In "A
            Most Peculiar Peculiar -
            Hexhamshire Testate Registrate"
            (Northumberland & Durham FHS
            J vol 6) [NU/PER]
1688-1799   Index of York Wills, etc probably
            relating to Hexham &
            Hexhamshire 1688-1799 (Mfc)
            [Apply to Staff]

HEYDOUR WITH WALTON, THE COURT OF THE PREBEND OF
Superior Court: Lincoln (Dean & Chapter);
merged with Lincoln (Consistory) in 1834
1669-1836   Lincoln Wills; vol 4: Cal of Wills &
            Admons at Lincoln;
            Archdeaconry of Stow, Peculiar
            Courts & Misc Courts - including
            the Court of the Prebend of

Heydour (with invents) (BRS vol 57) [BRS]; Index to Lincoln Peculiar Courts: Prebendal Court of Haydor Wills & Admons [Mf 759]

HIGHCLERE, THE COURT OF THE PECULIAR JURISDICTION OF
Superior Court: Winchester (Archdeaconry)
1668-1835 Cal of Hants Wills proved in the Prerogative & Peculiar Courts of Winchester with other Prob Docs: *Highclere - Separate Peculiar Wills* [HA/G 62]

HIGHAM FERRERS, THE BURGESS COURT OF
1390-1632 Extr from Wills in the Burgess Court Rolls 1390-1632 *In* "HMC Rep on the MSS of the Corp of Higham Ferrers" [Apply to Staff]

HIGHWORTH, THE COURT OF THE PREBEND OF
Superior Court: Sarum (Dean)
1623-1799 Peculiar & Prebendal Courts of the Diocese of Sarum - Indexes to Wills & Admons 1462-1810: *Prebendal Court of Highworth (with invents)* [Mf 836]
1800-1857 Wilts Wills Beneficiaries Index 1800-1858: Name Abst; vol 1: Corsham & Highworth 1800-1857 (Peculiar Court docs 1-137) [WL/G 67]
1800-1858 Sarum Courts, Deanery & Archdeaconry of Wiltshire; vol "A": Index for Wills & Admons 1800-1858 with names beginning A-B only [Mf 838]

(HITCHIN DIVISION), THE COURT OF THE ARCHDEACONRY OF HUNTINGDON see *Huntingdon (Archdeaconry - Hitchin)*

HOLME ARCHIEPISCOPI, THE COURT OF THE PREBEND OF
Superior Courts: York (Chancery); York (Dean & Chapter)
1663-1703 York Registry; Cal of Wills & Admons - Separate Peculiars & Dean & Chapter's General Peculiars: *Holme 1663-1703*; York Registry; Names of Peculiars wherein separate lists are kept of the wills etc proved therein *including Holme with Withernwick* [both Mf 879]

HOPE *in Barningham: see Arkengarthdale*

HORLEY and HORNTON, THE COURT OF THE PECULIAR JURISDICTION OF THE DEAN and CHAPTER OF LINCOLN IN see *Banbury*

HORNCHURCH IN THE LIBERTY OF HAVERING-ATTE-BOWER, THE COURT OF THE PECULIAR JURISDICTION OF THE COMMISSARY OF THE WARDEN, FELLOWS and SCHOLARS OF NEW COLLEGE AT OXFORD FOR
see also London (Commissary - Essex & Herts); Oxford (University)
1753-1839 Testmtry Docs of the Liberty of Havering-atte-Bower 1753-1839 *(Cal of Recs in New College Archives)* [ES Tracts]

HORNTON, THE COURT OF THE PECULIAR JURISDICTION OF HORLEY and see *Banbury*

HOUGHTON, THE TESTAMENTARY JURISDICTION OF THE PARISH OF
Superior Court: Winchester (Archdeaconry)
1613-1716 Cal of Hants Wills proved in the Prerogative & Peculiar Courts of Winchester with other Prob Docs: *Houghton - Separate Peculiar Wills* [HA/G 62]

HUNSINGORE, THE COURT OF THE MANOR OF
1607-1839 Manor Court of Hunsingore: Index of Wills, *Admons, Invents & Bonds* 1607-1839 [Mf 878]

HUNTINGDON, THE COURTS OF THE ARCHDEACONRY OF
ie the Court of the Commissary of the Bishop of Lincoln for the Archdeaconry of Huntingdon & the Court of the Archdeacon of Huntingdon
Superior Courts: Lincoln (Consistory) until 1837; Ely (Consistory) from 1837
1479-1652 Cal of Wills & Admons in the Act Books of the Archdeaconry of Huntingdon relating to the counties of Beds, Herts & Hunts *(wills 1479-1615, original wills 1615-1652 & admons 1559-1614)* & to the Peculiar Court of Brampton previous to 1660; now preserved in the Probate Registry of Peterborough (BRS vol 42) [Apply to Staff]
1615-1858 Archdeaconry of Huntingdon -

Cal of Wills; vols 1: 1615-1740,
2: 1740-1848 & vol 3: 1848-1858
[Mf 918 or 736]

**HUNTINGDON (HITCHIN DIVISION), THE
COURT OF THE ARCHDEACON OF**
Superior Court: Huntingdon (Archdeaconry)
1557-1843 Archdeaconry of Huntingdon
(Hitchin Registry) Indexes; vol 1:
Index of Registered Wills 1563-
1843; Index to Original &
Unregistered Wills 1557-1800
[*both* Mf 334]
1580-1609 Abst of Herts Wills *in the
Archdeaconry Court of
Huntingdon (Hitchin Registry)*;
*"Reg 3": 1579-1614 & "Reg 4":
1595-1601* (Herts Genealogist &
Antiquary vols 2 & 3) [*both*
HT/PER]
1635-1855 Archdeaconry of Huntingdon
(Hitchin Div) Admon Bonds &
Accounts: papers relating to
intestates whose surnames
began with the letter "G" (*1635-
1699, 1707-1855*) [Mf 2586]
1801-1857 Archdeaconry of Huntingdon
(Hitchin Registry) Indexes; vol 3:
Index to Wills 1801-1857 [Mf 334]

HULL *see Kingston-upon-Hull*

HUNTON *see Crawley*

**HURSLEY WITH OTTERBOURNE, THE
TESTAMENTARY JURISDICTION OF THE
PARISH OF**
Superior Court: Winchester (Archdeaconry)
1566-1705 Cal of Hants Wills proved in the
Prerogative & Peculiar Courts of
Winchester with other Prob Docs:
*Hursley including Otterbourne -
Separate Peculiar Wills* [HA/G
62]

**HURSTBOURNE and BURBAGE, THE
COURT OF THE PREBEND OF**
only recs for Burbage seem to have survived
Superior Court: Sarum (Dean)
1635-1799 Peculiar & Prebendal Courts of
the Diocese of Sarum - Indexes
to Wills & Admons 1462-1810:
*Prebendal Court of Hurstbourne
& Burbage (with invents)* [Mf 836]
1800-1856 Wilts Wills Beneficiaries Index
1800-1858: Name Abst; vol 5:
Durnford 1800-1857, Fordington
& Writhlington 1800-1855,

Hurstbourne & Burbage
1800-1856, Netheravon
1800-1854 (Peculiar Court docs
508-632) [WL/G 67]
1800-1858 Sarum Courts, Deanery &
Archdeaconry of Wiltshire; vol
"A": Index for Wills & *Admons*
1800-1858 with names beginning
A-B only [Mf 838]

**HURSTBOURNE PRIORS and ST MARY
BOURNE, THE TESTAMENTARY
JURISDICTION OF THE PARISH OF**
Superior Court: Winchester (Archdeaconry)
1577-1782 Cal of Hants Wills proved in the
Prerogative & Peculiar Courts of
Winchester with other Prob Docs:
*Hurstbourne Priors including St
Mary Bourne - Separate Peculiar
Wills* [HA/G 62]

**HUSTHWAITE, THE COURT OF THE
PREBEND OF**
Superior Courts: York (Chancery); York
(Dean & Chapter)
1661-1842 York Registry; Names of
Peculiars wherein separate lists
are kept of the wills etc proved
therein *including Husthwaite from
1714 to the present time*; York
Registry; Cal of Vacancy &
Prebendal Wills *including
Husthwaite* [*both* Mf 879]

HUSTING, THE COURT OF
*this was the court of the Corporation of the
City of London until 1688*
1258-1688 Cal of Wills proved & enrolled on
the Court of Husting 1258-1688;
abst preserved among the
archives of the Corp of the City of
London at the Guildhall; pts 1:
1258-1358 & 2: 1358-1688
[MX/G 245-246]; *errata* (N&Q 7th
ser vol 11 & 8th ser vol 3) [N&Q]

HYTHE *see Fawley*

**ILMINSTER, THE COURT OF THE ROYAL
PECULIAR JURISDICTION IN THE MANOR
OF**
Superior Court: Delegates (High Court)*; see
also Wells (Episcopal Consistory)*
1625-1696 Wells Wills; vol 13: Indexes to
Wells Registry Cals - Peculiar
Courts: *Ilminster Wills & Admons
1625 & 1673-1696* (Mfc) [Apply
to Staff]

1690-1857 Cal of Wills & Admons in the Court of the Ilminster Royal Peculiar (*admons with bonds from 1843*) (BRS vol 53) [BRS]

ILTON, THE COURT OF THE PREBEND OF
Superior Court: Wells (Dean)
1678-1848 Wells Wills; vol 13: Indexes to Wells Registry Cals - Peculiar Courts: *Ilton Wills, Admons, Invents & Tuit Bonds* (Mfc) [Apply to Staff]

INGOLDMELLS, THE COURT OF THE MANOR OF
1328-1442 *Extr of* Enrolled Wills *In* "Court Rolls of the Manor of Ingoldmells in the County of Lincoln" [LI/L 15]

INHURST *see Baughurst*

INVERNESS, THE COMMISSARIOT OF
Superior Court: Court of Session*; see also* Edinburgh (*Commissariot*)
1630-1800 Commissariot Rec of Inverness; Reg of Testmts 1630-1800 (Scottish Rec Soc vol 4 or BRS vol 20) [SC/PER or BRS]
1801-1823 *Inverness Reg of Testmts In* "Index to Regs of Testmts for various Commissariots 1801-1823" [Mf 2910]

IPSWICH *see Suffolk (Archdeaconry)*

ISLEHAM and FRECKENHAM, THE COURT OF THE PECULIAR JURISDICTION OF THE BISHOP OF ROCHESTER IN
Superior Court: Rochester (Consistory)*; see also Huntingdon (Archdeaconry); Norwich (Consistory)*
1354-1700 Index of the Prob Recs (*wills, admons & invents*) of the Court of the Archdeacon of Sudbury 1354-1700; vols 1 & 2 (BRS vols 95 & 96) [*both* BRS]
Note: *nothwithstanding the title & introduction, the index to these vols reveal many Isleham & Freckenham entries*

ISLES, THE COMMISSARIOT OF THE
Superior Court: Court of Session*; see also* Edinburgh (*Commissariot*)
1661-1800 Commissariot Rec of the Isles; Reg of Testmts 1661-1800 (Scottish Rec Soc vol 11) [SC/PER]

1801-1823 *The Isles Regs of Testmts & Invents In* "Index to Regs of Testmts for various Commissariots 1801-1823" [Mf 2910]

ITCHINGTON, THE COURT OF THE PREBEND OF BISHOPS *see Bishops Itchington*

KENDAL, THE DEANERY OF *see Richmond (Western Deaneries)*

KENN *see Yatton*

KETTON, THE COURT OF THE PREBEND OF
Superior Courts: Lincoln (Dean & Chapter) until 1834; Lincoln (Consistory) from 1834
1574-1820 Index to Wills & Admons proved & granted in the Archdeaconry Court of Leicester 1660-1750 & in the Peculiars of St Margaret Leicester & Rothley & in the Rutland Peculiars of Caldecott, Ketton with Tixover (*1574 & 1722-1820*) & Liddington prior to 1821; now preserved in the Probate Registry at Leicester (BRS vol 51) [Apply to Staff]
1666-1677 Lincoln Wills; vol 4: Cal of Wills & Admons at Lincoln; Archdeaconry of Stow, Peculiar Courts & Misc Courts - *including the Court of the Prebend of Ketton* (BRS vol 57) [BRS]

KILDARE, THE CONSISTORY COURT OF THE BISHOP OF
Superior Court: Armagh (PCA)
1661-1800 *Phillimore's* Indexes to Irish Wills; vol 1: Cal of Wills in the Dioceses of Ossory, Leighlin, Ferns & Kildare [IR/G 84]
1661-1826 Kildare Wills from Betham's Geneal Abst; pt 1: A-K 1661-1826 & pt 2: K-S 1661-1824 [Mf 332]

KILFENORA *see Killaloe*

KILLALA and ACHONRY, THE CONSISTORY COURT OF THE BISHOP OF
Superior Court: Armagh (PCA)
1698-1858 Index to Killala & Achonry Wills (*1698-1838 with a fragmentary list of testators to 1858*) (Irish Genealogist vol 3) [IR/PER]

1779-1856 Index to Killala & Achonry Admon Bonds (Irish Ancestor vol 7) [IR/PER]

KILLALOE and KILFENORA, THE CONSISTORY COURT OF THE BISHOP OF
Superior Court: Armagh (PCA)
1653-1800 *Phillimore's* Indexes to Irish Wills; vol 2: Cal of Wills in the Dioceses of Cashel & Emly, Killaloe & Kilfenora, Waterford & Lismore, Limerick, Ardfert & Aghadoe & the Peculiar Jurisdiction of the Dean of Lismore [IR/G 86]
1708-1724 *Index to the* Killaloe Caveat Book for 1708-1723/24 *In* appx 1A to "57th Rep of Deputy Keeper of Public Recs in Ireland" [IR/K]
1845 *Index to* Killaloe Admon Grants for 1845 *In* appx 1A to "57th Rep of Deputy Keeper of Public Recs in Ireland" [IR/K]

KILMACDUAGH *see Clonfert*

KILMESTON *see Cheriton*

KILMORE, THE CONSISTORY COURT OF THE BISHOP OF
Superior Court: Armagh (PCA)
1694-1770 Surname Index to the Swanzy MSS *(these MSS include will abst from the PRO, Dublin for the Diocese of Kilmore)* [IR/G 143]
1682-1857 Index to Kilmore Diocesan Wills to 1858 [IR/L 97 or IR/G 138]

KING'S LYNN, THE COURT OF THE MAYOR OF THE BOROUGH OF
formerly the Borough of Bishop's Lynn
1276-1751 Extr from the Roll of Enrolment of Wills 1276-1751 *In* "HMC Rep on the MSS of the Corp of King's Lynn" [Apply to Staff]

KINGS SUTTON, THE COURT OF THE PECULIAR JURISDICTION OF THE DEAN and CHAPTER OF LINCOLN IN *see Banbury*

KINGSBURY EPISCOPI and EAST LAMBROOK, THE COURT OF THE PECULIAR JURISDICTION OF THE CHANCELLOR OF THE CATHEDRAL CHURCH AT WELLS IN
Superior Court: Wells (Episcopal Consistory)
1661-1857 Wells Wills; vol 13: Indexes to Wells Registry Cals - Peculiar Courts: *Kingsbury & E Lambrook*

Wills, Admons & Tuits 1661-1857 & Admon Bonds, etc 1667-1739 (in 2 pts) (Mfc) [Apply to Staff]

KINGSTON-UPON-HULL, THE COURT OF THE MAYOR OF THE BOROUGH OF
1303-1791 City & County of Kingston upon Hull - Cal of the Ancient Deeds, Letters, Misc Old Docs, etc *including Wills* in the Archives of the Corp [YK/L 46 or YK/L 164]
1309-1426 Wills enrolled in the Liber Rubeus of Kingston-upon-Hull *(Index to Guildhall recs)* (Northern Genealogist vol 2) [PER/NOR]

KINOULTON, THE COURT OF THE PECULIAR JURISDICTION OF THE COMMISSARY FOR
Superior Court: York (Exchequer)
1724-1851 Abst of Wills & other Prob Papers 1724-1851 *In* "Gleanings from Parish Chests" [CA/L 12]
1758-1846 Peculiar Court of the Vicar of Kinoulton - Cal of Wills, Admons, etc 1758-1846 [Mf 796]

KIRKCUDBRIGHT, THE COMMISSARIOT OF
Superior Court: Court of Session; *see also Edinburgh (Commissariot)*
1663-1800 Commissariot Rec of Kirkcudbrightshire; Executry Papers 1663-1800 (Scottish Rec Soc vol 17) [SC/PER]
1801-1823 *Kirkcudbright Regs of Settlements, Testmts & Invents In* "Index to Regs of Testmts for various Commissariots 1801-1823" [Mf 2910]

KIRKBY-LE-SOKEN *see Sokens*

KIRTON-IN-LINDSEY, THE COURT OF THE PECULIAR JURISDICTION OF THE SUB DEAN OF LINCOLN IN
Superior Court: Lincoln (Dean & Chapter); *merged with Lincoln (Consistory) in 1834*
1536-1617 Index to Lincoln Peculiar Courts: Kirton in Lindsey Jurisdictionalia Subdecanatus Lincolnie - Index of Wills & Admons [Mf 759]
1566-1834 Lincoln Wills; vol 4: Cal of Wills & Admons at Lincoln; Archdeaconry of Stow, Peculiar Courts & Misc Courts - *including the Court of the Peculiar Jurisdiction of the Sub Dean of*

Lincoln in Kirton-in-Lindsey (with invents in 2 pts): 1536-1617 & 1566-1834 (BRS vol 57) [BRS]; Index to Lincoln Peculiar Courts: Prebendal Court of Kirton-in-Lindsey Wills & Admons [Mf 759]

KNARESBOROUGH, THE COURT OF THE HONOUR OF

1507-1858   *Abst of* Wills & Admons from the Knaresborough Court Rolls; vols 1: from temp 2 Henry 8 to 1668 & 2: 1640-1858 with an index to original wills, invents, etc (Surtees Soc vols 104 & 110) [*both* DU/PER]

1640-1858   Honor Court of Knaresborough - Index of Wills, Admons, Invents & Bonds 1640-1858 (*in 2 pts*) [Mf 878]

1640-1858   Wills & Admons etc: listings taken from cals of the old Diocese of York & the Diocese of Lincoln (with certain additions from Durham) (*index BUR-WRI*) (Fam Hist vols 2 & 3) [PER/FAM]

KNOWLE, THE COURT OF THE MANOR OF

1675-1790   Cals of Original Wills & Admon Papers transmitted (*to Birmingham Probate Registry*) from the registers of Barston, Bishops Itchington, Baddesley Clinton, Knowle, Packwood, Tachbrook & Temple Balsall from 1675 to 1790 inclusive (BRS vol 7) [BRS]

1726-1858   Cal of Wills & Admons of Peculiar Jurisdictions in the Diocese of Lichfield; vols 1 & 2 *including*: Manorial Court of Knowle 1726-1858 [Mf 801]

1726-1790   List of Wills proved & Admons granted in the Manor Court of Knowle 1726-1790 *In* "Recs of Knowle" [WA/R 18]

1727-1890   Cal of Original Wills & Admon Papers from the Regs of *Knowle* (*with invents*) [Mf 802]

KNOWLE ST GILES *see Cudworth*

LAFFORD *see Sleaford*

LAMBETH PALACE, THE LIBRARY OF THE ARCHBISHOP OF CANTERBURY AT

although not a court, the Palace Library holds Regs & other probate papers of the Archbishops of Canterbury & their commissaries especially for probates arising during vacancies; collections relating to locations, counties or countries or for particular groups are shown under the appropriate place or group; see also Canterbury (PCC); Arches (Deanery); Arches (High Court); Bocking; Croydon; S Malling; Monks Risborough; Pagham & Tarring; Shoreham

1292-1635   Cal of Lambeth Wills (The Genealogist vols 5-6 & new ser vols 34-35) [PER/GEN]

1313-1644   Cal of Lambeth Admons (The Genealogist vol 7 & new ser vol 1) [PER/GEN]

1414-1443   Reg of Henry Chichele, Archbishop of Canterbury 1414-1443; vol 2: *Abst of* Wills proved before the Archbishop or his Commissaries (Canterbury & York Soc vol 42) [KE/G 21]

1454-1477   Commissions for proving Wills & Collecting & Administering the Estates of Intestates 1454-1467 & 1477 *In* "Registrum Thome Bourgchier Cantuariensis Archiepiscopal/Reg of Thomas Bourchier, Archbishop of Canterbury" (Canterbury & York Soc vol 54) [KE/G 24]

1487-1493   Reg of John Morton, Archbishop of Canterbury 1486-1500; vol 2: *Abst of* Reg of Testmts pertaining to the Prerogative Jurisdiction of the Archbishop proved in the Diocese of Exeter from the Feast of St Peter ad Vincula (Canterbury & York Soc vol 78) [CE/GEN]

1559-1575   Abst of Wills *In* "Registrum Matthei Parker Diocesis Cantuarienses 1559-1575/Reg of Matthew Parker, Diocese of Canterbury" (Canterbury & York Soc vol 36) [KE/G 25]

1690-1823   Catalogue of MSS in Lambeth Palace Lib - MSS 1222-1860: Prob Acts of Peculiars etc (*includes MS 1488: Grants of Prob or Admon*) [TB/BIB]

LAMBROOK, EAST *see Kingsbury Episcopi*

LANARK, THE COMMISSARIOT OF
Superior Court: Court of Session; *see also*
Edinburgh (Commissariot)
1595-1800 Commissariot Rec of Lanark;
Reg of Testmts 1595-1800
(Scottish Rec Soc vol 19)
[SC/PER]
1801-1823 *Lanark Regs of Testmts &*
Invents In "Index to Regs of
Testmts for various
Commissariots 1801-1823" [Mf
2910]

LANCASTER, THE CHANCERY COURT OF
THE DUCHY OF
Superior Court: The Privy Council; *see also*
Chancery (High Court)
1700-1793 Lancs & Cheshire Depositions
Indexed 1700-1793 [LA/G 60]

LANGFORD ECCLESIA, THE COURT OF
THE PREBEND OF
Superior Courts: Lincoln (Dean & Chapter)
until 1834; Lincoln (Consistory) from 1834
1550-1856 *Index to Berks, Bucks & Oxon*
Peculiars - Wills & Admons 1550-
1858 (*also Invents & Bonds*):
Peculiar Court Langford Ecclesia
[Mf 913]

LANGTOFT, THE COURT OF THE
PREBEND OF
Superior Courts: York (Chancery); York
(Dean & Chapter)
1647-1738 York Registry; Cal of Wills &
Admons - Separate Peculiars &
Dean & Chapter's General
Peculiars: *Langtoft 1647-1699 &*
1702-1738 [Mf 879]

LAUDER, THE COMMISSARIOT OF
Superior Court: Court of Session; *see also*
Edinburgh (Commissariot)
1561-1800 Commissariot Rec of Lauder;
Reg of Testmts 1561-1800
(Scottish Rec Soc vol 18)
[SC/PER]
1801-1823 *Lauder Regs of Testmts &*
Invents In "Index to Regs of
Testmts for various
Commissariots 1801-1823" [Mf
2910]

LEICESTER, THE ARCHIDIACONAL
COURTS OF
ie the Court of the Commissary of the Bishop
of Lincoln for the Archdeaconry of Leicester,
the Court of the Archdeacon of Leicester &

the Court of the Vicar General of Leicester;
these Courts' recs are combined
Superior Court: Lincoln (Consistory)
1489-1538 Leicester Archdeaconry Court;
Leics Uncalendared Wills 1489-
1538 with later items (*cals of*
wills, admons & invents) *In* "Leics
Miscellany" (Leics Archl Soc *extra*
publication, Summer 1951) [LE/G
25]
1495-1649 Cal of Wills & Admons relating to
the County of Leicester, proved
in the Archdeaconry Court of
Leicester 1495-1649 (*admons*
from 1556) & in the Peculiars of
St Margaret Leicester, Rothley,
Groby, Evington & unproved
Wills previous to 1801; all now
preserved in the Probate Registry
at Leicester (BRS vol 27) [BRS]
1500-1579 Archdeaconry Court of Leicester;
Index to Wills 1500-1579 [Mf
750]
16-19 C Oldaker Coll of Wills: *see the*
note on this coll in the General
Collections of Wills, Indexes, etc
part of the NATIONAL section
1528-1529 Some Unindexed Wills at
Lincoln; Leicester Archdeaconry
1528-1529 & wills in the Court of
the Dean & Chapter 1555
(Associated Archl Socs Reps &
Papers vol 21) [PER/ASS]
1556-1586 Archdeaconry Court Proceedings
- Leicester Cal of Wills & Admons
In "Leics Miscellany" (Leics Archl
Soc *extra vol*) [LE/G 25]
1576-1800 Archdeaconry of Leicester; Index
to Wills, Admons, etc not
completed 1576-1800 (BRS vol
27) [BRS]
1619-1750 Index to Wills & Admons proved
& granted in the Archdeaconry
Court of Leicester 1660-1750
(*including the Commissary Court*
of Leicester, the Vicar-General's
Court & miscellaneous recs,
bonds & invents 1619-1744) & in
the Peculiars of St Margaret
Leicester & Rothley & in the
Rutland Peculiars of Caldecott,
Ketton & Tixover & Liddington
prior to 1821; now preserved in
the Probate Registry at Leicester
(BRS vol 51) [Apply to Staff]
1750-1858 Archdeaconry Court of Leicester;
Index to Wills & Admons 1750-
1858 (*in 4 pts*) [Mf 750]

LEICESTER, THE COURT OF THE VICAR-GENERAL OF see Leicester (Archdeaconry)

LEICESTER, THE COURT OF THE PREBEND OF ST MARGARET IN
Superior Courts: Lincoln (Dean & Chapter) until 1834; Lincoln (Consistory) from 1834
1543-1800 Cal of Wills & Admons relating to the County of Leicester, proved in the Archdeaconry Court of Leicester 1495-1649 & in the Peculiars of St Margaret Leicester, Rothley, Groby, Evington & unproved Wills previous to 1801; all now preserved in the Probate Registry at Leicester (BRS vol 27) [BRS]
1642-1720 Index to Wills & Admons proved & granted in the Archdeaconry Court of Leicester 1660-1750 & in the Peculiars of St Margaret Leicester (additional admons only) & Rothley & in the Rutland Peculiars of Caldecott, Ketton & Tixover & Liddington prior to 1821; now preserved in the Probate Registry at Leicester (BRS vol 51) [Apply to Staff]

LEIGH see Lyme Regis; Yetminster

LEIGHLIN, THE CONSISTORY COURT OF THE BISHOP OF
Superior Court: Armagh (PCA)
1652-1800 Phillimore's Indexes to Irish Wills; vol 1: Cal of Wills in the Dioceses of Ossory, Leighlin, Ferns & Kildare [IR/G 84]
1694-1845 Index to Leighlin Admon Bonds (supp vol of Irish Ancestor for 1972) [IR/G 134]
1703-1802 Ossory & Leighlin Admons Intestate; Grants of admon of the goods of intestates in the Dioceses of Ossory & Leighlin (1703 & 1716-1802) from the Carrigan MSS (Irish Genealogist vol 4) [IR/PER]

LEIGHTON BUZZARD, THE COURT OF THE PREBEND OF
Superior Courts: Lincoln (Dean & Chapter) until 1834; Lincoln (Consistory) from 1834; see also Aylesbury; Northampton (Archdeaconry)
1537-1846 Index of Beds Prob Recs 1484-1858 (wills, admons, invents, guardnshp & other bonds, etc in the Court of Leighton Buzzard Peculiar - Wills: 1537-1554, 1736-1795 & 1797-1846; Admons: 1772-1842); pts 1 & 2 (BRS vols 104 & 105) [both BRS]
18th C Index to 18th C Leighton Buzzard Wills & Admon Bonds now in the Bedford County RO In "Index to Berks, Bucks & Oxon Peculiars - Wills & Admons 1550-1858" [Mf 913]

LEWES, THE CONSISTORIAL COURT OF THE BISHOP OF CHICHESTER FOR THE ARCHDEACONRY OF
Superior Court: Chichester (Consistory)
1518-1659 Cals of Wills & Admons in the Archdeaconry Court of Lewes in the Bishopric of Chichester together with those in the Archbishop of Canterbury's Peculiar Jurisdiction of S Malling & the Peculiar of the Deanery of Battle comprising together the whole of the Eastern division of the County of Sussex & the parish of Edburton in W Sussex, from the earliest extant instruments in the reign of Henry VIII to the Commonwealth (BRS vol 24) [BRS]; Lewes Probs 1645-1646 (an Act Book of Wills omitted from BRS vol 24) (Sussex FHn vol 3) [SX/PER]
1528-1543 Extr from Lewes Archdeaconry Wills in Reg "Ala" (Sussex FHn vol 2) [SX/PER]
1528-1548 Cal of Wills at Lewes 1543-1548 with a list of Archdeaconry of Lewes Wills 1528-1541 (Sussex Archl Colls vol 32) [SX/PER]
1550-1551 Archdeaconry of Lewes: Abst of Wills & Admons [Apply to Staff]
1557-1829 List of Invents from Lewes Registry in E Sussex RO (Sussex Geneal & Loc Hn vol 1) [SX/PER]
1563-1729 Unpublished Notes of Wills from the Probate Registry at Lewes (extr from stray wills) (Misc Gen et Her 2nd ser vol 1) [PER/MIS]
1660-1799 Archdeaconry Court of Lewes; Index to Registered Will Books & Admon Act Books 1660-1799 (in 3 pts) [Mf 826]
1685-1696 Lewes Probate Registry: Sede Vacante Reg 1685 & 1696 Wills; Full Index to all the Wills in the vol (compiled directly from the

wills) also abst of all the Admon Acts in the same vol [SX/G 52]

1800-1858 Archdeaconry Court of Lewes; Cals of Wills & Admons: 1800-1858 (*in 2 pts*) [Mf 827]
Note: *this series continues to 1896: see Lewes (District Registry)*

1849-1851 Testamenta Probata Acta No 83 (Lewes Will Book for 1849-1851) [Mf 828]

LEWES, THE DISTRICT PROBATE REGISTRY IN
Superior Registry: London (Principal Probate Registry)
1858-1896 Lewes Probate Court; Cals of Wills & Admons: 1858-1896 (*in 3 pts*) [Mf 827]
Note: *this is a continuation from the series beginning in 1800: see Lewes (Archdeaconry)*

LICHFIELD and COVENTRY, THE CONSISTORY COURT OF THE BISHOP OF
Superior Court: Canterbury (PCC)
1472-1650 Lichfield Consistory Court Index to Wills; vols 1 & 2: 1472-1650 [Mf 803 & 804]

16-19 C Oldaker Coll of Wills: *see the note on this coll in the General Collections of Wills, Indexes, etc part of the NATIONAL section*

1516-1652 Cals of Wills & Admons in the Consistory Court of the Bishop of Lichfield & Coventry 1516-1652 (*1516-1526, 1528-1640, 1526-1561 & 1562-1652*); also those in the "Peculiars" now deposited in the Probate Registries at Lichfield, Birmingham & Derby (BRS vol 7) [BRS]; Lichfield Wills & Admons registered in the Consistory Court of the Bishop of Lichfield & Coventry 1516-1629 (offprint from BRS vol 7); ser 1: 1516-1526; ser 2: 1528-1540; ser 3: 1526-1527 & 1533-1561; ser 4: 1562-1599 (*AA-AP only*) [ST/G 26]; *see also* Cal of Wills & Admons 1516-1652 [ST/G 30]

1529-1650 *Cal of Clerical Wills at Lichfield* (Salop N&Q 3rd ser vol 3) [SH/PER]

1535-1840 Lichfield Probate Registry Extracts *from Consistory Court Wills & Admons* (*Oldaker MSS*) [ST/G 30]

1597-1614 Typical Invents of Clergymen c1600 (*abst at Lichfield 1597-1614*) *In* "Clerical Invents" (appx 4 to Wm Salt/Staffs Rec Soc 3rd ser vol for 1915) [ST/PER]

1651-1725 Diocese of Lichfield & Coventry - Cal of Wills & Admons; vol 4: *1651-1700 & 1701-1725* [Mf 805]

1655-1671 Diocese of Lichfield & Coventry - Cal of Wills & Admons; vol 3: The Black Book of Lichfield (*copies of wills*) [Mf 804]

1726-1858 Diocese of Lichfield & Coventry - Cal of Wills & Admons; vols 5: 1726-1750 & 6: 1751-1775; 7: 1776-1800 & 8: 1801-1820; 9: 1821-1840 & 10: 1841-1858 [Mf 806-808 or (*vol 10*) Mf 809]
Note: *this series continues to 1860: see Birmingham (District Registry)*

LICHFIELD, THE COURT OF THE PECULIAR JURISDICTION OF THE DEAN OF
Superior Court: Lichfield (Consistory); *see also Lichfield (Dean & Chapter)*
1529-1652 Cal of Wills & Admons registered in the various Peculiar Courts now preserved at the Lichfield Registry 1529-1652 (BRS vol 7) [BRS]

1568-1680 Abst of Prob Invents of Lichfield & District (*in the Peculiar Courts of the Dean & of the Dean & Chapter*) (Wm Salt/Staffs Rec Soc 4th ser vol 5) [ST/PER]

1570-1858 Cal of Wills & Admons of Peculiar Jurisdictions in the Diocese of Lichfield; vols 1 & 2 *including*: Peculiar Court of the Dean of Lichfield 1570-1858 [Mf 801]

LICHFIELD, THE COURT OF THE DEAN and CHAPTER OF
Superior Court: Lichfield (Consistory); *see also Lichfield (Dean)*
1510-1858 Cal of Wills & Admons of Peculiar Jurisdictions in the Diocese of Lichfield; vols 1 & 2 *including*: Peculiar Court of the Dean & Chapter of Lichfield 1510-1858 [Mf 801]

1529-1650 *Cal of Clerical Wills at Lichfield* (Salop N&Q 3rd ser vol 3) [SH/PER]

1529-1652 Cal of Wills & Admons registered

in the various Peculiar Courts now preserved at the Lichfield Registry 1529-1652 (BRS vol 7) [BRS]

1568-1680 *Abst of* Prob Invents of Lichfield & District (*in the Peculiar Courts of the Dean & of the Dean & Chapter*) (Wm Salt/Staffs Rec Soc 4th ser vol 5) [ST/PER]

LIDDINGTON, THE COURT OF THE PREBEND OF

Superior Courts: Lincoln (Dean & Chapter) until 1834; Lincoln (Consistory) from 1834; *see also Caldecott*

1723-1819 Index to Wills & Admons proved & granted in the Archdeaconry Court of Leicester 1660-1750 & in the Peculiars of St Margaret Leicester & Rothley & in the Rutland Peculiars of Caldecott, Ketton & Tixover & Liddington prior to 1821 *with Invents*; now preserved in the Probate Registry at Leicester (BRS vol 51) [Apply to Staff]

1668-1810 Lincoln Wills; vol 4: Cal of Wills & Admons at Lincoln; Archdeaconry of Stow, Peculiar Courts & Misc Courts - *including the Court of the Prebend of Liddington* (BRS vol 57) [BRS]

LIMERICK, THE CONSISTORY COURT OF THE BISHOP OF

Superior Court: Armagh (PCA)

1615-1800 *Phillimore's* Indexes to Irish Wills; vol 2: Cal of Wills in the Dioceses of Cashel & Emly, Killaloe & Kilfenora, Waterford & Lismore, Limerick, Ardfert & Aghadoe & the Peculiar Jurisdiction of the Dean of Lismore [IR/G 86]

LINCOLN, THE CONSISTORY COURT OF THE BISHOP OF

Superior Court: Canterbury (PCC)

1271-1526 *Abst of* Lincs Wills registered in the District Probate Registry at Lincoln; vol 1: 1271-1526 (Lincoln Rec ser vol 5) [LI/PER]

1280-1547 Index to the Wills & Admons recorded in the Episcopal Regs at Lincoln 1280-1847 [Mf 751]; Early Lincoln Wills: an abstract of all wills & admons recorded in the old Diocese of Lincoln, comprising the counties of Lincoln, Rutland, Northampton, Huntingdon, Bedford, Buckingham, Oxford, Leicester & Hertford 1280-1547 (Lincoln Rec ser vol 1) [LI/G 32]

1320-1547 Lincoln Wills; vol 1: Cal of Wills & Admons recorded in the Episcopal Regs of the Ancient Diocese of Lincoln 1320-1547; Misc Wills in the Episcopal Registry 1489-1588; & Misc Wills 1489-1588 & Wills proved in the Consistory Court of Lincoln 1506-1600 (BRS vol 28) [BRS]

1419-1420 Abst of sede vacante Wills 1419-1420 *In* "Reg of Richard Fleming, Bishop of Lincoln 1420-1431 vol 1" (Canterbury & York Soc vol 73) [Apply to Staff]

1489-1511 Lincoln Consistory Court - Visitation Books (*Leics entries for wills, admons & invents 1489-1491, 1498-1499 & 1509-1511*) *In* "Leics Miscellany" (Leics Archl Soc *extra publication,* Summer 1951) [LE/G 25]

1489-1588 Lincoln Wills; vol 1: Cal of Wills & Admons recorded in the Episcopal Regs of the Ancient Diocese of Lincoln 1320-1547 & *also* Misc Wills in the Episcopal Registry of the Ancient Diocese of Lincoln 1489-1588 (BRS vol 28) [BRS]

16-19 C Oldaker Coll of Wills*: see the note on this coll in the General Collections of Wills, Indexes, etc part of the NATIONAL section*

1505-1530 *Abst of* Lincs Wills registered in the District Probate Registry at Lincoln; vol 2: 1505-1530 (Lincoln Rec ser vol 10) [LI/PER]

1506-1531 Wills in the Consistory Court of Lincoln: 1506 & subsequent years (*1506 et seq & 1520-1531 A-SCR*) [LI/G 31]

1506-1580 Consistory Court of Lincoln - Cal of Wills; vols 1: 1506-1558 & 2: 1558-1580 [Mf 751]

1506-1600 Lincoln Wills; vol 1: Cal of Wills & Admons recorded in the Episcopal Regs of the Ancient Diocese of Lincoln 1320-1547 & *also* Wills proved in the Consistory Court of Lincoln 1506-1600 (BRS vol 28) [BRS]

1508-1730 Lincoln Wills; vol 4: Cal of Wills & Admons at Lincoln;

Archeaconry of Stow, Peculiar Courts & Misc Courts - *including Misc Wills, Admons, Invents & Bonds in Bundles A-H at the District Probate Registry, Lincoln 1549-1730 (with "Foreign" recs for outside the county of Lincoln) & Sundry Wills, Admons, Invents & Bonds in the Diocesan Registry 1508-1608* (BRS vol 57) [BRS]

1521-1531 Wills in the Consistory Court of Lincoln 1521-1531 *In* "Some Indexes to Lincs Wills & Admons" (*A-SCR*) [LI/G 31]

1530-1532 *Abst of* Lincs Wills registered in the District Probate Registry at Lincoln; vol 3: 1530-1532 (Lincoln Rec ser vol 24) [LI/PER]

1540-1659 Lincoln Wills; vol 3: Cal of Admons in the Consistory Court of Lincoln 1540-1659 (BRS vol 52) [BRS]

1560-1695 Some Unindexed wills at Lincoln found in the Bishop's Registry *amongst Marriage & Admon Bonds 1560, 1580-1595, 1632, 1638-1640, 1652 & 1695)* (Misc Gen et Her 2nd ser vol 3) [PER/MIS]

1581-1609 Consistory Court of Lincoln - Cal of Wills; vol 3: 1581-1609 [Mf 752]

1600-1637 Consistory Court of Lincoln - Cal of Admons; vol 1: 1600-1637 [Mf 756]

1601-1652 Lincoln Wills; vol 2: Cal of Wills & Admons proved in the Consistory Court of Lincoln 1601-1652 (BRS vol 41) [BRS]

1610-1699 Consistory Court of Lincoln - Cal of Wills; vols 4: 1610-1630; 5: 1630-1669 & 6: 1670-1699 [Mf 752-753]

1638-1699 Consistory Court of Lincoln - Cal of Admons; vol 2: 1638-1699 [Mf 756]

1660-1700 Lincoln Wills; vol 5: Index of Lincoln Consistory Court Wills & Invents 1660-1700 (BRS vol 101) [BRS]

1699-1857 Wills & Admons etc: listings taken from cals of the old Diocese of York & the Diocese of Lincoln (with certain additions from Durham) (*index BUR-WRI*) (Fam Hist vols 2 & 3) [PER/FAM]

1699-1857 Consistory Court of Lincoln - Cal of Wills; vols 7: 1699-1731 & 8: 1732-1765; 9: 1766-1808, 10: 1809-1841 & 11: 1842-1857 [Mf 754-755]

1700-1857 Consistory Court of Lincoln - Cal of Admons; vols 3: 1700-1730 & 4: 1730-1810; 5: 1811-1857 [Mf 756-757]

LINCOLN, THE ARCHIDIACONAL COURTS OF

ie the Court of the Commissary of the Bishop of Lincoln for the Archdeaconry of Lincoln & the Court of the Archdeacon of Lincoln; records of these courts do not appear to have been kept separately from the Consistory Court of Lincoln (qv)

LINCOLN, THE COURT OF THE DEAN and CHAPTER OF

Superior Court: Lincoln (Consistory) *until merged with* Lincoln (Consistory) *in 1834*

1520-1536 Wills in the Chapter Acts of the Dean & Chapter of Lincoln (Lincoln Rec ser vol 12) [LI/PER])

1534-1780 Wills & Admons in the Court of the Dean & Chapter of Lincoln 1534-1780 (*A-R*) *In* "Some Indexes to Lincs Wills & Admons" [LI/G 31]

1534-1834 Lincoln Wills; vol 4: Cal of Wills & Admons at Lincoln; Archdeaconry of Stow, Peculiar Courts & Misc Courts *including the Court of the Peculiar Jurisdiction of the Dean & Chapter of Lincoln (with invents)* (BRS vol 57) [BRS]

1555 Some Unindexed Wills at Lincoln; Leicester Archdeaconry 1528-1529 & wills in the Court of the Dean & Chapter 1555 (Associated Archl Socs Reps & Papers vol 21) [PER/ASS]

1700-1800 Wills & Admons etc: listings taken from cals of the old Diocese of York & the Diocese of Lincoln (with certain additions from Durham) (*index BUR-WRI*) (Fam Hist vols 2 & 3) [PER/FAM]

1747-1798 Abst of Wills proved in the Court of the Dean & Chapter of Lincoln (Lincs N&Q vol 11) [LI/PER]

LINCOLN, THE COURT OF THE CHANCELLOR OF

also Commissary of the Bishop of Lincoln: see Buckingham (Archdeaconry); Stow (Archdeaconry)

LINCOLN IN KIRTON-IN-LINDSEY, THE COURT OF THE PECULIAR JURISDICTION OF THE SUB DEAN OF see *Kirton-in-Lindsey*

LINCOLN, THE COURT OF THE MAYOR OF THE CITY OF
1492-1610 List of Wills in Lincoln Corp Regs *In* "HMC Rep on the MSS of the Corp of Lincoln" [Apply to Staff]
1661-1714 *Abst of* Prob Invents of Lincoln Citizens 1661-1714 (Lincoln Rec ser vol 80) [LI/PER]

LINTON ON OUSE, THE COURT OF PECULIAR JURISDICTION IN THE MANOR OF
Superior Court: York (Dean & Chapter)
1710-1735 York Registry; Names of Peculiars wherein separate lists are kept of the wills etc proved therein *including Linton upon 'Grange'* [Mf 879]

LISMORE, THE COURT OF THE PECULIAR JURISDICTION OF THE DEAN OF
Superior Court: Waterford & Lismore
1693-1799 *Phillimore's* Indexes to Irish Wills; vol 2: Cal of Wills in the Dioceses of Cashel & Emly, Killaloe & Kilfenora, Waterford & Lismore, Limerick, Ardfert & Aghadoe & the Peculiar Jurisdiction of the Dean of Lismore [IR/G 86]

LITTLETON, THE TESTAMENTARY JURISDICTION OF THE PARISH OF
Superior Court: Winchester (Archdeaconry)
1630-1735 Cal of Hants Wills proved in the Prerogative & Peculiar Courts of Winchester with other Prob Docs: *Littleton - Enrolled Peculiar Wills 1630 & 1639 & Separate Peculiar Wills 1689-1735* [HA/G 62]

LITTON, THE COURT OF THE PECULIAR JURISDICTION OF THE PRECENTOR OF THE CATHEDRAL CHURCH AT WELLS IN THE PREBEND OF
Superior Court: Wells (Dean)
1661-1848 Wells Wills; vol 13: Indexes to Wells Registry Cals - Peculiar Courts: *Litton Wills, Admons & Tuit Bonds* (Mfc) [Apply to Staff]

LLANDAFF, THE CONSISTORY COURT OF THE BISHOP OF
Superior Court: Canterbury (PCC)
1504-1736 Llandaff Probate Registry - an index [Topo Docs Coll: Wales]
1575-1857 Consistory Court of Llandaff - Indexes of Wills; vol 1: 1575-1799; vol 2: 1799-1857 [Mf 880]
1753-1857 Mynegai i Ewyllysiau Llandaf/*Prob Index Llandaff 1753-1857 (index to wills, admon bonds & invents in the National Lib of Wales)*; vols 1 & 2 [WS/G 120-121]

LLANDAFF, THE ARCHDEACONRY OF
not a probate jurisdiction: see Llandaff (Consistory)

LONDON, THE CONSISTORY COURT OF THE BISHOP OF
including jurisdiction exercised by the Vicar General of London
Superior Court: Canterbury (PCC)
1313-1548 List of Wills & Admons in the Episcopal Reg Books of the See of London 1313-1548 [Apply to Staff]
1492-1547 London Consistory Court Wills 1492-1547 *(will & invent abst in Reg "Palmer" 1492 & 1514-1520 with abst of separate wills for 1508 & 1526-1547)* (London Rec Soc vol 3) [MX/PER]
1514-1559 Consistory Court of London *Will Book Abst*; vols 1: Reg "Palmer" 1514-1520; 2: Reg "Thirlby" 1540-1548; 3: Reg "Wymesley" 1548-1556 [Mf 773]; 4: Reg "Horn" 1549-1559 [Mf 773]
1514-1641 Consistory Court of London - Index to Regs of Wills 1541-1641 [Mf 773]
1534-1559 *Abst of* Wills in the Office of the Vicar-General of London (Misc Gen et Her 5th ser vol 7) [PER/MIS]

LONDON (ESSEX and HERTFORDSHIRE DIVISION), THE COURT OF THE COMMISSARY OF
ie the Court of the Commissary of the Bishop of London for the Parts of Essex & Herts
Superior Court: London (Consistory); *see also London (Commissary - London) until 1483*
1431-1660 Commissary Court of London for Essex & Herts - Cals of Wills 1431-1660 (vols 1-4) [Mf 760]
1441-1620 Wills at Chelmsford *including the Commissary Court of London (Essex & Herts Jurisdiction) from*

1441; Index to Wills now preserved in the Essex RO at Chelmsford; vol 1: 1400-1619 (BRS vol 78) [BRS]

1558-1603 *Abst of* Essex Wills 1558-1603; pt 2: Wills proved in the Bishop of London's Commissary Court; vol 8: 1558-1569 (*original & registered wills*) (Essex RO Pub no 124); vol 9: 1569-1578 (*original wills*) (Essex RO Pub no 127); vol 10: 1578-1588 (Essex RO Pub no 129) [*all* ES/PER]; *vols 11-12: 1589-1603 on order*

1620-1720 Wills at Chelmsford *including the Commissary Court of London (Essex & Herts Jurisdiction)*; Index to Wills now preserved in the Essex RO at Chelmsford; vol 2: 1620-1720 (BRS vol 79) [BRS]

1661-1858 Commissary Court of London for Essex & Herts - Cals of Wills (vols 6-8) 1660-1783; Cals of Wills (vols 9-12) 1697-1858 (*Admons from 1699*) [Mf 761-762]

1721-1858 Wills at Chelmsford *including the Commissary Court of London (Essex & Herts Jurisdiction)*; Index to Wills now preserved in the Essex RO at Chelmsford; vol 3: 1721-1858 (BRS vol 84) [BRS]

LONDON (LONDON DIVISION), THE COURT OF THE COMMISSARY OF

ie the Court of the Commissary of the Bishop of London for the Parts of London, Middlesex & Essex

Superior Court: London (Consistory)

1374-1603 Commissary Court of London (London Div) - Cal of Wills, Prob & Admon Acts; vols 35: 1374-1449, 36: 1450-1539 & 37: 1539-1603 [Mf 765]

1374-1570 Index to Testmtry Recs in the Commissary Court of London (London Div) now preserved in the Guildhall Lib; vols 1: 1374-1488 & 2: 1489-1570 (BRS vols 82 & 86) [*both* BRS or, *as* HMC JP nos 12-13, MX/G 243-244]

15-16 C Index of Wills; an arbitrary coll of 15th & 16th C wills (*including some from London Commissary Court*) (*Soper*) [WILLS/GEN]

1545-1562 Commissary Court of London (London Div) - Cal of Original Wills & Prob Acts; vol 38A: 1545-1562 [Mf 767]

1571-1625 Index to Testmtry Recs in the Commissary Court of London (London Div) now preserved in the Guildhall Lib; vol 3: 1571-1625 (BRS vol 97) [BRS]

1577-1585 Commissary Court of London (London Div) - Cal of Prob Acts & Unregistered Wills; vol 38B: 1577-1585 [Mf 767]

1558-1603 Elizabethan Wills of SW Essex (*abst from the Commissary Court (London Div)*) [ES/G 63]

1585-1638 Commissary Court of London (London Div) - Cal of Admon & Prob Acts; vol 1: 1585-1638 [Mf 768]

1603-1621 Commissary Court of London (London Div) - Cal of Wills, Prob & Admon Acts; vols 38: 1603-1607 & 39: 1607-1611; vol 40: Cal of Wills 1611-1621; vol 41: Cal of Admons 1612-1621 [Mf 766]

1611-1693 *Americans in* London Commissary Court Recs (*prob abst*) (Nat Geneal Soc Qtrly vol 76) [US/PER]

1622-1629 Commissary Court of London (London Div) - Cal of Wills, Prob & Admon Acts; vols 42: 1622-1625 & 43: 1626-1629 [Mf 766]

1626-1700 Index to Testmtry Recs in the Commissary Court of London (London Div) now preserved in the Guildhall Lib; vol 4: 1626-1649, 1661-1700 (A-G) (BRS vol 102) [BRS]

1639-1665 Commissary Court of London (London Div) - Cal of Wills, Prob & Admon Acts; vols 2: Act Book for Probs & Admons 1639-1647 & 3: Act Book for Probs & Admons 1647-1665 [Mf 768]

1662-1679 Commissary Court of London (London Div) - Cal of Wills, Prob & Admon Acts; vols 4: 1662-1669; 5: 1670-1674 & 6: 1675-1679 [Mf 768-769]

1681-1685 Commissary Court of London (London Div) - Cal of Wills, Prob & Admon Acts; vol 8: Act Book for Probs & Admons 1681-1685 [Mf 769]

1685-1858 Commissary Court of London (London Div) - Cal of Prob & Admon Acts; vols 9: 1685-1687, 10: 1688-1690, 11: 1691-1693 &

12: 1694-1696; 13: 1697-1700, 14: 1701-1704, 15: 1705-1710, 16: 1711-1716, 17: 1717-1719, 18: 1720-1722, 19: 1723-1727, 20: 1728-1730 & 21: 1731-1737; 22: 1738-1742, 23: 1743-1746, 24: 1747-1750, 25: 1750-1756, 26: 1757-1771, 27: 1772-1790, 28: 1791-1799 & 29: 1800-1805; 30: 1805-1807, 31: 1806-1811, 32: 1812-1820, 33: 1821-1840; & 34: 1841-1858 [Mf 769-772]

1792-1794 Table of *Commissary Court* Wills in Treasury Miscellanea, Various (PRO Class T 64) *In* "List of Wills, Admons, etc in the PRO, London, England from 12-19th C" [WILLS/GEN]

LONDON (LONDON DIVISION), THE COURT OF THE ARCHDEACON OF

"(London Division)" is usually omitted
Superior Court: London (Consistory)
1368-1662 Index to Testmtry Recs in the Archdeaconry Court of London & now preserved in the Guildhall Lib; vol 1: 1363-1649 (*wills & admons*) (BRS vol 89) [BRS]

1400-1415 *Abst of* Ten English wills from the Archdeaconry of London 1400-1415 (the first wills in the English tongue) (Ancestor vol 5) [PER/ANC]

1549-1560 *Abst of* Wills & *Admons* - Archdeaconry of London 1549-60 (*Pescod MSS*) [MX/G 267]

1661-1700 Index to Testmtry Recs in the Archdeaconry Court of London & now preserved in the Guildhall Lib; vol 2: 1661-1700 (*wills, admons & invents*) & Index of Testmtry Recs of the Deanery of the Arches & now preserved in the Lambeth Court Lib 1620-1845 (BRS vol 98) [BRS]

1700-1807 Index of Wills proved in the Archdeaconry Court of London 1700-1807 [MX/G 274]

LONDON (MIDDLESEX DIVISION), THE COURT OF THE ARCHDEACON OF *see* Middlesex (Archdeaconry - Middx)

LONDON, THE COURT OF THE DEAN and CHAPTER OF ST PAUL'S CATHEDRAL CHURCH AT

Superior Court: London (Consistory)
1226-1552 Extr from Wills *In* "HMC Rep on the MSS of the Dean & Chapter of St Paul's" (appx to "9th HMC Rep") [SP/HMC]

1535-1857 Cals of the Peculiar Court of the Dean & Chapter of St Paul's; vols 1: Index to Wills 1535-1672, 2: Cal of Prob & Admon Acts 1646-1665 & Caveats 1647-1665, 3: Cal of Prob & Admon Acts 1665-1672 & Caveats 1665-1674, 4-6: Cals of Prob & Admon Acts 1672-1694; vols 6-10: 1694-1857 [Mf 763-764]

LONDON, THE COURT OF THE VICAR GENERAL OF *see* London (Consistory)

LONDON, THE COURT OF THE LORD MAYOR OF THE CITY OF

1641-1736 Lord Mayor's Court of London Depositions relating to Americans 1641-1736 (*with* PCC testmtry cases) [US/G 76]

LONDON, THE COURT OF HUSTING IN THE CITY OF *see* Husting

LONDON, THE ORPHAN'S COURT OF THE CITY OF

1541 1541 Great Orphans' Book (London Rec Soc vol 22) [MX/PER]

LONDON, THE PRINCIPAL PROBATE REGISTRY AT SOMERSET HOUSE IN

1858-1930 Indexes to Wills & Admons 1858-1930 (Mf) [Lower Library: Somerset House Prob Index cabinet]; *series in progress & on order*

LONGDON, THE COURT OF THE PREBEND OF

Superior Court: Lichfield (Dean & Chapter)
1529-1652 Cal of Wills & Admons registered in the various Peculiar Courts now preserved at the Lichfield Registry 1529-1652 (BRS vol 7) [BRS]

1685-1858 Cal of Wills & Admons of Peculiar Jurisdictions in the Diocese of Lichfield; vols 1 & 2 *including*: Prebendal Court of Longdon 1685-1858 [Mf 801]

LONGDON-UPON-TERN, THE COURT OF THE MANOR OF

1777-1838 Cal of Salop Wills & Admons

(with invents) deposited in Shrewsbury District Probate Registry *including: Manor of Longdon-upon-Terne* (supps to Trans Salop Archl & Nat Hist Soc 4th ser vols 12 *now 45* & 46) [Mf 800 or SH/PER]

LONGSTOW or STOW LONGA, THE COURT OF THE PREBEND OF
Superior Courts: Lincoln (Dean & Chapter) until 1834; Lincoln (Consistory) from 1834; *see also Huntingdon (Archdeaconry)*
1736-1744 Lincoln Wills; vol 4: Cal of Wills & Admons at Lincoln; Archdeaconry of Stow, Peculiar Courts & Misc Courts - *including wills proved in the Court of the Prebend of Long Stow or Stow Longa* (BRS vol 57) [BRS]

LONSDALE, THE DEANERY OF *see Richmond (Western Deaneries)*

LOUTH, THE COURT OF THE PREBEND OF
Superior Courts: Lincoln (Dean & Chapter) until 1834; Lincoln (Consistory) from 1834
1612-1879 Lincoln Wills; vol 4: Cal of Wills & Admons at Lincoln; Archdeaconry of Stow, Peculiar Courts & Misc Courts - *including the Court of the Prebend of Louth (with invents)* (BRS vol 57) [BRS]; Wills & Admons etc: listings taken from cals of the old Diocese of York & the Diocese of Lincoln (with certain additions from Durham) (*index BUR-WRI*) (Fam Hist vols 2 & 3) [PER/FAM]; Index to Lincoln Peculiar Courts: Prebendal Court of Louth Wills & Admons [Mf 759]
1659-1857 *Indexes of* Wills & Admons in the Peculiar Courts at Lincoln: *Louth Prebendal Court* (Northern Genealogist vols 1 & 2) [PER/NOR]

LYDFORD, THE COURT OF THE PECULIAR JURISDICTION OF WEST
Superior Court: Wells (Episcopal Consistory)
1669-1857 Wells Wills; vol 13: Indexes to Wells Registry Cals - Peculiar Courts: *W Lydford Wills, Admons & Tuit Bonds* (Mfc) [Apply to Staff]

LYME REGIS and HALSTOCK, THE COURT OF THE PREBEND OF
Superior Court: Sarum (Dean)
1664-1799 Cal of Wills & Admons relating to Dorset in the Courts of Sarum & elsewhere (*including Lyme Regis with Halstock, Leigh & Colway*) (BRS vol 53) [BRS]
1664-1857 Peculiar & Prebendal Courts of the Diocese of Sarum - Indexes to Wills & Admons 1462-1810: *Prebendal Court of Lyme Regis & Halstock (with invents)* [Mf 836]
1800-1858 Sarum Courts, Deanery & Archdeaconry of Wiltshire; vol "A": Index for Wills & *Admons* 1800-1858 with names beginning A-B only [Mf 838]

LYME REGIS, THE COURT OF THE MAYOR OF THE BOROUGH OF
1544 Cal of Wills & Admons relating to Dorset in the Courts of Sarum; *from Borough of Lyme Regis recs* (BRS vol 53) [BRS]

LYNEALL, THE COURT OF THE MANOR OF
see also Ellesmere
1738-1801 Cal of Salop Wills & Admons *(with invents)* deposited in Shrewsbury District Probate Registry *including: Manor of Lyneall* (supps to Trans Salop Archl & Nat Hist Soc 4th ser vols 12 *now 45* & 46) [Mf 800 or SH/PER]

MALDON, THE COURT OF THE COMMISSARY OF THE ROYAL COLLEGIATE CHURCH OF ST MARTIN LE GRAND FOR THE PREBEND OF ST MARY'S PARISH IN *see Westminster (Abbot/Dean & Chapter)*

MALLING, THE COURT OF THE PECULIAR JURISDICTION OF THE ARCHBISHOP OF CANTERBURY IN THE DEANERY OF SOUTH
Superior Court: Canterbury (PCC); *see also Lambeth Palace; Pagham & Tarring; Lewes (Archdeaconry)*
1559-1575 Cal of Admons 1555-1800 granted in the Consistory Court of the Bishop of Chichester with cal of Wills & Admons in the Peculiar Court of the Archbishop *in Pagham & Tarring with some S Malling Wills: 1559-1569 & 1574-*

1575 & with cal of Wills &
Admons 1577-1800 for the
Peculiar Court of the Dean of
Chichester (BRS vol 64) [BRS]

1560-1567 Index to some Wills proved &
Admons granted in the peculiar
of the Deanery of S Malling
(reprinted from Sussex Archl
Colls vol 50) *In* "Sussex tracts vol
1" [SX/G 2]; *also* an Index to 216
other Sussex Wills (Sussex Archl
Colls vol 50) [SX/G 51 or
SX/PER]

1588-1600 Cals of Wills & Admons in the
Archdeaconry Court of Lewes in
the Bishopric of Chichester
together with those in the
Archbishop of Canterbury's
Peculiar Jurisdiction of S Malling
(*wills only*) & the Peculiar of the
Deanery of Battle comprising
together the whole of the Eastern
division of the County of Sussex
& the parish of Edburton in W
Sussex, from the earliest extant
instruments in the reign of Henry
VIII to the Commonwealth (BRS
vol 24) [BRS]

**MAN, THE HIGH COURT OF JUSTICE OF
THE ISLE OF**
Superior Court: The Privy Council
1885-1949 Cals of Isle of Man Wills &
Admons 1885-1949 (*in 3 pts*) [Mf
775]
Note: *this is a continuation from
the series beginning in 1659: see
Man (Consistory)*

**MAN, THE CONSISTORY COURT OF THE
BISHOP OF SODOR and**
Superior Courts: York (PCY) *until 1858;* Man
*(High Court) from 1858; see also Man
(Archdeaconry)*
1659-1884 Episcopal Consistory Court of the
Isle of Man - Cals of Wills 1659-
*1664, 1668-1680, 1697-1809 (in
6 pts*); Cal of Wills & Admons
1800-1884 [Mf 775]
Note: *this series continues to
1949: see Man (High Court)*
1713-1716 Consistory Court Book of Wills
1713-1716 *with Invents & Prob
Accounts* [Mf 776]

**MAN, THE COURT OF THE ARCHDEACON
OF THE ISLE OF**
Superior Court: Man (Consistory)
1631-1884 Archidiaconal Court of the Isle of
Man - Cals of Wills 1631-1800 (*in
2 pts*); Cal of Wills & Admons
1800-1884 [Mf 774]

MANGERTON *see Netherbury*

**MANSFIELD, THE COURT OF THE MANOR
OF**
1640-1695 *Abst in* cal of Wills, Admons (&
other papers) of the Peculiar
Court of Mansfield, County Notts
1640-1695 [NT/G 25]
1640-1858 Manorial Court of Mansfield -
Index of Wills, *Admons, Invents,
Bonds & Trust Papers* 1640-1858
[Mf 796]

**MAPPLETON, THE COURT OF THE
PECULIAR JURISDICTION OF THE
ARCHDEACON OF THE EAST RIDING OR
YORKSHIRE IN**
Superior Court: York (Chancery)
1572-1778 York Registry; Names of
Peculiars wherein separate lists
are kept of the wills etc proved
therein *including Mappleton* [Mf
879]

MARKET WEIGHTON *see Weighton*

**MARSDEN, THE COURT OF THE MANOR
OF**
1654-1855 *Indexes to* Wills &c in the
Peculiar Courts at Wakefield:
Marsden Manor Court (Northern
Genealogist vol 2) [PER/NOR]
1655-1855 Manorial Court of Marsden -
Index of Wills & Admons 1655-
1855 [Mf 878]

**MASHAM, THE COURT OF THE PECULIAR
JURISDICTION OF**
*a Prebendal Court in the Diocese of York until
1546 when the jurisdiction was assumed by
Trinity College, Cambridge*
Superior Courts: York (Dean & Chapter); *see
also Cambridge (University)*
1438-1756 Peculiar Court of Masham:
Collation of the Indexes at
Somerset House & at York
Probate Registry from the
Commencement down to 1709
(*A-ROW*) (Northern Genealogist
vols 4-8) [PER/NOR]

1548-1858 Masham Peculier (*sic*) Court - An Indexed Cal of Wills & Admons *with Bonds, Tuits & Invents*; pts 1: The Cal & 2: The Indexes [YK/L 198]

1572-1858 Peculiar Court of Masham - Cals of Wills *from 1572* & of Admons *from 1614* to 1858 (*in 4 pts*) [Mf 862]

1609-1707 York Registry; Cal of Wills & Admons - Separate Peculiars & Dean & Chapter's General Peculiars: *'Massam' 1609-1707*; York Registry; Names of Peculiars wherein separate lists are kept of the wills etc proved therein *including Masham 1609-1707* [both Mf 879]

1745-1858 Wills & Admons etc: listings taken from cals of the old Diocese of York & the Diocese of Lincoln (with certain additions from Durham) (*index BUR-WRI*) (Fam Hist vols 2 & 3) [PER/FAM]

MEDSTEAD *see Alresford*

MEON WITH FROXFIELD and STEEP, THE TESTAMENTARY JURISDICTION OF THE PARISH OF EAST
Superior Court: Winchester (Archdeaconry)
1569-1845 Cal of Hants Wills proved in the Prerogative & Peculiar Courts of Winchester with other Prob Docs: *E Meon - Separate Peculiar Wills* [HA/G 62]

1625-1637 Diocese of Winchester; Index to Registered Copies of Wills in the charge of the Diocesan Registrar (*Peculiar of E Meon with Froxfield & Steed*); Wills, Admons & Invents with the Winchester Diocesan Recs; *index to Registered Wills in the Peculiar Court of Alverstoke* [HA/G 67 & 40]

MEON WITH PRIVETT, THE TESTAMENTARY JURISDICTION OF THE PARISH OF WEST
Superior Court: Winchester (Archdeaconry)
1571-1839 Cal of Hants Wills proved in the Prerogative & Peculiar Courts of Winchester with other Prob Docs: *W Meon including Privett - Separate Peculiar Wills* [HA/G 62]

1625-1637 Diocese of Winchester; Index to Registered Copies of Wills in the charge of the Diocesan Registrar (*Peculiar of W Meon*); Wills, Admons & Invents with the Winchester Diocesan Recs; *index to Registered Wills in the Peculiar Court of Alverstoke* [HA/G 67 & 40]

MEONSTOKE and SOBERTON, THE COURT OF THE PECULIAR JURISDICTION OF
Superior Court: Winchester (Archdeaconry)
1562-1839 Cal of Hants Wills proved in the PCC & in the Peculiar Courts of Winchester with other Prob Docs: *Meonstoke including Soberton - Separate Peculiar Wills* [HA/G 62]

MEREVALE, THE COURT OF THE PECULIAR JURISDICTION IN THE MANOR OF
Superior Court: Lichfield (Consistory)
1529-1652 Cal of Wills & Admons registered in the various Peculiar Courts now preserved at the Lichfield Registry 1529-1652 (BRS vol 7) [BRS]

1770-1858 Cal of Wills & Admons of Peculiar Jurisdictions in the Diocese of Lichfield; vols 1 & 2 *including*: Peculiar & Manorial Court of Merevale 1770-1858 [Mf 801]

MEXBOROUGH and RAVENFIELD, THE COURT OF THE PECULIAR JURISDICTION OF THE ARCHDEACON OF YORK OR THE WEST RIDING OF YORKSHIRE IN
Superior Court: York (Chancery)
1662-1839 York Registry; Cal of Wills & Admons - Separate Peculiars & Dean & Chapter's General Peculiars: *Archdeaconry of York ('Mexbrough & Ranfield') 1662-1740 & 1760-1839*; York Registry; Names of Peculiars wherein separate lists are kept of the wills etc proved therein *including Mexborough with Ravenfield 1662-1740 & 1760 to the present time* [both Mf 879]

MICHELMERSH, THE TESTAMENTARY JURISDICTION OF THE PARISH OF
Superior Court: Winchester (Archdeaconry)
1593-1694 Cal of Hants Wills proved in the

Prerogative & Peculiar Courts of
Winchester with other Prob Docs:
*Michelmersh - Separate Peculiar
Wills* [HA/G 62]

MIDDLEHAM, THE COURT OF THE ROYAL PECULIAR JURISDICTION OF THE DEAN OF THE COLLEGIATE CHURCH OF
Superior Court: Delegates (High Court); *see
also York (Dean & Chapter); Richmond
(Eastern Deaneries)*
1637-1854 York Registry; Middleham Act
Book 1637-1642 [Mf 879]
1722-1854 York Registry; Cal of Wills &
Admons: *Middleham* [Mf 879]
1789-1846 York Registry; Middleham
Deanery Surrogate Deeds [Mf
879]

MIDDLESEX (ESSEX and HERTFORDSHIRE DIVISION), THE COURT OF THE ARCHDEACON OF
*also called the "Court of the Archdeacon of
Middlesex (Essex Division)"*
Superior Court: London (Consistory): *see
also London (Commissary - Essex & Herts)*
1554-1619 Wills at Chelmsford *including the
Archdeaconry Court of Middlesex
(Essex & Herts Jurisdiction) from
1554*; Index to Wills now
preserved in the Essex RO at
Chelmsford; vol 1: 1400-1619
(BRS vol 78) [BRS]
1554-1721 Archdeaconry Court of Middlesex
(Essex & Herts Div); Cal of
Registered Wills, Acts &
Assignations 1554-1721 (vol 1)
[Mf 917]
1558-1603 *Abst of* Essex Wills 1558-1603;
pt 1: Wills proved in the
Archdeaconry of Essex, the
Archdeaconry of Colchester &
the Archdeaconry of Middlesex
(Essex Div); vol 1: 1558-1565
(Nat Geneal Soc Spec Pub no
51); vol 2: 1565-1571 (NEHG Soc
Spec Pub); vol 3: 1571-1577
(*with additions for 1559-1571*)
(NEHG Soc *Spec Pub*); vol 4:
1577-1584 (*with unregistered
wills 1581-1588*) (Essex RO Pub
no 96); vol 5: 1583-1592 (Essex
RO Pub no 101); vol 6: 1591-
1597 (Essex RO Pub no 114); vol
7: 1597-1603 (Essex RO Pub no
107) [*all* ES/PER]
1564-1574 Abst of Herts Wills in Reg
"Raymond" *in the Archdeaconry*

*Court of Middlesex (Essex &
Herts Div)* (Herts Genealogist &
Antiquary vol 1) [Mf 2587 or
HT/PER]
1582-1590 Abst of Herts Wills in Reg
"Barker" *in the Archdeaconry
Court of Middlesex (Essex &
Herts Div)* (Herts Genealogist &
Antiquary vol 2) [HT/PER]
1617-1720 Archdeaconry Court of Middlesex
(Essex & Herts Div); Cal of
Original Wills 1617-1720 (vol 2)
[Mf 917]
1620-1720 Wills at Chelmsford *including the
Archdeaconry Court of Middlesex
(Essex & Herts Jurisdiction)*;
Index to Wills now preserved in
the Essex RO at Chelmsford; vol
2: 1620-1720 (BRS vol 79) [BRS]
1708-1857 Archdeaconry Court of Middlesex
(Essex & Herts Div); Cal of Wills
& Admons 1708-1857 (vol 3) [Mf
917]
1721-1858 Wills at Chelmsford *including the
Archdeaconry Court of Middlesex
(Essex & Herts Jurisdiction)*;
Index to Wills now preserved in
the Essex RO at Chelmsford; vol
3: 1721-1858 (BRS vol 84) [BRS]

MIDDLESEX (MIDDLESEX DIVISION), THE COURT OF THE ARCHDEACON OF
*including the Court of the Archdeaconry of
London (Middlesex Division) & sometimes
called "(London Division)"*
Superior Court: London (Consistory): *see
also London (Archdeaconry - London)*
1608-1810 Archdeaconry Court of Middlesex
(Middx Div) - Cal of Wills &
Admons 1608-1810 [Mf 917]

MILTON ABBAS, THE COURT OF THE ROYAL PECULIAR JURISDICTION OF
Superior Court: Delegates (High Court); *see
also Canterbury (PCC); Dorset
(Archdeaconry)*
1675-1811 Cal of Wills & Admons relating to
the County of Dorset, proved in
the Consistory Court (Dorset Div)
of the late Diocese of Bristol
1681-1792, in the Archdeaconry
Court of Dorset 1568-1792 & in
the several peculiars 1660-1799 -
with wills, invents & admons in
the Court of the Royal Peculiar of
Milton Abbas together with
Whitcombe, Woolland &
Holwarth previous to 1792 (BRS

vol 22) [BRS]

MONKS RISBOROUGH, THE COURT OF THE PECULIAR JURISDICTION OF THE ARCHBISHOP OF CANTERBURY IN THE DEANERY OF
including the Peculiar Jurisdiction of Halton (Bucks) & the Prebend of Newington (Oxon)
Superior Court: Canterbury (PCC)*; see also Aylesbury; Banbury; Lambeth Palace*
1550-1856 *Index to* Berks, Bucks & Oxon Peculiars - Wills & Admons 1550-1858 *(also Invents & Bonds): Peculiar Court Monks Risborough* [Mf 913]

MORAY, THE COMMISSARIOT OF
Superior Court: Court of Session*; see also Edinburgh (Commissariot)*
1684-1800 Commissariot Rec of Moray; Reg of Testmts 1684-1800 (Scottish Rec Soc vol 20) [SC/PER]
1801-1823 *Moray Regs of Testmts & Invents In* "Index to Regs of Testmts for various Commissariots 1801-1823" [Mf 2910]

MORESTEAD, THE TESTAMENTARY JURISDICTION OF THE PARISH OF
Superior Court: Winchester (Archdeaconry)
1637-1696 Cal of Hants Wills proved in the Prerogative & Peculiar Courts of Winchester with other Prob Docs: *Morestead - Separate Peculiar Wills* [HA/G 62]

MORETON-UPON-LUGG, THE COURT OF THE PREBEND OF
also called Moreton Magna
Superior Court: Hereford (Dean)
1668-1854 Moreton-upon-Lugg in the County of Hereford & Peculiar of the Prebendary of Moreton-upon-Lugg - *Wills* 20th Oct 1668-16th May 1854: Index of Wills & Admons together with Copies of Registered Wills [Mf 2591]

MOTCOMBE *see Gillingham*

MOURNE *see Newry*

NASSINGTON, THE COURT OF THE PREBEND OF
Superior Courts: Lincoln (Dean & Chapter) until 1834; Lincoln (Consistory) from 1834*; see also Huntingdon (Archdeaconry)*
1702-1744 Lincoln Wills; vol 4: Cal of Wills &

Admons at Lincoln; Archdeaconry of Stow, Peculiar Courts & Misc Courts - *including the Court of the Prebend of Nassington (with invents)* (BRS vol 57) [BRS]

NETHERAVON, THE COURT OF THE PREBEND OF
Superior Court: Sarum (Dean)
1595-1795 Peculiar & Prebendal Courts of the Diocese of Sarum - Indexes to Wills & Admons 1462-1810*: Prebendal Court of Netheravon (with invents)* [Mf 836]
1800-1854 Wilts Wills Beneficiaries Index 1800-1858: Name Abst; vol 5: Durnford 1800-1857, Fordington & Writhlington 1800-1855, Hurstbourne & Burbage 1800-1856, Netheravon 1800-1854 (Peculiar Court docs 508-632) [WL/G 67]
1800-1858 Sarum Courts, Deanery & Archdeaconry of Wiltshire; vol "A": Index for Wills & *Admons* 1800-1858 with names beginning A-B only [Mf 838]

NETHERBURY IN ECCLESIA, THE COURT OF THE PREBEND OF
Superior Court: Sarum (Dean)
1608-1799 Peculiar & Prebendal Courts of the Diocese of Sarum - Indexes to Wills & Admons 1462-1810*: Prebendal Court of Netherbury in Ecclesia (with invents)* [Mf 836]; Cal of Wills & Admons relating to Dorset in the Courts of Sarum & elsewhere *(including Netherbury in Ecclesia with Beaminster & Mangerton)* (BRS vol 53) [BRS]
1800-1858 Sarum Courts, Deanery & Archdeaconry of Wiltshire; vol "A": Index for Wills & *Admons* 1800-1858 with names beginning A-B only [Mf 838]

NEWBALD, THE COURT OF THE PREBEND OF NORTH
Superior Courts: York (Chancery); York (Dean & Chapter)
1633-1734 York Registry; Cal of Wills & Admons - Separate Peculiars & Dean & Chapter's General Peculiars*: N Newbald*; York Registry; Names of Peculiars wherein separate lists are kept of

the wills etc proved therein
including N Newbald [both Mf
879]

NEWCASTLE-UNDER-LYME, THE COURT OF THE MANOR OF
1661-1686 Cal of the Wills recorded in the Manor Rolls of Newcastle-under-Lyme (Genealogists' Ref J vol 1 pts 2-3) [PER/GEN]

NEW COLLEGE AT OXFORD, THE PECULIAR JURISDICTIONS OF THE MASTER, FELLOWS and SCHOLARS OF
see Hornchurch; Sokens; Writtle; see also Oxford (University)

NEWINGTON (Oxon), THE COURT OF THE PREBEND OF *see Monks Risborough*

NEWPORT, THE COURT OF THE PECULIAR JURISDICTION OF THE BISHOP OF LONDON IN
prior to the Reformation this was the Court of the Commissary of the Royal Collegiate Church of St Martin le Grand for the Prebend of Newport - see Westminster (Abbot/Dean & Chapter) until 1540 & London (Consistory) from 1540

NEWRY and MOURNE, THE COURT OF THE PECULIAR JURISDICTION OF
Superior Court: Dromore (Consistory)
1727-1858 *Phillimore's* Indexes to Irish Wills; vol 4: Cal of Wills in the Diocese of Dromore & the Exempt Jurisdiction of Newry & Mourne [IR/G 87]
1811-1857 *Index to* Admons from the Peculiar of Newry & Mourne (Irish Ancestor vol 1) [IR/PER]

NEWTON *see Burghclere*

NORFOLK, THE COURTS OF THE ARCHDEACONRY
ie the Court of the Commissary of the Bishop of Norwich for the Archdeaconry of Norfolk & the Court of the Archdeacon of Norfolk
Superior Court: Norwich (Consistory)
1453-1542 Index of Wills proved in the Norfolk Archdeaconry Court; vol 1: 1453-1542 (Norfolk Genealogy vol 3) [NF/PER]
1460-1606 Archdeaconry Court of Norfolk - Cal of Wills; vol 1: 1460-1606 [Mf 782]
1542-1604 Index of Wills proved in the

Norfolk Archdeaconry Court; vols 2: 1542-1560 & 3: 1560, *1603-1604* (Norfolk Genealogy vols 5 & 10) [*both* NF/PER]
1607-1784 Archdeaconry Court of Norfolk - Cal of Wills; vols 2: 1607-1629 & 3: 1630-1784; 4: 1630-1784 [Mf 782-783]
1671-1680 Archdeaconry Court of Norfolk - Court Accounts Book 1671-1680 [Mf 784]
1691-1794 Archdeaconry Court of Norfolk - Cal of Wills; *supp to* vol 5: *1691-1794* [Mf 784]
1785-1857 Archdeaconry Court of Norfolk - Cal of Wills; vol 5: 1785-1857 [Mf 784]
1838-1858 Index to Norfolk (England) Wills 1838-1858 (*nominal index to Salt Lake City Lib mf of Archdeaconry of Norfolk Wills*) [Apply to Staff]

NORMANTON *see Altofts*

NORTHAMPTON, THE COURT OF THE ARCHDEACON OF
Superior Courts: Lincoln (Consistory) until 1541; Peterborough (Consistory) from 1541
1467-1506 Archdeaconry Court of Northampton; Regular Copy Wills in the District Probate Court of Birmingham 1467-1506 *with Cal* [Mf 789]
1467-1510 Prob Recs *of the* Archdeaconry of Northampton: the first surviving Regs of Wills 1467-1510; pt 1: *Index to* Early Northants Wills [Apply to Staff]
16-19 C Oldaker Coll of Wills*: see the note on this coll in the General Collections of Wills, Indexes, etc part of the NATIONAL section*
1510-1652 Cal of Wills relating to the counties of Northampton & Rutland 1510-1652 (BRS vol 1) [BRS or Mf 790]
1510-1670 Cal of Wills in the Archdeaconry of Northampton & the Consistory Court of Peterborough prefaced by an index of courts & a list of the several registers of the Court of Probate; vol 1: 1510-1670 [Mf 793 or Mf 912]
1510-1752 Geneal Recs vol containing extr from Wills in the Northampton Registry (*Norman Coll*) [Mf 920]
1545-1676 Admons of the Archdeaconry of Northampton (*1545-1546, 1552,*

1638, 1641 & 1660-1676)
(*extracted from* Misc Gen et Her
5th ser vols 9-10) [NH/G 38]

1603-1622 Archdeaconry Court of
Northampton; Regular Copy Wills
in the District Probate Court of
Birmingham 1603-1622 [Mf 789]

1607-1719 Index to Northampton &
Consistory Wills; vols 1: Books A-
N, 1607-1672 (*in 3 pts*) & 2:
Books O-Z, 1673-1719 [Mf 791]

1608-1723 Archdeaconry Court of
Northampton - Cal of Wills 1608-
1723 [Mf 792]

1660-1800 Cal of Admon *Acts* (*with Invents
List 1660-1710*) granted in the
Archdeaconry of Northampton &
now preserved in the District
Probate Registry at Northampton;
vols 1: 1677-1710 & 2: 1711-
1800 (BRS vol 70 & 92) [*both*
BRS]

1676-1858 Cals of Wills & Admons in the
Archdeaconry of Northampton &
the Consistory Court of
Peterborough prefaced by an
index of courts & a list of the
several registers of the Court of
Probate; vols 2: 1676-1704, 3:
1704-1724, 4: 1705-1751 & 5:
1752-1858 [Mf 793 or Mf 912]

**NORTON or NORTON EPISCOPI, THE
COURT OF THE PREBEND OF BISHOP** *see
Bishop Norton*

**NORWICH, THE CONSISTORY COURT OF
THE BISHOP OF**
*including the Peculiar Jurisdiction of the
Bishop of Norwich in Thorpe-next-Norwich*
Superior Court: Canterbury (PCC)

1370-1383 Early Norfolk Wills from the
Norwich Registry (*notes on
interesting wills in Reg "Heydon"*)
(Norfolk Antqn Miscellany vol 1 pt
2) [NF/PER]

1370-1550 Index of Wills proved in the
Consistory Court of Norwich &
now preserved in the District
Probate Registry at Norwich; vol
1: 1370-1550 (BRS vol 69 or
Norfolk Recs Soc vol 16) [BRS or
NF/PER]

1371-1545 *Extr from* Old Wills now
preserved in the District Registry
of the Court of Probate of
Norwich (E Anglian vols 1, 2 & 4)
[NF/PER]

1416-1530 Consistory Court of Norwich - Cal
of Wills; vol 1: 1416-1530 [Mf
777]

1419-1530 Norwich Consistory Court
Depositions 1419-1512 & 1518-
1530 (*includes testmtry Causes
of Action*) (Norfolk Rec Soc vol
10) [NF/PER]

1500-1503 *List of* Wills proved in the
Diocese of Norwich *In* "8th HMC
Rep" [SP/HMC]

1535-1557 Consistory Court of Norwich - Cal
of Wills; vol 2: 1535-1557 [Mf
777]

1550-1603 Index of Wills proved in the
Consistory Court of Norwich &
now preserved in the District
Probate Registry at Norwich; vol
2: 1550-1603 (BRS vol 73 or
Norfolk Recs Soc vol 21) [BRS or
NF/PER]

1556-1691 Consistory Court of Norwich -
Cals of Wills; vols 3: 1556-1691
("second copy") & 4: 1556-1691
[Mf 777-778]

1564-1617 Consistory Court of Norwich -
Admon Acts Book 1564-1617 (*pt
of vol 8A*) [Mf 779]

1592-1625 Consistory Court of Norwich -
Cals of Wills; vol 5: 1592-1625
[Mf 778]

1604-1686 Index of Wills proved in the
Consistory Court of Norwich &
now preserved in the District
Probate Registry at Norwich; vol
3: 1604-1686 (Norfolk Recs Soc
vol 28) [NF/PER]

1626-1719 Consistory Court of Norwich -
Cals of Wills; vols 6: 1626-1649
& 7: 1650-1719 [Mf 778-779]

1660-1779 Consistory Court of Norwich -
Index of Wills; vol 8A: 1660-1779
[Mf 779]

1666-1699 Consistory Court of Norwich -
Admon Acts Book; vol 1: 1666-
1699; vol 2: 1673-1688 [Mf 781]

1673-1745 Consistory Court of Norwich -
Index of Unproved Wills (*pt of vol
8*) [Mf 779]

1687-1750 Index of Wills proved in the
Consistory Court of Norwich &
now preserved in the District
Probate Registry at Norwich; vol
4: 1687-1750 (Norfolk Recs Soc
vol 34) [NF/PER]

1700-1811 Consistory Court of Norwich - Cal
of Admons Granted; vol 3: 1700-
1811 [Mf 781]

1720-1763 Consistory Court of Norwich - Cal of Wills; vol 8: 1720-1763 [Mf 779]

1751-1818 Index of Wills proved in the Consistory Court of Norwich & now preserved in the District Probate Registry at Norwich; vol 5: 1751-1818 (Norfolk Recs Soc vol 38) [NF/PER]

1764-1820 Consistory Court of Norwich - Index of Wills; vol 9: 1764-1820 [Mf 780]

1811-1857 Consistory Court of Norwich - Cal of Admons Granted; vol 4: 1811-1857 [Mf 781]

1819-1857 Index of Wills proved in the Consistory Court of Norwich & now preserved in the District Probate Registry at Norwich; vol 6: 1819-1857 (Norfolk Recs Soc vol 47) [NF/PER]

1821-1858 Consistory Court of Norwich - Index of Wills; vol 10: 1821-1844; vol 11: 1845-1858 [Mf 780]

NORWICH, THE COURTS OF THE ARCHDEACONRY OF
ie the Court of the Commissary of the Bishop of Norwich for the Archdeaconry of Norwich & the Court of the Archdeacon of Norwich
Superior Court: Norwich (Consistory)

1469-1728 Archdeaconry Court of Norwich - Cal of Wills; vols 1: 1469-1584, 2: 1573-1604 & 3: 1660-1728 [Mf 785]

1700-1811 Archdeaconry Court of Norwich - Cal of Admons; vol 1: 1700-1811 [Mf 787]

1728-1811 Archdeaconry Court of Norwich - Cal of Wills; vol 4: 1728-1811 [Mf 786]

1812-1858 Archdeaconry Court of Norwich - Cal of Wills; vol 5: 1812-1858 [Mf 786]; Cal of Admons; vol 2: 1812-1858 [Mf 787]

NORWICH, THE COURT OF THE DEAN and CHAPTER OF
Superior Court: Norwich (Consistory)

1416-1857 Norfolk Peculiar Jurisdictions; *index of* wills & other prob recs: the Peculiar of the Dean & Chapter of Norwich 1416-1857; Prob Invents (*in the Dean & Chapter Archives*) 1688-*1694, 1717 & 1727*-1782; the Peculiar of Great Cressingham 1675-

1754; the Peculiar of Castle Rising 1624-1724 (Norfolk Genealogy vol 16) [NF/PER]

1600-1857 Peculiar Court of the Dean & Chapter of Norwich - Cal of Wills 1600-1857 [Mf 788]

NORWICH IN THORPE-NEXT-NORWICH, THE COURT OF THE PECULIAR JURISDICTION OF THE BISHOP OF *see Norwich (Consistory)*

NORWICH, THE COURT OF THE MAYOR OF THE CITY OF

1298-1508 Index of Wills proved in the Court of the City of Norwich & now preserved in the Norwich Enrolled Deeds in the Muniments Room of Norwich Castle 1298-1339, 1378-1405, 1413-1508 (BRS vol 69 or Norfolk Recs Soc vol 16) [BRS or NF/PER]

NOTTINGHAM, THE ARCHDEACONRY OF
although not a probate jurisdiction the Archdeacon's papers include wills; probate powers throughout the Archdeaconry were exercised by the Exchequer Court of the Archbishop of York (qv); see also Southwell

1712-1857 Copies of Unproved Wills in the Archdeaconry of Nottingham 1712-1857 [Mf 799]

OFFLEY and FLIXTON, THE COURT OF THE PREBEND OF HIGH
Superior Court: Lichfield (Dean & Chapter)

1529-1652 Cal of Wills & Admons registered in the various Peculiar Courts now preserved at the Lichfield Registry 1529-1652 (BRS vol 7) [BRS]

1706-1858 Cal of Wills & Admons of Peculiar Jurisdictions in the Diocese of Lichfield; vols 1 & 2 *including*: Prebendal Court of High Offley & Flixton 1706-1858 [Mf 801]

ORFORD, THE COURT OF THE MAYOR OF THE CORPORATION OF

1468-1614 *Extr from* Wills in the Recs of the dissolved Corp of Orford *In* "HMC Rep on Various Colls vol 4" [Apply to Staff]

ORKNEY and SHETLAND, THE COMMISSARIOT OF
Superior Court: Court of Session; *see also Edinburgh (Commissariot)*
1611-1688 Commissariot Rec of Orkney & Shetland; Reg of Testmts; pts 1: Orkney 1611-1684, 2: Shetland 1611-1649 *(with ts index)* & *3*: Orkney 1685-1688 *ts index in front of* the vol (Scottish Rec Soc vol 21) [SC/PER]
1573-1615 Orkney Testmts & Invents 1573-1615 *(abst, wills from 1613)* (Scottish Rec Soc new ser vol 6) [SC/PER]

ORKNEY SHERIFF'S COURT
Superior Court: Court of Session
1806-1831 Orkney Sheriff's Court: Index to Reg of Confirmations 1806-1823 & Index to Reg of Invents 1809-1831 [Mf 2909]

OSBALDWICK, THE COURT OF THE PREBEND OF
Superior Courts: York (Chancery); York (Dean & Chapter)
1631-1739 York Registry; Names of Peculiars wherein separate lists are kept of the wills etc proved therein *including Osbaldwick with Gate Helmsley 1631-1739*; York Registry; Cal of Wills & Admons - Separate Peculiars & Dean & Chapter's General Peculiars: *Osbaldwick 1631-1739 [both* Mf 879]

OSSORY, THE CONSISTORY COURT OF THE BISHOP OF
Superior Court: Armagh (PCA)
1536-1800 *Phillimore's* Indexes to Irish Wills; vol 1: Cal of Wills in the Dioceses of Ossory, Leighlin, Ferns & Kildare [IR/G 84]
1612-1843 Index to Irish Wills in the Carrigan MSS at St Kieran's College, Kilkenny *(wills collected for a history of the Diocese of Ossory)* (Irish Genealogist vol 4) [IR/PER]
1660-1804 Ossory & Leighlin Admons Intestate; Grants of admon of the goods of intestates in the Dioceses of Ossory & Leighlin from the Carrigan MSS (Irish Genealogist vol 4) [IR/PER]
1848-1858 Index to Admons Grant Book for 1848-1858 *In* appx 1A to "57th

Rep of Deputy Keeper of Public Recs in Ireland" [IR/K]

OTTERBOURNE *see Hursley*

OVERTON and TADLEY, THE TESTAMENTARY JURISDICTION OF THE PARISH OF
Superior Court: Winchester (Archdeaconry)
1562-1841 Cal of Hants Wills proved in the Prerogative & Peculiar Courts of Winchester with other Prob Docs: *Overton including Tadley - Separate Peculiar Wills* [HA/G 62]

OVINGTON, THE TESTAMENTARY JURISDICTION OF THE PARISH OF
Superior Court: Winchester (Archdeaconry)
1626-1721 Cal of Hants Wills proved in the Prerogative & Peculiar Courts of Winchester with other Prob Docs: *Ovington - Separate Peculiar Wills* [HA/G 62]

OWSLEBURY *see Twyford*

OXFORD, THE CONSISTORY COURT OF THE BISHOP OF
Superior Court: Canterbury (PCC); *see also Oxford (Archdeaconry)*
1516-1732 Oxford Archdeaconry & Consistory Courts - *Combined* Index to Wills, *Invents* & Admon *Bond*s: 1516-1732 [Mf 914]; Prob Recs *(wills, admons & invents)* of the Courts of the Bishop & Archdeacon of Oxford 1516-1732; vols 1 & 2 (BRS vols 93 & 94) [*both* BRS]
1542-1586 Testmtry Abst *In* "Oxford Church Courts Depositions - 1542-1550; 1570-1574; 1581-1586" [*all* OX/G 38]; *3 pts to date: series in progress & on order*
1700-1858 Oxford Consistory Court - Cal of Wills & Admons: 1700-1858 [Mf 915]

OXFORD, THE COURT OF THE ARCHDEACON OF
Superior Courts: Lincoln (Consistory) until 1541; Oxford (Consistory) from 1542
1516-1732 Oxford Archdeaconry & Consistory Courts - *Combined* Index to Wills, *Invents* & Admon *Bond*s: 1516-1732 [Mf 914]; Prob Recs *(wills, admons & invents)* of

the Courts of the Bishop & Archdeacon of Oxford 1516-1732; vols 1 & 2 (BRS vol 93 & 94) [*both* BRS]

1542-1586 Testmtry Abst *In* "Oxford Church Courts Depositions - 1542-1550; 1570-1574; 1581-1586"[*all* OX/G 38]; *3 pts to date: series in progress & on order*

1732-1745 Oxford Archdeaconry Admons 1732-1745 (*Snell MSS*) [BK/G 13]

1733-1857 Oxford Archdeaconry Court - Cal of Wills & Admons: 1733-1857 (*in 2 pts*) [Mf 915]

OXFORD, THE COURT OF THE CHANCELLOR, MASTERS and SCHOLARS OF THE UNIVERSITY OF

Superior Court: Delegates (High Court)

1413-1814 Social Hist of Property & Possessions; pt 1: Invents & Wills including Renaissance Lib Catalogues from the Bodleian Lib, Oxford 1436-1814 consisting of an index to Wills proved in the Court of the Chancellor of the University of Oxford & to such of the recs of that Court as relate to matters or causes testmtry (with ms annotations) - *abst of wills & admon bonds 1436-1814, of invents 1443-1740 & of prob accounts 1413-1514 & 1527-1661* [Mf 1756-1767]

1436-1814 Index to Wills proved in the Court of the Chancellor of the University of Oxford & to such of the recs & other instruments & papers of that court as relate to matters or causes testmtry (*wills 1436-1814, invents 1443-1740, accounts 1453-1719*) [OX/G 37]

OXFORD, THE COURT OF THE MAYOR OF THE CITY OF

1276-1646 Oxford Book of Wills (*abst from Mayor's Court recs*) [OX/L 31]

OXFORD, THE PECULIAR JURISDICTIONS OF THE MASTER, FELLOWS and SCHOLARS OF NEW COLLEGE AT *see Hornchurch; Sokens; Writtle; see also Oxford (University)*

PACKWOOD, THE COURT OF THE PECULIAR JURISDICTION IN THE MANOR OF

Superior Court: Lichfield (Consistory)

1675-1790 Cals of Original Wills & Admon Papers transmitted (*to Birmingham Probate Registry*) from the registers of Barston, Bishops Itchington, Baddesley Clinton, Knowle, Packwood, Tachbrook & Temple Balsall from 1675-1790 inclusive (BRS vol 7) [BRS]

1759-1850 Cal of Original Wills & Admon Papers from the Regs of *Packwood (with invents)* [Mf 802]

PAGHAM and TARRING, THE COURT OF THE PECULIAR JURISDICTION OF THE ARCHBISHOP OF CANTERBURY IN THE DEANERIES OF

this Court was also the **Court of the Commissary of the Archbishop of Canterbury for Pagham and Tarring** *during archiepiscopal vacancies*

Superior Court: Canterbury (PCC); *see also Chichester (Archdeaconry); Lambeth Palace*

1520-1670 Cal of Admons 1555-1800 granted in the Consistory Court of the Bishop of Chichester with cal of Wills & Admons in the Peculiar Court of the Archbishop *in Pagham & Tarring - Wills: 1520-1526, 1553-1670 (including wills proved in London 1615-1670) & Admons: 1569-1668 -* & with cal of Wills & Admons 1577-1800 for the Peculiar Court of the Dean of Chichester (BRS vol 64) [BRS]

1781-1857 Consistory Court for the Archdeaconry of Chichester Cals; vol 13: Archbishop's Peculiar (*ie Pagham & Tarring*) & Dean's Peculiar Admons 1781-1857 [Mf 834]

PEAK FOREST, THE COURT OF THE PECULIAR JURISDICTION OF

Superior Court: Lichfield (Consistory)

1529-1652 Cal of Wills & Admons registered in the various Peculiar Courts now preserved at the Lichfield Registry 1529-1652 (BRS vol 7) [BRS]

1667-1858 Cal of Wills & Admons of Peculiar Jurisdictions in the Diocese of Lichfield; vols 1 & 2 *including*: Peculiar Court of Peak Forest 1667-1858 [Mf 801]

PEEBLES, THE COMMISSARIOT OF
Superior Court: Court of Session; *see also*
Edinburgh (Commissariot)
1681-1699 Commissariot Rec of the
Peebles; Reg of Testmts 1681-
1699 (Scottish Rec Soc vol 12)
[SC/PER]
1785-1827 Index to Reg of Testmts: Peebles
1785-1827 [Mf 2909]

PENKRIDGE, THE COURT OF THE ROYAL
PECULIAR JURISDICTION OF
Superior Court: Delegates (High Court); *see*
also Lichfield (Consistory)
1529-1652 Cal of Wills & Admons registered
in the various Peculiar Courts
now preserved at the Lichfield
Registry 1529-1652 (BRS vol 7)
[BRS]
1660-1858 Cal of Wills & Admons of Peculiar
Jurisdictions in the Diocese of
Lichfield; vols 1 & 2 *including*:
Royal Peculiar Court of
Penkridge 1660-1858 [Mf 801]

PETERBOROUGH, THE CONSISTORY
COURT OF THE BISHOP OF
Superior Courts: Lincoln (Consistory) until
1541; Canterbury (PCC) from 1541; *see also*
Northampton (Archdeaconry) from 1541 until
1598
1510-1670 Cal of Wills in the Archdeaconry
of Northampton & the Consistory
Court of Peterborough prefaced
by an index of courts & a list of
the several registers of the Court
of Probate; vol 1: 1510-1670 [Mf
793 or Mf 912]
1541-1608 Consistory Court of Peterborough
- Cals of Wills; vol 1: 1541-1608
[Mf 794]
1604-1719 Index to Wills proved in the
Consistory Court of Peterborough
1604-1719 including the counties
of Rutland & Northants (mostly
Northern portion) & the Soke of
Peterborough; vols 1 & 2 [Mf 795
or NH/G 39 & NH/G 40]
1607-1719 Index to Northampton &
Consistory Wills; vol 1: Books A-
N, 1607-1672 (*in 3 pts*); vol 2:
Books O-Z, 1673-1719 [Mf 791]
1609-1646 Consistory Court of Peterborough
- Cal of Wills; vol 2: 1609-1646
[Mf 794]
1719-1858 Consistory Court of Peterborough
- Cal of Wills & Admons 1719-
1858 (*in 2 pts*) [Mf 906]

PETERBOROUGH, THE COURT OF THE
ARCHDEACONRY OF
not a probate jurisdiction: see Northampton
(Archdeaconry) for the Western Deaneries;
Peterborough (Consistory) for the Eastern
Deaneries (from 1598)

PILTON and NORTH WOOTTON, THE
COURT OF THE PECULIAR JURISDICTION
OF
Superior Court: Wells (Episcopal Consistory)
1661-1856 Wells Wills; vol 13: Indexes to
Wells Registry Cals - Peculiar
Courts: *Pilton & N Wootton Wills*
& Admon Bonds (Mfc) [Apply to
Staff]

POCKLINGTON *see York (Dean)*

PIPE MINOR *see Prees*

POOLE, THE COURT OF THE MAYOR OF
THE BOROUGH OF
see also Canford
1408-1463 Cal of Wills & Admons relating to
Dorset in the Courts of Sarum;
from Borough of Poole recs (BRS
vol 53) [BRS]

PORTSMOUTH, THE COURT OF THE
MAYOR OF THE BOROUGH OF
1527-1592 *Abst of* Wills 1527-1592 *In* "Extr
from Recs in the possession of
the Municipal Corp of the
Borough of Portsmouth & from
other docs relating thereto" [HA/L
35]

PREES otherwise PIPE MINOR, THE
COURT OF THE PREBEND OF
includes Tipton
Superior Court: Lichfield (Dean & Chapter)
1529-1652 Cal of Wills & Admons registered
in the various Peculiar Courts
now preserved at the Lichfield
Registry 1529-1652 (BRS vol 7)
[BRS]
1698-1858 Cal of Wills & Admons of
Peculiar Jurisdictions in the
Diocese of Lichfield; vols 1 & 2
including: Prebendal Court of
Prees otherwise Pipe Major
1698-1858 [Mf 801]
1698-1863 Cal of Salop Wills & Admons & *of*
Invents deposited in Shrewsbury
District Probate Registry
including: Index to Prees Grants -
Prees Wills & Admons in the

Ellesmere Manorial Court Book
(supps to Trans Salop Archl &
Nat Hist Soc 4th ser vols 12 *now*
45 & 46) [Mf 800 or SH/PER]

PREROGATIVE COURTS OF THE BRITISH ISLES

ARMAGH: *see Armagh (PCA)*
CANTERBURY: *see Canterbury (PCC)*
"EDINBURGH": *see Edinburgh (Commissariot)*
YORK: *see York (PCY)*

PRESTON, THE COURT OF THE PREBEND OF

Superior Court: Sarum (Dean)
1761-1799 Peculiar & Prebendal Courts of
the Diocese of Sarum - Indexes
to Wills & Admons 1462-1810*:
Prebendal Court of Preston &
Sutton Pointz (with Admon
Bonds)* [Mf 836]; Cal of Wills &
Admons relating to Dorset in the
Courts of Sarum & *elsewhere
(including Preston with Sutton
Poyntz 1761-1799)* (BRS vol 53)
[BRS]
1800-1858 Sarum Courts, Deanery &
Archdeaconry of Wiltshire; vol
"A": Index for Wills & *Admons*
1800-1858 with names beginning
A-B only [Mf 838]

PRESTON IN HOLDERNESS, THE COURT OF THE PECULIAR JURISDICTION OF THE SUB DEAN OF YORK IN THE PREBEND OF

Superior Courts: York (Chancery); York
(Dean & Chapter)
1676-1729 York Registry; Cal of Wills &
Admons - Separate Peculiars &
Dean & Chapter's General
Peculiars*: Subdeanery*; York
Registry; Names of Peculiars
wherein separate lists are kept of
the wills etc proved therein
*including the Subdeanery
(Preston in Holderness)* [*both* Mf
879]

PRINCIPAL PROBATE REGISTRIES *see
under name of town (London, Edinburgh or
Dublin)*

PRIVETT *see Meon, West*

PRIVY COUNCIL, THE JUDICIAL COMMITTEE OF THE

*this committee formally assumed the probate
appellate powers of the High Court of
Delegates in 1832 but the Sovereign in
Council exercised ultimate power long before
that date*
Superior Court: *This was the final court of
appeal in the British Empire*
1832-1851 *Index to* Wills & Admons before
the Judicial Committee of the
Privy Council (The Genealogist
new ser vols 11 & 12)
[PER/GEN]

PUDSEY, THE COURT OF THE MANOR OF
see Crossley

PUXTON *see Banwell*

RAPHOE, THE CONSISTORY COURT OF THE BISHOP OF

Superior Court: Armagh (PCA)
1684-1858 *Phillimore's* Indexes to Irish Wills;
vol 5: Cal of Wills in the Dioceses
of Derry & Raphoe [IR/G 88]

RATBY *see Groby*

RAVENFIELD *see Mexborough*

RICCALL, THE COURT OF THE PREBEND OF

Superior Courts: York (Chancery); York
(Dean & Chapter)*; see also Fenton*
1690-1833 York Registry; Names of
Peculiars wherein separate lists
are kept of the wills etc proved
therein *including Riccall from an
early period to the present time*;
York Registry; Cal of Vacancy &
Prebendal Wills *including Riccall*
[*both* Mf 879]

RICHMOND, THE CONSISTORIAL COURT OF THE ARCHDEACONRY OF

*Founded in 1090, the Archdeaconry's
jurisdiction originally covered much of
Northern England but it was gradually
reduced by the creation of diocesan courts as
each See was founded until the Archdeaconry
was transferred to the new See of Chester in
1541 when the Archdeacon's powers passed
from* **The Consistory Court of the
Archdeacon of Richmond** *to* **The
Consistory Court of the Commissary of the
Bishop of Chester for the Archdeaconry of
Richmond**. *The site of the Court's registry*

moved in the 18th C from Richmond to Kendal then to Lancaster & then back again in 1748 to Richmond, losing papers in the process. Surviving records of the Court are generally divided into two divisions - one for the **Eastern Deaneries (ie Boroughbridge, Catterick and Richmond)** & one for the **Western Deaneries (ie Amounderness, Copeland, Furness, Kendal and Lonsdale)**; it is not always clear as to which Deanery the material refers so BOTH divisions should be searched
Superior Courts: York (Chancery) until 1541; Chester (Consistory) from 1541

The Eastern Deaneries
1352-1699   Archdeaconry Court of Richmond - Cal of Wills & Admons; vol 25: to 1699 [Mf 871]
1410-1611   Archdeaconry Court of Richmond - Script Indexes to Wills; vols 1-19: 1410-1610 [Mf 863-868]
1411-1601   *Abst of* some *Unregistered* Wills from the Richmond Registry (Northern Genealogist vols 2-4 & 6) [PER/NOR]
1418-1438   Cal of Wills *1418-1438 In* "Regs of the Archdeaconry of Richmond 1361-1442" (Yorks Arch & Topo J vols 25, 30 & 32) [YK/PER]; *also In* "Yorks Tracts vol 2" (*offprint*) [Apply to Staff]
1427-1610   Richmondshire Wills (*Cal to the Eastern Deaneries*) (supp to Northern Genealogist vol 2) (*A-GRI*) [PER/NOR]
1442-1579   *Abst of* Wills & Invents from the Registry of the Archdeaconry of Richmond, extending over portions of the counties of York, Westmorland, Cumberland & Lancaster (Surtees Soc vol 26) [DU/PER]; *Surname* Index to Wills deposited in the Registry at Richmond & published by the Surtees Soc in 1853 [Topo Docs Coll: Yorks]
1457-1548   Richmond Wills - List of Archdeaconry of Richmond Wills relating to Cumbrians in the W Riding RO at Leeds (*1457 & 1529-1548*) (Cumbria FHS N/L no 56) [CU/PER]
1529-1579   Archdeaconry Court of Richmond; Regs 1-3 & "A": 1529-1551; Reg "B": 1564-1573, Reg "C": 1552-1568 & Regs "D" & "F": Copy Wills 1529-1579 [Mf 873-

874]
1610-1857   Archdeaconry Court of Richmond - Cals of Wills & Admons; vols 20-24: 1611-1700 [Mf 869-870]; vols 26-27: 1700-1857 [Mf 872]

The Western Deaneries
1442-1579   Wills & Invents from the Registry of the Archdeaconry of Richmond, extending over portions of the counties of York, Westmorland, Cumberland & Lancaster (*selected abst*) (Surtees Soc vol 26) [DU/PER]; *Surname* Index to Wills deposited in the Registry at Richmond & published by the Surtees Soc in 1853 [Topo Docs Coll: Yorks]
1528-1548   *Extr from* Richmond Wills *connected with Cumbria* (Cumbria FHS N/L no 56) [CU/PER]
1531-1652   List of Lancs Wills, *admons, invents & bonds* proved within the Archdeaconry of Richmond; pt 1: 1457-1680 (*Towneley abst 1531-1652 in BM Add MSS 32,115*); List of abst (*Towneley abst 1569-1603 in BM Add MSS 32,115*) of Westmorland & Cumberland Wills belonging to the Deanery of Lonsdale but found in the Deanery of Amounderness 1569-1603 (*both* Lancs & Cheshire Rec Soc Procs vol 10) [LA/PER]
1574-1667   *Abst of* Wills of the Fam of Benn & others, in that part of Cumberland formerly known as the Copeland Deanery of the Archdeaconry of Richmond, Yorks *In* "FH Tracts vol 6" [FH Tracts]
1633-1855   Strays amongst the Copeland Wills (*cal of wills, admons, etc*) (Cumbria FHS J nos 79 & 80) [CU/PER]
1681-1858   List of Lancs Wills, *admons, invents & bonds* proved within the Archdeaconry of Richmond; pts 2: 1681-1748, 3: 1748-1792, 4: 1793-1812, 5: 1813-1837 & 6: 1838-1858 (Lancs & Cheshire Rec Soc Procs vols 13, 23, 66, 99 & 105) [*all* LA/PER]

RICHMOND, THE DEANERY OF *see Richmond (Eastern Deaneries)*

RINGWOOD WITH HARBRIDGE, THE TESTAMENTARY JURISDICTION OF THE PARISH OF
Superior Court: Winchester (Archdeaconry)
1605-1842   Cal of Hants Wills proved in the Prerogative & Peculiar Courts of Winchester with other Prob Docs: *Ringwood - Index of Peculiar Courts* [HA/G 62]

RIPON, THE COURT OF THE PECULIAR JURISDICTION OF THE ARCHBISHOP OF YORK IN THE MANOR and LIBERTY OF *formerly the Court of the Chapter of the Collegiate Church of Sts Peter & Wilfrid at Ripon*
Superior Court: York (PCY); *see also York (Exchequer)*
1346-1718   *Extr from* Wills *In* "Memorials of the Church of Sts Peter & Wilfrid, Ripon vol 2" (Surtees Soc vol 78) [DU/PER]
1354-1560   Entries *de latio testamenti* in the Fabric Rolls 1354-1542, the Chamberlain's Rolls 1410-1541 (including mortuary payments 1541-1650) & a paper book c1520 *In* "Memorials of the Church of Sts Peter & Wilfrid, Ripon vol 3" (Surtees Soc vol 81) [DU/PER]
1371-1437   *Abst of* Wills in the Ingilby MSS *In* "Memorials of the Church of Sts Peter & Wilfrid, Ripon vol 4" (Surtees Soc vol 115) [DU/PER]
1452-1513   *Abst of* Enrolled Wills & Testmtry Matters 1452-1506 & *of* Some Other Wills & Admons (*1507-1513*) *In* "Acts of Chapter of the Collegiate Church of Sts Peter & Wilfrid, Ripon 1452-1502" (Surtees Soc vol 64) [DU/PER]
1460-1624   *Abst of* Wills & Invents preserved in their Original Form & not in the Act Book *In* appx 3 to "Acts of Chapter of the Collegiate Church of Sts Peter & Wilfrid, Ripon 1452-1502" (Surtees Soc vol 64) [DU/PER]

ROCHESTER, THE CONSISTORY COURT OF THE BISHOP OF
Superior Court: Canterbury (PCC); *see also Rochester (Archdeaconry)*
1323-1348   *Abst of Prob Acts In* "Registrum Hamonis Hethe Diocesis Roffensis/*Reg of Hamo de Hethe, Diocese of Rochester* 1319-1352; vols 1 & 2" (Canterbury & York Soc vols 48 & 49) [KE/G 26-27]
1440-1561   Index of Wills proved in the Rochester Consistory Court 1440-1561 (Kent Recs vol 9) [KE/G 66]; *commentary* (Archaeologica Cantiana vol 38) [KE/PER]
1440-1605   Consistory Court of Rochester - Index to Wills; vols 1: 1440-1605 & 2: "Reg 1" 1440-1453 [Mf 745]
1508-1679   Archdeaconry & Consistory Courts of Rochester - *Combined* Index of Wills 1671-1679 & of Supp Wills & Admons *1508*-1600 [Mf 737]
1596-1622   Consistory Court of Rochester - Index to Wills; vol 3 (pt 1): 1596-1622 & (pt 2): 1604-1622 [Mf 745]
1600-1718   Consistory Court of Rochester - Indexes to Wills - 1600-1674 & 1680-1718; Index to Admons 1635-1644 & 1660-1782 [Mf 746]
1678-1858   Consistory Court of Rochester - Indexes to Wills & Admons - 1678-1858 (*in 3 pts*) [Mf 748]
1841-1857   Consistory Court of Rochester - Index to Unregistered Wills & Admons 1841-1857 [Mf 747]

ROCHESTER, THE COURT OF THE ARCHDEACON OF
Superior Court: Rochester (Consistory)
1508-1679   Archdeaconry & Consistory Courts of Rochester - *Combined* Index of Wills 1671-1679 [Mf 737]
1680-1857   Archdeaconry Court of Rochester - Index to Wills & Admons; vols "A": 1680-1728, "B": 1728-1823 & "C": 1729-1857 [Mf 749]

ROSS (Ireland) *see Cork*

ROSS (Scotland), THE COMMISSARIOT OF
Superior Court: Court of Session; *see also Edinburgh (Commissariot)*
1801-1823   *Ross Reg of Testmts In* "Index to Regs of Testmts for various Commissariots 1801-1823" [Mf 2910]

ROTHLEY, THE COURT OF THE COMMISSARY OF THE BISHOP OF LINCOLN FOR THE MANOR OF
Superior Court: Lincoln (Consistory)
1533-1609 Notes concerning the pretended peculiar of Rothley Temple, etc (*list of wills*) *In* appx to "Leics Uncalendared Wills" (*In* "Leics Miscellany", Leics Archl Soc *extra pub*, Summer 1951) [LE/G 25]
1575-1800 Cal of Wills & Admons relating to the County of Leicester, proved in the Archdeaconry Court of Leicester 1495-1649 & in the Peculiars of St Margaret Leicester, Rothley, Groby, Evington & unproved Wills previous to 1801; all now preserved in the Probate Registry at Leicester (*admons from 1712*) (BRS vol 27) [BRS]
1626-1633 Index to Wills & Admons proved & granted in the Archdeaconry Court of Leicester 1660-1750 & in the Peculiars of St Margaret Leicester & Rothley (*additional registered wills*) & in the Rutland Peculiars of Caldecott, Ketton & Tixover & Liddington prior to 1821; now preserved in the Probate Registry at Leicester (BRS vol 51) [Apply to Staff]

ROXWELL *see Writtle*

RUYTON OF THE ELEVEN TOWNS, THE COURT OF THE MANOR OF
1665-1709 *Cal of* Wills & *Invents* proved in the Manorial Court of Ruyton-of-the-Eleven-Towns (Trans Salop Archl & Nat Hist Soc vol 52) [SH/PER]

RYE, THE COURT OF THE MAYOR OF THE BOROUGH OF
1475-1728 *Extr from Prob Docs In* "Recs of Rye Corp" [SX/L 36]

ST ALBANS, THE COURT OF THE ARCHDEACON OF
the Peculiar Jurisdiction of the Abbey of St Albans until 1550
Superior Court: London (Consistory)
1415-1470 Cal of Wills & Admons - Archdeaconry of St Albans; pt 1: Reg "Stonham" 1415-1470 [HT/G 39]; Abst of Herts Wills in Reg "Stoneham" *in the Archdeaconry*

Court of St Albans (1415-1451) (Herts Genealogist & Antiquary vols 1-3) [HT/PER or (*vol 1 to 1434*) Mf 2587]
1415-1857 Archdeaconry Court of St Albans - Cal of Wills & Admon Acts 1415-1857 [Mf 735]
1471-1500 *Index to* St Albans Wills & Admons 1471-1500 (Herts Rec Pubs vol 9) [HT/PER]

ST ANDREWS, THE COMMISSARIOT OF
Superior Court: Court of Session; *see also Edinburgh (Commissariot)*
1549-1800 Commissariot Rec of St Andrews; Reg of Testmts 1549-1800 (Scottish Rec Soc vol 8) [SC/PER]
1801-1823 Index to Testmts of the Commissariot of St Andrews 1801-1823 [Mf 2909]

ST ASAPH, THE CONSISTORY COURT OF THE BISHOP OF
Superior Court: Canterbury (PCC)
1583-1729 Consistory Court of St Asaph - Index of Wills 1583-1729 [Mf 883]
1658-1793 St Asaph Wills (*Myddleton MSS: abst 1658-1793*) [Topo Docs Coll: Wales]
1750-1858 Mynegai i Ewyllysiau Llanelwy/*Prob Index St Asaph* 1750-1858 (*will, admon bond & invent index in the National Lib of Wales*); vols 1 & 2 [WS/G 107 & WS/G 108]

ST ASAPH, THE ARCHDEACONRY OF
not a probate jurisdiction: see St Asaph (Consistory)

ST BURYAN, THE COURT OF THE ROYAL PECULIAR JURISDICTION IN THE DEANERY OF
Superior Court: Delegates (High Court); *see also Canterbury (PCC)*
1569-1799 Cal of Wills, Admons & Accounts relating to the counties of Devon & Cornwall in the Consistorial Archidiaconal Court of Cornwall (with which are included the recs of the Royal Peculiar of St Buryan) now preserved in the District Probate Registry at Bodmin; pts 1: 1569-1699 & 2: 1700-1799 (BRS vols 56 & 59) [*both* BRS]

1605-1857 Cornwall RO - Index to Cornish Estate Duty & Deanery of St Buryan Wills, *Admons & Invents* [CO/G 16]

ST CROSS AT WINCHESTER, THE COURT OF THE PECULIAR JURISDICTION OF THE MASTER OF THE HOSPITAL OF *see Winchester (St Cross)*

ST DAVID'S, THE EPISCOPAL CONSISTORY COURT OF THE BISHOP OF
Superior Court: Canterbury (PCC)
1564-1750 St David's Diocese Wills - Testators index to abst of original wills 1564-1750: all of St David's Diocese Episcopal Consistory Court (excluding Archdeaconries), index of testators by parish or town ... (Mfc) [Apply to Staff]
1750-1858 Mynegai i Ewyllysiau Tyddewi/*Prob Index St David's* 1750-1858 (*will, admon bond & invent index in the National Lib of Wales*); vols 1-4 [WS/G 114-117]

ST DAVID'S, THE CONSISTORIAL COURT OF THE ARCHDEACON OF
Superior Court: St David's (Episcopal Consistory)
1594-1858 Cals of Wills & Admons including the Archdeaconries of Cardigan, Carmarthen & St David's (*in 9 pts including Invents & Bonds*); vols 1: 1594-1629, 2: 1700-1747, 3: 1746-1798, 4: 1799-1836, 9: 1700-1740 (*Admons only*) & 8: 1837-1858 [Mf 881-882]

ST DECUMANS, THE COURT OF THE PREBEND OF
Superior Court: Wells (Dean)
1636-1857 Wells Wills; vol 13: Indexes to Wells Registry Cals - Peculiar Courts: *St Decumans Wills, Admons & Tuit Bonds (1636 & 1661-1857) & Admon Bonds, etc (1641 & 1681-1745) (in 2 pts)* (Mfc) [Apply to Staff]

ST FAITH'S *see Winchester (St Cross)*

ST LEONARD IN YORK, THE COURT OF THE PECULIAR JURISDICTION OF THE GUARDIAN OF THE SPRITUALITIES OF THE HOSPITAL OF *see York (St Leonard's)*

ST MARGARET IN LEICESTER, THE COURT OF THE PREBEND OF *see Leicester (St Margaret)*

ST MARTIN LE GRAND IN WESTMINSTER, THE COURT OF THE COMMISSARY OF THE ROYAL COLLEGIATE CHURCH OF *see Westminster (Abbott/Dean & Chapter)*

ST MARY BOURNE *see Hurstbourne Priors*

ST MARY EXTRA, SOUTH STONEHAM and WESTON, THE TESTAMENTARY JURISDICTION OF THE PARISH OF
Superior Court: Winchester (Archdeaconry)
1628-1727 Cal of Hants Wills proved in the Prerogative & Peculiar Courts of Winchester with other Prob Docs: *St Mary Extra including S Stoneham, Weston - Separate Peculiar Wills* [HA/G 62]

ST MARY'S PARISH IN MALDON *see Maldon*

ST MARY'S, SHREWSBURY *see Shrewsbury*

ST PAUL'S CATHEDRAL CHURCH AT LONDON *see London (Dean & Chapter of St Paul's)*

ST PETER IN WESTMINSTER, THE CONSISTORIAL COURT OF THE DEAN and CHAPTER OF THE ROYAL COLLEGIATE CHURCH OF *see Westminster (Abbot/Dean & Chapter)*

ST SWITHIN'S WORCESTER *see Worcester (St Swithin)*

SALISBURY *see Sarum*

SALOP, THE ARCHDEACONRY OF
not a probate jurisdiction - for the Northern Deaneries: see Lichfield (Consistory); for the Southern Deaneries: see Hereford (Consistory)

SARUM, THE CONSISTORY COURT OF THE BISHOP OF
Superior Court: Canterbury (PCC)
1408-1412 *Abst of* Wills proved *In* "Reg of Robert Hallum, Bishop of Salisbury 1407-1417" (Canterbury & York Soc vol 71) [WL/G 11]
1526-1799 Consistory Court of Sarum - Cal of Wills & Admon Acts 1538-1799 [Mf 837]

1533-1744 List (Unofficial) of Wills & Admons *with Invents* (originals & copies) remaining at The Diocesan Registry, Salisbury [(*ms*) Topo Docs Coll: Wilts or (*ts*) Apply to Staff]

1540-1809 Wilts Wills still preserved in the Diocesan Registry, Salisbury (*will, admon, invent, etc index for Hurst, Wokingham & Wilts*) (Wilts Archl & Nat Hist Mag vol 45) [WL/PER]; *also (offprint) In* Wilts Tracts vol 1 [WL Tracts]

1540-1857 Testmtry Papers at Salisbury; pt 2: Wilts Wills, Admons, Invents, etc still preserved at the Diocesan Registry, Salisbury 1540-1857 (*offprint index from Wilts Mag 1930*) [WL/G 52]

1561-1672 Extr from Salisbury Diocesan Recs (*probs in Boucher MSS*) [WL/G 15]

1597-1599 Sarum Diocesan Court Recs (*Cal of Wilts & Dorset Witnesses*) (Genealogists' Mag vol 7) [PER/GEN]

1653-1837 Cal of Wills & Admons relating to Dorset in the Courts of Sarum (BRS vol 53) [BRS]; *see* DORSET *for details*

1800-1858 Sarum Courts, Deanery & Archdeaconry of Wiltshire; vol "A": Index for Wills & *Admons* 1800-1858 with names beginning A-B only [Mf 838]

SARUM, THE COURT OF THE ARCHDEACON OF
Superior Court: Sarum (Consistory)

1538-1799 Archdeaconry Court of Sarum - Index to Wills & Admons 1528-1799 [Mf 835]

1800-1858 Sarum Courts, Deanery & Archdeaconry of Wiltshire; vol "A": Index for Wills & *Admons* 1800-1858 with names beginning A-B only [Mf 838]

SARUM, THE PECULIAR JURISDICTION OF THE BISHOP OF
probate jurisdiction in the Peculiars of the Bishop of Sarum was undertaken by the Consistory Court of Sarum (qv)

SARUM, THE COURT OF THE PECULIAR JURISDICTION OF THE DEAN OF
Superior Court: Sarum (Consistory)

1404-1407 Abst of Wills *In* "Reg of John Chandler, Dean of Salisbury 1404-1407" (Wilts Rec Soc vol 39) [WL/PER]

1501-1801 Peculiar Court of the Dean of Sarum - Cal of Wills & Admon Acts *1501 & 1557-1801* [Mf 837]

1800-1808 Peculiar Court of the Dean of Sarum - Copies of Wills & *Bonds* chronologically arranged 1800-1808 [Mf 839]

1800-1858 Sarum Courts, Deanery & Archdeaconry of Wiltshire; vols "I": Dean of Sarum's Catalogue Book of Wills, etc 1800-1858 & "A": Index to Wills & *Admons* 1800-1858 with names beginning A-B only [*both* Mf 838]

SARUM, THE ARCHIDIACONAL COURT OF THE SUB DEAN OF
Superior Court: Sarum (Consistory)

1581-1588 Peculiar & Prebendal Courts of the Diocese of Sarum - Indexes to Wills & Admons 1462-1810: *Archidiaconal Court of the Sub Dean of Sarum (wills & admons registered)* [Mf 836]

1610-1799 Peculiar & Prebendal Courts of the Diocese of Sarum - Indexes to Wills & Admons 1462-1810: *Archidiaconal Court of the Sub Dean of Sarum (wills & admons not registered & also invents)* [Mf 836]

1800-1858 Sarum Courts, Deanery & Archdeaconry of Wiltshire; vol "A": Index for Wills & *Admons* 1800-1858 with names beginning A-B only [Mf 838]

SARUM, THE COURT OF THE DEAN and CHAPTER OF
Superior Court: Sarum (Consistory)

1604-1799 Peculiar & Prebendal Courts of the Diocese of Sarum - Indexes to Wills & Admons 1462-1810: *Peculiar Court of the Dean & Chapter of Sarum* [Mf 836]

1800-1857 Wilts Wills Beneficiaries Index 1800-1858: Name Abst; vols 2 & 3: Savernake Forest 1800-1829 & Dean & Chapter of Sarum (*pts 1-2*) 1800-1857 (Peculiar Court docs 138-397) [WL/G 67]

1800-1858 Sarum Courts, Deanery & Archdeaconry of Wiltshire; vol "A": Index for Wills & *Admons* 1800-1858 with names beginning

A-B only [Mf 838]

SARUM, THE COURT OF THE PECULIAR JURISDICTION OF THE PRECENTOR OF THE CATHEDRAL CHURCH AT
also the Court of the Chantor of Sarum Cathedral
Superior Court: Sarum (Dean)
1614-1799 Peculiar & Prebendal Courts of the Diocese of Sarum - Indexes to Wills & Admons 1462-1810: *Peculiar Court of the Precentor or Chantor of Sarum (with invents)* [Mf 836]
1800-1858 Sarum Courts, Deanery & Archdeaconry of Wiltshire; vol "A": Index for Wills & *Admons* 1800-1858 with names beginning A-B only [Mf 838]

SARUM, THE COURT OF THE PECULIAR JURISDICTION OF THE TREASURER OF THE CATHEDRAL CHURCH AT
with the Court of the Prebend of Calne united thereto
Superior Court: Sarum (Dean)
1599-1799 Peculiar & Prebendal Courts of the Diocese of Sarum - Indexes to Wills & Admons 1462-1810: *Peculiar Court of the Treasurer of the Cathedral Church of Sarum annexed with the Prebendal Stall of Calne (1599 & 1610-1799 & with invents)* [Mf 836]
1800-1858 Wilts Wills Beneficiaries Index 1800-1858: Name Abst; vol 8: *Prebend of Calne* (Peculiar Court docs 844-1095) (Mfc) [Apply to Staff]
1800-1858 Sarum Courts, Deanery & Archdeaconry of Wiltshire; vol "A": Index for Wills & *Admons* 1800-1858 with names beginning A-B only [Mf 838]

SAVERNAKE FOREST, THE COURT OF THE PECULIAR JURISDICTION OF THE LORD WARDEN OF
Superior Court: Sarum (Dean) *until 1829 when this lay prebend was dissolved*
1617-1799 Peculiar & Prebendal Courts of the Diocese of Sarum - Indexes to Wills & Admons 1462-1810: *Peculiar Court of the Lord Warden of Savernake Forest (with invents)* [Mf 836]
1800-1829 Wilts Wills Beneficiaries Index 1800-1858: Name Abst; vols 2 &

3: Savernake Forest 1800-1829 & Dean & Chapter of Sarum 1800-1857 (Peculiar Court docs 138-397) [WL/G 67]
1800-1858 Sarum Courts, Deanery & Archdeaconry of Wiltshire; vol "A": Index for Wills & *Admons* 1800-1858 with names beginning A-B only [Mf 838]

SAWLEY, THE COURT OF THE PREBEND OF
Superior Court: Lichfield (Dean & Chapter)
1529-1652 Cal of Wills & Admons registered in the various Peculiar Courts now preserved at the Lichfield Registry 1529-1652 (BRS vol 7) [BRS]
1712-1858 Cal of Wills & Admons of Peculiar Jurisdictions in the Diocese of Lichfield; vols 1 & 2 *including*: Prebendal Court of Sawley 1712-1858 [Mf 801]

SEDGLEY, THE COURT OF THE MANOR OF
1612-1763 Abst of Wills, *Admons* & Invents 1612-1763 *In* "Sedgley Manor Court Rolls" [ST/R 107 or ST Tracts]
1614-1804 Wills & Letters of Admon recorded in the Court Rolls of the Manor of Sedgley, County Stafford (*Tildesley's abst with invents*) [Apply to Staff]

SELBY, THE COURT OF THE TESTAMENTARY JURISDICTION OF
a Peculiar Jurisdiction in lay hands
Superior Court: York (Dean & Chapter)
1634-1710 Selby Wills (*will, admon, invent, bonds, etc abst from the Peculiar Court 1634-1639 & 1650-1710*) (Yorks Archl Soc rec ser vol 47) [YK/PER]
1681-1858 Selby Act Books 1681-1788 & 1681-1858 [Mf 879]

SHAFTESBURY, THE COURT OF THE MAYOR OF THE BOROUGH OF
1348-1510 Cal of Wills & Admons relating to Dorset in the Courts of Sarum; *from Borough of Shaftesbury recs* (BRS vol 53) [BRS]

SHETLAND *see Orkney (Commissariot)*

SHERBURN *see Fenton*

SHIPTON *see Weighton*

**SHOREHAM, THE COURT OF THE
PECULIAR JURISDICTION OF THE
ARCHBISHOP OF CANTERBURY IN THE
DEANERY OF**
Superior Court: Canterbury (PCC); *see also
Arches (Deanery); Croydon; Lambeth Palace*
1664-1738 Peculiars of the Arches of
London, Shoreham, Kent &
Croydon, Surrey - *Cal of* Invents
& Admons 1664-1738 with a list
of non-testmtry docs [KE/G 69]
1664-1841 *Index to* Wills Registered in the
Deanery of Shoreham (*1664-
1813, 1816-1821, 1841*) [KE/G
69]

**SHREWSBURY, THE DONATIVE COURT OF
THE ROYAL PECULIAR OF ST MARY'S IN**
Superior Court: Delegates (High Court); *see
also Lichfield (Consistory)*
1661-1857 Cal of Salop Wills & Admons
(with invents) deposited in
Shrewsbury District Probate
Registry *including: The Peculiar
Court of St Mary's Repertory,
Shrewsbury* (supps to Trans
Salop Archl & Nat Hist Soc 4th
ser vols 12 *now 45* & 46) [Mf 800
or SH/PER]

**SHREWSBURY, THE DISTRICT PROBATE
REGISTRY IN**
Superior Registry: London (Principal Probate
Registry)
1858-1940 Index to Salop & Montgomery
wills proved in the Shrewsbury
District Probate Registry 1858-
1940 & held in the Salop Recs &
Res Centre (Mfc) [Apply to Staff]

**SHREWSBURY, THE COURT OF THE
MAYOR OF THE BOROUGH OF**
1336-1404 Extr from Wills & Invents in the
Municipal Regs 1336-1404 *In*
"HMC Rep on the Municipal Recs
of Shrewsbury" [Apply to Staff]

SHROPSHIRE *see Salop*

SIBFORD, THE COURT OF THE MANOR OF
also called Sibford Gower; see also Banbury
1550-1856 *Index to* Berks, Bucks & Oxon
Peculiars - Wills & Admons 1550-
1858 (*also Invents & Bonds*):
Manorial Court of Sibford [Mf
913]

1680-1758 Wills from the Manorial Court of
Sibford Gower (*index to wills,
invents & bonds 1680 & 1724-
1758 in BM Add Ch. 46,206-
46,280*) (Oxon FHn vol 2 no 8)
[OX/PER]
1732-1829 Index to Wills & *Admons* proved
in the Court of the Dean &
Chapter of Lincoln in the Peculiar
of Banbury 1542-1858 & *in the
Manorial Court of Sibford Gower*
(Oxford Rec Soc vol 40 or
Banbury Hist Soc no 1) [*both*
OX/PER]

SILSDEN, THE COURT OF THE MANOR OF
1587-1737 *Indexes to* Wills &c in the
Peculiar Courts at Wakefield:
Silsden Manor Court (Northern
Genealogist vol 1) [PER/NOR]
1587-1809 Manorial Court of Silsden: Index
of Wills; vols "A": 1587, *1663-
1727* & "B": *1654*-1809 [Mf 878]

**SLEAFORD OR LAFFORD, THE COURT OF
THE PREBEND OF NEW**
Superior Court: Lincoln (Dean & Chapter);
merged with Lincoln (Consistory) in 1834
1610-1833 Lincoln Wills; vol 4: Cal of Wills &
Admons at Lincoln;
Archdeaconry of Stow, Peculiar
Courts & Misc Courts - *including
the Court of the Prebend of
Sleaford (with invents)* (BRS vol
57) [BRS]; Index to Lincoln
Peculiar Courts: New Sleaford
peculiar Wills & Admons [Mf 759]

**SNAITH, THE COURT OF THE
TESTAMENTARY JURISDICTION OF**
a Peculiar Jurisdiction in lay hands
Superior Court: York (Dean & Chapter)
1568-1858 Peculiar Court of Snaith - Index
to Wills, Admons & Invents; vol 1:
1568-1719; vol 2: 1715-1858 [Mf
876]
1658-1879 Wills & Admons etc: listings
taken from cals of the old
Diocese of York & the Diocese of
Lincoln (with certain additions
from Durham) (*index BUR-WRI*)
(Fam Hist vols 2 & 3) [PER/FAM]

SOBERTON *see Meonstoke*

**SODOR and MAN, THE CONSISTORY
COURT OF THE BISHOP OF** *see Man
(Consistory)*

SOKENS, THE COURT OF THE COMMISSARY OF THE LIBERTY OF THE
ie Kirkby-le-Soken, Thorpe-le-Soken & Walton-le-Soken; also known as the Court of the Commissary for the Lords of the Liberty of the Soken; the Lordship was held by the Warden, Fellows & Scholars of New College, Oxford; see also London (Commissary - Essex & Herts); Oxford (University); Suffolk (Archdeaconry)

1632-1855   Abst of Wills & Admon Bonds of the Peculiar Jurisdiction of the Liberty of the Soken in the Essex RO: *Wills 1644-1855 & Bonds 1632-1749 with additional will abst in the supp from the Will Book 1775-1813 & Proceedings Book 1777-1822* [ES/G 64]

1644-1858   Wills at Chelmsford *including the Peculiar Court of the Liberty of the Sokens from 1644*; Index to Wills now preserved in the Essex RO at Chelmsford; vols 2: 1620-1720 & 3: 1721-1858 (BRS vols 79 & 84) [*both* BRS]

SOUTHAMPTON, THE COURT OF THE MAYOR OF THE BOROUGH OF
1392-1558   Black Book of Southampton; vols 1-3 (*abst of enrolled wills 1392-1513 & 1558*) (Southampton Rec Soc Pubs vols 13, 14 & 17) [HA/PER]

1447-1575   Southampton Prob Invents 1447-1575 (*abst of wills & invents*); vols 1: 1447-1566 & 2: 1566-1575 (Southampton Rec Soc Pubs vols 34 & 35) [*both* HA/PER]

SOUTHWELL, THE COURT OF THE PECULIAR JURISDICTION OF THE CHAPTER OF THE COLLEGIATE CHURCH AT
Superior Court: York (Exchequer)
1470-1537   List of Wills contained in the Regs of Chapter Acts *In* "HMC Rep on the MSS of Southwell Cathedral" [Apply to Staff]

1470-1600   Peculiar Court of the Chapter of Southwell - Cal of Wills & Admons; pt 1: 1470-1600 [Mf 797]

1512-1568   Notts Household Invents (*abst from the Peculiar of Southwell*) (Thoroton Soc rec ser vol 22) [NT/PER]

1538-1547   Copy Book of Wills & *Invents*

proved in the Peculiar Court of Southwell (*cal*) *In* "HMC Rep on the MSS of Southwell Cathedral" [Apply to Staff]

1601-1857   Peculiar Court of the Chapter of Southwell - Cal of Wills & Admons; pts 2: 1601-1650; pts 3-4: 1639-1726, 5: Wills 1680-1857 & 6: Admons 1771-1857 [Mf 797-798]

STAFFORD, THE COURT OF THE COMMISSARY OF THE BISHOP OF LICHFIELD FOR THE PECULIAR JURISDICTION OF THE CHAPTER OF THE COLLEGIATE CHURCH AT
Superior Church: Lichfield (Consistory)
1531-1583   Reg of Stafford & other Loc Wills *1531-1558, 1575-1577 & 1583* (Wm Salt/Staffs Rec Soc 3rd ser vol for 1926) [ST/PER]

STAFFORD, THE ARCHDEACONRY OF
not a probate jurisdiction: see Lichfield (Consistory)

STAMP OFFICe (THE) *see Estate Duty Office*

STEEP *see Meon, East*

STIRLING, THE COMMISSARIOT OF
Superior Court: Court of Session; *see also Edinburgh (Commissariot)*
1607-1800   Commissariot Rec of Stirling; Reg of Testmts 1607-1800 (Scottish Rec Soc vol 22) [SC/PER]

1801-1823   *Stirling Regs of Testmts & Invents In* "Index to Regs of Testmts for various Commissariots 1801-1823" [Mf 2910]

STOCKTON *see Bugthorpe*

STONEHAM, SOUTH *see St Mary Extra*

STOUR, EAST and WEST *see Gillingham*

STOW, THE COURTS OF THE ARCHDEACONRY OF
ie the Court of the Commissary of the Bishop of Lincoln for the Archdeaconry of Stow & the Court of the Archdeacon of Stow
Superior Court: Lincoln (Dean & Chapter); *merged with Lincoln (Consistory) in 1834*
1499   Archdeaconry of Stow: list of wills

1499 *compiled from fee accounts*
(Lincs FHn vol 1 no 1) [LI/PER]

1530-1699 Archdeaconry Court of Stow - Cal
of Wills; vol 1: 1530-1699 [Mf
758]; Lincoln Wills; vol 4: Cal of
Wills & Admons at Lincoln;
Archdeaconry of Stow (*wills
proved 1530-1699, prob grants &
admons from 1580 & also
invents*), Peculiar Courts & Misc
Courts (BRS vol 57) [BRS]

1610-1728 Index to Lincoln Peculiar Courts:
Stow Wills & Admons prior to
1730 [Mf 759]

1700-1808 Archdeaconry Court of Stow - Cal
of Wills; vol 2: 1700-1808 [Mf
758]

1700-1834 Wills & Admons etc: listings
taken from cals of the old
Diocese of York & the Diocese of
Lincoln (with certain additions
from Durham) (*index BUR-WRI*)
(Fam Hist vols 2 & 3) [PER/FAM]

1730-1833 Index to Lincoln Peculiar Courts:
Stow Wills & Admons 1730-1833
[Mf 759]

**STOW-IN-LINDSEY, THE COURT OF THE
PREBEND OF**
Superior Court: Lincoln (Dean & Chapter)*;
merged with Lincoln (Consistory) in 1834*

1610-1833 Lincoln Wills; vol 4: Cal of Wills &
Admons at Lincoln; Archdeaconry
of Stow, Peculiar Courts & Misc
Courts - *including the Court of the
Prebend of Stow in Lindsey (with
invents)* (BRS vol 57) [BRS]

**STRENSALL, THE COURT OF THE
PREBEND OF**
Superior Courts: York (Chancery); York
(Dean & Chapter)

1640-1739 York Registry; Cal of Wills &
Admons - Separate Peculiars &
Dean & Chapter's General
Peculiars*: 'Stransall'*; York
Registry; Names of Peculiars
wherein separate lists are kept of
the wills etc proved therein
including Strensall Prebend [*both*
Mf 879]

STOW LONGA *see Longstow*

**STURMINSTER MARSHALL, THE COURT
OF THE PECULIAR JURISDICTION OF**
Superior Court: Dorset (Archdeaconry)
1641-1799 Cal of Wills & Admons relating to

the County of Dorset, proved in
the Consistory Court (Dorset Div)
of the late Diocese of Bristol
1681-1792, in the Archdeaconry
Court of Dorset 1568-1792 & in
the several peculiars 1660-1799 -
including wills & admons of the
Peculiar of Sturminster Marshall
(*wills 1641-1642 & 1661-1799,
invents 1719-1799 & admons
1719-1799*) (BRS vol 22) [BRS]

1800-1857 Cal of Wills & Admons relating to
the County of Dorset preserved
in the Probate Registry at
Blandford & among the
Ecclesiastical Recs of Wimborne
Minster to 1857 (*including the
Peculiar Court of Sturminster
Marshall*) (*Fry MSS*) [Apply to
Staff]

**SUDBURY, THE COURTS OF THE
ARCHDEACONRY OF**
*ie the Court of the Sacrist of St Edmund's
Abbey at Bury St Edmunds (which became
the Court of the Commissary of the Bishop of
Norwich at Bury St Edmunds in 1539 before
being annexed to the Archdeaconry Court in
1844) & the Court of the Archdeacon of
Sudbury; these courts shared a common
registry from 1566*
Superior Courts: Norwich (Consistory) until
1837; Ely (Consistory) from 1837

962-1461 *List of some* Wills (*962-1070 &
1408-1461*) In "Archives of the
Abbey of Bury St Edmunds"
(Suffolk Rec Soc vol 21)
[SF/PER]

1354-1472 Archdeaconry Court of the
Sudbury - Cal of Wills; vol 1:
1354-1472 [Mf 816]

1354-1538 Cal of Pre-Reformation Wills,
Testmts, Probs, Admons,
registered at the Probate Office,
Bury St Edmunds [SF/G 65]

1354-1652 Index to Registered Wills &
Admons 1354-1652 (*Crossfield
MSS*) [Mf 819-820]

1354-1700 Index of the Prob Recs (*wills,
admons & invents*) of the Court
of the Archdeacon of Sudbury
1354-1700; vols 1 & 2 (BRS vols
95 & 96) [*both* BRS]

1370-1652 *Abst of* Wills & Invents from the
Regs of the Commissary of Bury
St Edmunds & the Archdeacon of
Sudbury (Camden Soc old ser
vol 49) [PER/CS or SF/G 74]

1473-1535 Archdeaconry Court of the Sudbury - Cal of Wills; vol 2: 1473-1535 [Mf 816]

1520-1626 Archdeaconry Court of the Sudbury - Cal of Wills; vol 3: 1520-1626 [Mf 817]

1605-1612 Archdeaconry Court of Sudbury - Admon Acts; vol 2: 1605-1612 [Mf 823]

1626-1691 Archdeaconry Court of the Sudbury - Cal of Wills; vol 4: 1627-1691 [Mf 817]

1630-1635 *Abst of* Wills of the Archdeaconry of Sudbury; vol 1: 1630-1635 (Suffolk Rec Soc vol 29) [SF/PER]

1630-1652 Archdeaconry Court of Sudbury - Admon Acts; vol 3: 1630-1652 [Mf 823]

1636-1638 *Abst of* Wills of the Archdeaconry of Sudbury; vol 2: 1636-1638 (Suffolk Rec Soc vol 35) [SF/PER]

1660-1678 Archdeaconry Court of Sudbury - Admon Acts; vol 4: 1660-1678 [Mf 823]

1660-1857 Episcopal Commissary Court of Bury St Edmunds - Index to Wills & Admons for the 1660-1858 (*Crossfield MSS*) [Mf 821-822]

1692-1857 Archdeaconry Court of the Sudbury - Cal of Wills; vol 3: 1692-1761; vol 4: 1762-1839; vol 5: 1840-1857 [Mf 818]

1699-1759 Some newly discovered Suffolk & Cambs Prob Invents (*Archdeaconry of Sudbury listing*) (Suffolk Roots vol 2 no 2) [SF/PER]

SUFFOLK, THE COURTS OF THE ARCHDEACONRY OF
ie the Court of the Commissary of the Bishop of Norwich at Ipswich & the Court of the Archdeacon of Suffolk
Superior Court: Norwich (Consistory)

1444-1477 Cal of Early Suffolk Wills in the Ipswich Registry 1444-1620 (*1444-1457 & 1458-1477 A-S*) (E Anglian new ser vols 1-5) [NF/PER]

1444-1600 Cal of Wills at Ipswich 1444-1600 [SF/G 67]; *Crisp's Surname List In* "List of Parish Regs & other Geneal Works" (*1897 ed*) [UK/R]; (*1904 & 1908 eds*) [TB/BIB]

1444-1700 Index of the Prob Recs (*wills, admons & invents*) of the Court of

the Archdeacon of Suffolk 1444-1700; vols 1 & 2 (BRS vols 90 & 91) [*both* BRS]

1444-1620 Archdeaconry Court of Suffolk - Indexes to Regs of Wills; vol 1: 1444-1620 [Mf 810]

1525-1640 Admon Grants of the Archdeaconry of Suffolk 1610-1640 with additions from the earliest Induction Book for that Archdeaconry 1525-1629 [SF/G 69]

1582-1702 Archdeaconry Court of Suffolk - Index to *the* Reg of Prob Invents 1582-1702 [Mf 814]

1609-1699 Ipswich Admons (Acts for 1609-1699) [Mf 813]

1602-1652 Archdeaconry of Suffolk - Cal of Wills 1602-1652 [SF/G 68]

1620-1624 *Abst of* Wills of the Archdeaconry of Suffolk; vol 1: 1620-1624 (Suffolk Rec Soc vol 31) [SF/PER]

1620-1660 Archdeaconry Court of Suffolk - Indexes to Regs of Wills; vol 2: 1620-1660 [Mf 810]

1625-1626 *Abst of* Wills of the Archdeaconry of Suffolk; vol 2: 1625-1626 (Suffolk Rec Soc vol 37) [SF/PER]

1640-1681 Ipswich Admons 1640-1681 (*index*) [SF/G 71]

1660-1736 Archdeaconry Court of Suffolk - Indexes to Regs of Wills; vol 3: 1660-1736 [Mf 810]

1674-1782 Archdeaconry Court of Suffolk - Indexes to Regs of Admons; vol 1: 1674-1782 [Mf 812]

1738-1805 Archdeaconry Court of Suffolk - Indexes to Regs of Wills; vol 4: 1738-1805 [Mf 811]

1751-1793 Cal of Wills at Ipswich 1751-1793 [SF/G 72]

1783-1857 Archdeaconry Court of Suffolk - Indexes to Regs of Admons; vol 2: 1783-1857 [Mf 812]

1806-1857 Archdeaconry Court of Suffolk - Indexes to Regs of Wills; vol 5: 1806-1857 [Mf 811]

SURREY, THE COURT OF THE COMMISSARY OF THE BISHOP OF WINCHESTER FOR THE PARTS OF
Superior Court: Winchester (Consistory)*; see also Surrey (Archdeaconry)*

1469-1649 Union Index of Surrey Prob Recs which survive before the year 1650 *including Commissary*

Court of Surrey recs (BRS vol 99)
[BRS]

1752-1858 Commissary Court of the Bishop
of Winchester; Index to the
Original Wills (collated with the
Act Books & Will Regs, etc; also
Peculiar Court of the Archbishop
of Canterbury in the Deanery of
Croydon - Index to Wills - 1752-
1858 (W Surrey FHS rec ser no
3; 2nd ed) *with Commissary
Invents List 1752-1821*
[SR/PER]; (W Surrey FHS rec ser
no 3; 1st ed) [Apply to Staff]

SURREY, THE COURT OF THE
ARCHDEACON OF
Superior Court: Winchester (Consistory) until
1660; Surrey (Commissary) from 1660

1469-1649 Union Index of Surrey Prob Recs
which survive before the year
1650 - *including Archdeacon's
Court of Surrey recs* (BRS vol 99)
[BRS]

1484-1490 Abst of Surrey Wills
(Archdeaconry Court "Spage"
Reg 1484-1490) (Surrey Rec Soc
vol 5, *no 17*) [SR/PER]

1532-1537 Surrey Will Abst; vol 3:
Archdeaconry Court of Surrey,
Reg "Heats" 1532-1537 (*BM Add
MSS 24,925*) [SR/G 54]

1544 Surrey Will Abst; vol 1: BM Add
MSS 24,925 (*stray Archdeaconry
Reg for 1544*) [SR/G 54]

1595-1608 Abst of Surrey Wills
(Archdeaconry Court
"Herningman" Reg 1595-1608)
(Surrey Rec ser vol 4, *nos 3, 7 &
15*) [SR/PER]

1595-1649 Surrey Will Abst; vol 2: Abst of
unfilmed wills in the
Archdeaconry Court of Surrey
1595-1649 (*BM Add MSS
24,925*) [SR/G 54]

1752-1858 Archdeaconry Court of Surrey -
Index to the Original Wills 1752-
1858 (collated with Act Books &
Will Regs) (W Surrey FHS rec ser
no 1; 2nd ed) *with Lists of
Nuncupative Wills 1752-1761 &
of Invents 1753-1828* [SR/PER];
also In "Surrey Wills" [SR/G 56];
(W Surrey FHS rec ser no 1; 1st
ed) [Apply to Staff]

SUTTON POYNTZ *see Preston*

SUTTON SCOTNEY *see Wonston*

**TACHBROOK, THE COURT OF THE
PREBEND OF BISHOPS** *see Bishops
Tachbrook*

TADLEY *see Overton*

TARRING *see Pagham*

TAUNTON, THE CONSISTORIAL COURT OF
THE ARCHDEACON OF
Superior Court: Wells (Episcopal Consistory)

15-16 C Index of Wills; an arbitrary coll of
15th & 16th C wills (*including
some from Taunton*) (*Soper*)
[WILLS/GEN]

1537-1799 Cal of Wills & Admons in the
Court of the Archdeacon of
Taunton; pts 1 & 2: Wills 1537-
1593 & 1597-1797; 3: Admons
1596-1799 (BRS vols 45 & 53)
[BRS]

1559-1777 Somerset Testmtry Docs
(*Archdeacon's Court of Taunton
will, admon, invent, etc index*)
(Genealogists' Mag vol 5)
[PER/GEN]

1561-1731 Taunton Archdeaconry: List of
Wills, Admons, Invents, Bonds,
Oath & Prob Cases ... *with abst*
[SO/G 65]

1729-1747 Somerset Prob Invents 1729-
1747 (*Archdeaconry of Taunton
cal*) (Studies in Somerset Hist
from Loc Recs for 1971) [SO/G
39 or SO Tracts]

TEMPLE BALSALL, THE COURT OF THE
MANOR OF
1675-1790 Cals of Original Wills & Admon
Papers transmitted (*to
Birmingham Probate Registry*)
from the registers of Barston,
Bishops Itchington, Baddesley
Clinton, Knowle, Packwood,
Tachbrook & Temple Balsall from
1675-1790 inclusive (BRS vol 7)
[BRS]

1743-1854 Cal of Original Wills & Admon
Papers from the Regs of *Temple
Balsall (with invents)* [Mf 802]

TEMPLE NEWSAM, THE COURT OF THE
MANOR OF
1612-1701 *Indexes to Wills &c in the
Peculiar Courts at Wakefield:
Temple Newsam Manor Court*

(Northern Genealogist vol 1) [PER/NOR]; Manorial Court of Temple Newsam - Index of Wills, Admons & Invents [Mf 878]

1612-1701 Abst of Wills, Admons, Invents, Tuits & Bonds of the Manor Court of Temple Newsam, W Riding of Yorks (Thoresby Soc Pubs vol 33) [YK/PER]

TEMPLETON, THE COURT OF THE MANOR OF

1670-1784 List of Wills, Admon Bonds & Invents In "Manorial Courts in Devon" (Genealogists' Mag vol 18) [PER/GEN]

TETTENHALL, THE COURT OF THE ROYAL PECULIAR JURISDICTION OF

formerly the Court of the Royal Peculiar Jurisdiction of the Dean & College of Tettenhall until its jurisdictions were sold by King Edward VI from which time the court became similar to other manorial jurisdictions; see also Lichfield (Consistory)

1529-1652 Cal of Wills & Admons registered in the various Peculiar Courts now preserved at the Lichfield Registry 1529-1652 (BRS vol 7) [BRS]

1661-1858 Cal of Wills & Admons of Peculiar Jurisdictions in the Diocese of Lichfield; vols 1 & 2 including: Royal Peculiar Court of Tettenhall 1661-1858 [Mf 801]

THAME, THE COURT OF THE PECULIAR JURISDICTION OF THE DEAN and CHAPTER OF LINCOLN IN

Superior Courts: Lincoln (Dean & Chapter) until 1834; Lincoln (Consistory) from 1834; see also Aylesbury; Banbury

1598-1633 List of Thame Invents 1598-1633 In "Farming Activities at Thame & Woodstock in the early 17th C: the evidence of Prob Invents" (Oxon Loc Hist vol 3 no 7) [OX/PER]

1603-1688 List of Thame Wills 1603-1688 In "Occupational Structure of Thame c1600-c1700" (Oxon Loc Hist vol 4 no 2) [OX/PER]

1698-1858 Index to Berks, Bucks & Oxon Peculiars - Wills & Admons with Invents & Bonds 1550-1858: Peculiar Court of Thame [Mf 913]

THORNEY, THE COURT OF THE PECULIAR JURISDICTION OF

Superior Court: Ely (Consistory); see also Canterbury (PCC); Huntingdon (Archdeaconry)

1775-1857 Index to Wills proved in the Peculiar Court of Thorney In "Episcopal Consistory Court of Ely - Wills Index; vol 3: 1764-1858 & Thorney Peculiars" [Mf 952]

THORPE-LE-SOKEN see Sokens

THORPE-NEXT-NORWICH, THE COURT OF THE PECULIAR JURISDICTION OF THE BISHOP OF NORWICH IN

the records of this Court appear to be merged with those of the Consistory Court of Norwich

TICHBORNE see Cheriton

TIMBERSCOMBE, THE COURT OF THE PREBEND OF

Superior Court: Wells (Episcopal Consistory)

1689-1850 Wells Wills; vol 13: Indexes to Wells Registry Cals - Peculiar Courts: Timberscombe Wills & Admons (Mfc) [Apply to Staff]

TIPTON see PREES

TIXOVER see Ketton

TOLLERTON see Alne

TOTNES, THE CONSISTORIAL COURT OF THE ARCHDEACON OF

Note: no index has survived apparently for this Archdeaconry

Superior Court: Exeter (Episcopal Principal Registry)

1529-1812 Index to copies of Lost Prob Recs of the Diocese of Exeter in the Library of the Society of Genealogists, London & other sources outside Devon, up to 1812 (wills, admons, invents, etc) [DE/G 25]

TREASURY SOLICITOR, THE OFFICE OF THE

see also Next of Kin Tracing & Other Monetary Records in the NATIONAL section

1808-1857 Bona Vacantia Div: Admon of Estates - Letters of Admon Case Papers 1808-1857: Index to PRO Class TS 17 [WILLS/GEN]

TRINITY COLLEGE AT CAMBRIDGE, THE PECULIAR JURISDICTION OF see Masham; see also Cambridge (University)

TWYFORD and OWSLEBURY, THE TESTAMENTARY JURISDICTION OF THE PARISH OF
Superior Court: Winchester (Archdeaconry)
1725-1775 Cal of Hants Wills proved in the Prerogative & Peculiar Courts of Winchester with other Prob Docs: Twyford including Owslebury - Separate Peculiar Wills [HA/G 62]

TYRLEY, THE COURT OF THE MANOR OF
1695-1841 Cal of Salop Wills & Admons (with invents) deposited in Shrewsbury District Probate Registry including: Manor of Tyrley (supps to Trans Salop Archl & Nat Hist Soc 4th ser vols 12 now 45 & 46) [Mf 800 or SH/PER]

UFFCULME, THE COURT OF THE PREBEND OF
Superior Court: Sarum (Dean)
1545-1799 Peculiar & Prebendal Courts of the Diocese of Sarum - Indexes to Wills & Admons with invents 1462-1810: Prebendary Court of Uffculme [Mf 836]
1555-1810 Index to Testmtry Papers at Salisbury; pt 1: Berks, Dorset & Uffculme Wills, Admons, Invents, etc preserved at Sarum (Genealogists' Mag vol 5) [PER/GEN or WL/G 52]
1800-1858 Sarum Courts, Deanery & Archdeaconry of Wiltshire; vol "A": Index for Wills & Admons 1800-1858 with names beginning A-B only [Mf 838]

UPHAM and DURLEY, THE TESTAMENTARY JURISDICTION OF THE PARISH OF
Superior Court: Winchester (Archdeaconry)
1569-1840 Cal of Hants Wills proved in the Prerogative & Peculiar Courts of Winchester with other Prob Docs: Upham & Durley - Separate Peculiar Wills [HA/G 62]

VICAR-GENERAL OF LEICESTER, THE COURT OF see Leicester (Archdeaconry)

VICAR-GENERAL OF LONDON, THE COURT OF THE see London (Consistory)

WADWORTH, THE COURT OF THE IMPROPRIATOR OF
formerly part of the Prebend of S Cave (qv)
Superior Courts: York (Chancery); York (Dean & Chapter)
1708-1760 York Registry; Cal of Wills & Admons - Separate Peculiars & Dean & Chapter's General Peculiars: Wadworth; York Registry; Names of Peculiars wherein separate lists are kept of the wills etc proved therein including Wadworth [both Mf 879]

WAKEFIELD, THE COURT OF THE MANOR OF
see also Barnoldswick; Crossley; Marsden; Silsden; Temple Newsam
1790-1792 Extr from Wills in the Court Rolls of the Manor of Wakefield (Wakefield Court Rolls ser of the Yorks Archl Soc vol 10) [YK/PER]

WALTHAM, BISHOPS see Bishops Waltham

WALTHAM, THE TESTAMENTARY JURISDICTION OF THE PARISH OF
Superior Court: Winchester (Archdeaconry)
1569-1840 Cal of Hants Wills proved in the Prerogative & Peculiar Courts of Winchester with other Prob Docs: N Waltham - Separate Peculiar Wills [HA/G 62]

WALTON (Bucks): see Aylesbury

WALTON (Lincs): see Heydour

WALTON-LE-SOKEN see Sokens

WANTAGE, THE COURT OF THE PECULIAR JURISDICTION OF THE DEAN and CANONS OF WINDSOR IN
Superior Court: Sarum (Dean)
1550-1856 Index to Berks, Bucks & Oxon Peculiars - Wills & Admons with Invents & Bonds 1550-1858: Peculiar Court of the Dean & Canons of Windsor in Wantage [Mf 913]
1582-1668 Prob Recs of the Court of the Dean & Canons of Windsor, (index of Wills & Invents) 1582-1668, from Oxon RO In "Berks Wills from Various Sources"

[BK/G 76]

1613-1799 Peculiar & Prebendal Courts of
the Diocese of Sarum - Indexes
to Wills & Admons 1462-1810:
*Peculiar Court of the Dean &
Canons of Windsor (1613, 1668-
1779)* [Mf 836]

1668-1840 Peculiar Court of the Dean &
Canons of Windsor - *Index to*
Wills & Admons 1668-1840, from
Wilts RO [*In* "Berks Wills from
Various Sources" BK/G 76 or, *as
a separate book*, BK/G 78]

1800-1858 Sarum Courts, Deanery &
Archeaconry of Wiltshire; vol
"A": Index for Wills & *Admons*
1800-1858 with names beginning
A-B only [Mf 838]

WARDS and LIVERIES, THE HIGH COURT OF

Superior Court: Chancery (High Court)

1608-1661 *Cal of* Depositions - Court of
Wards 1608-1627 & 1631-1645
(Bundles 34-61) (*Fothergill's
abst*); Index to Depositions: Court
of Wards (Fothergill's MSS) -
1608-1627 & 1631-1645
(Bundles 34-61) [*both* SP/WAR]

WARMFIELD WITH HEATH, THE COURT OF THE MANOR OF

1613-1691 Manor Court of Warmfield with
Heath, County Yorks - *Index to*
Wills & Admons (Northern
Genealogist vol 1) [PER/NOR]

WARTHILL, THE COURT OF THE PREBEND OF

Superior Courts: York (Chancery); York
(Dean & Chapter)

1661-1837 York Registry; Names of
Peculiars wherein separate lists
are kept of the wills etc proved
therein *including Warthill from
1681 to the present time*; York
Registry; Cal of Vacancy &
Prebendal Wills *including Warthill*
[*both* Mf 879]

WASPERTON see Alveston

WATERFORD and LISMORE, THE CONSISTORY COURT OF THE BISHOP OF

Superior Court: Armagh (PCA)

1645-1800 *Phillimore's* Indexes to Irish Wills;
vol 2: Cal of Wills in the Dioceses
of Cashel & Emly, Killaloe &

Kilfenora, Waterford & Lismore,
Limerick, Ardfert & Aghadoe &
the Peculiar Jurisdiction of the
Dean of Lismore [IR/G 86]

WEEFORD see Alrewas

WEIGHTON, THE COURT OF THE PREBEND OF

also called Market Weighton

Superior Courts: York (Chancery); York
(Dean & Chapter)

1660-1856 York Registry; Names of
Peculiars wherein separate lists
are kept of the wills etc proved
therein *including Weighton &
Shipton 1660 to the present time*;
York Registry; Cal of Vacancy &
Prebendal Wills *including
Weighton* [*both* Mf 879]

WELL see Sutton, Long

WELLS, THE EPISCOPAL CONSISTORY COURT OF THE BISHOP OF BATH and

Superior Court: Canterbury (PCC)

1311-1377 *Abst of* Wells Wills of the 14th C
(Somerset & Dorset N&Q vol 8)
[SO/PER]

1528-1536 Wells Wills arranged in parishes
& annotated (*Weaver's abst of
will books in the District Probate
Registry at Wells*) [SO/G 54]

1528-1585 Wells Wills; vol 1 i: Index to
Wells Registry Cals - Index to
Copy Wills - pt 1: Books 1-19
(Mfc) [Apply to Staff]

1528-1600 Somerset Wills from Exeter -
Cals of Wells Wills; pts 1: Copies
of Wills at Wells 1528-1585 & 2:
Index of Copies of Wills 1573-
1600; pt 3 Index of Original Wills
1543-1600 (Somerset Rec Soc
vol 62) [SO/PER]

1539-1541 Wells Wills; abst of Somerset
Wills in the Serel Coll (Procs
Somerset Archl & Nat Hist Soc
vol 61) [SO/PER]

1543-1648 Wells Wills; vols 1 ii: Index to
Wells Registry Cals - Index to
Copy Wills - pt 2: Books 20-47
(*1573-1635*) & 1 iii: Index to
Wells Registry Cals - Index to
Original Wills (*1543-1648*) (*both*
Mfc) [Apply to Staff]

1660-1830 Wells Wills; vols 2 & 3 (*in 2 pts*):
Index to Bishop's Court Wills
(*1660-1739*), 4: Index to Bishop's

Court Wills (*1740-1759*), 5: Index to Bishop's Court Wills (*1760-1780*), 6: Index to Bishop's Court Wills (*1780-1799*) & 7 i: Index to Bishop's Court Wills (*1800-1830*) (*all* Mfc) [Apply to Staff]

WELLS, THE CONSISTORIAL COURT OF THE ARCHDEACON OF
Superior Court: Wells (Episcopal Consistory)
1543-1556 *Abst of* Somerset Medieval Wills; 4th ser: wills from Wells deposited in the Diocesan Registry, Wells *1543-1546* & *1554-1556* (Somerset Rec Soc vol 40) [SO/PER]
1660-1800 Wells Wills; vols 8: Index to Archdeacon's Court Wills - pt 1: *1660-1699*, 9: Index to Archdeacon's Court Wills - pt 2: *1700-1755* & 10: Index to Archdeacon's Court Wills - pt 3: *1756-1800* (*all* Mfc) [Apply to Staff]

WELLS, THE CONSISTORIAL COURT OF THE DEAN OF
Superior Court: Wells (Episcopal Consistory); *see also Wells (Dean & Chapter)*
1558 Wills proved at the Deanery of Wells (*list for 1558*) (Somerset & Dorset N&Q vol 7) [SO/PER]
1660-1804 Wells Wills; vol 11: Index to Dean's Court Wills & Admons (Mfc) [Apply to Staff]
1712-1775 Wells Wills; vols 7 ii: Index to Dean's Court Admons & 12 ii: Index to Dean's Court Admons (*both* Mfc) [Apply to Staff]

WELLS, THE COURT OF THE SUB DEAN OF *see Wookey*

WELLS, THE CONSISTORIAL COURT OF THE DEAN and CHAPTER OF
Superior Court: Wells (Episcopal Consistory); *see also Wells (Dean)*
1254-1380 Abst of Enrolled Wills & Admons 1254-1380 *In* "HMC Cal of the MSS of the Dean & Chapter of Wells; vol 1" [Apply to Staff]
1311-1496 Abst of Wills in Wells Cathedral Charters 1311-1496 *In* "HMC Cal of the MSS of the Dean & Chapter of Wells; vol 2" [Apply to Staff]
1372-1484 Prob Copies of Wills at Wells (*abst from the Dean & Chapter's*

Additional MSS) In "3rd HMC Rep" [SP/HMC]
1660-1858 Wells Wills; vols 12 iii: Index to Dean & Chapter's Court Invents & Admon Papers (*1660-1837*) & 12 i: Index to Dean & Chapter's Court Wills (*1660-1720*) & Admons (*1837-1858*) (*both* Mfc) [Apply to Staff]

WELLS, THE COURT OF THE CHANCELLOR THE CATHEDRAL CHURCH AT *see Kingsbury Episcopi*

WELLS, THE COURT OF THE PRECENTOR THE CATHEDRAL CHURCH AT *see Litton*

WELSHAMPTON *see Ellesmere*

WESTBURY *see Sarum (Precentor)*

WESTERDALE, THE COURT OF THE MANOR OF
1550-1765 *List of* Wills on the Westerdale Court Rolls (*1669-1765 with abst for 1550-1575*) *In* "Miscellanea vol 2" (Yorks Archl Soc rec ser vol 74) [YK/PER]

WESTMINSTER, THE CONSISTORY COURT OF THE BISHOP OF *see Westminster (Abbot/Dean & Chapter); see also London (Consistory)*

WESTMINSTER, THE CONSISTORIAL COURT OF THE DEAN and CHAPTER OF THE ROYAL COLLEGIATE CHURCH OF ST PETER AT
until 1540 this was the Court of the Abbot & Chapter of Westminster & then the Consistory Court of the Bishop of Westminster until 1550; this included the Court of the Commissary of the Royal Collegiate Church of St Martin le Grand & the Essex Prebends of Creshall (until 1540), of Good Easter (until 1540), of Newport (until 1540) & of St Mary's Parish in Maldon
Superior Court: Delegates (High Court); *see also London (Consistory) & Middlesex (Archdeaconry - Middx)*
1228-1700 *Index to* Misc Testmtry Recs 1228-1700 preserved amongst the muniments of Westminster Abbey *In* "Indexes to the Ancient Testmtry Recs of Westminster" [MX/G 242]
1310-1674 *List of* Wills, Letters of Admons, etc *In* "Cal of Muniments of Westminster Abbey; portion

entitled 'Miscellanea'" ("4th HMC Rep") [SP/HMC]

1322-1675 *Extr from* Westminster Wills (N&Q vols 172 & 173) [N&Q]

1504-1700 Index to wills proved in the Peculiar Court of Westminster 1504-1700 *In* "Indexes to the Ancient Testmtry Recs of Westminster" [MX/G 242]

1504-1829 Cal of the Grants of Prob & Admon & of other Testmtry of the Commissary Court of the Venerable Dean & Chapter of Westminster *including St Mary's parish, Maldon 1504-1609, 1622-1641 & 1660-1829* [Mf 904]

1541-1550 Consistory Court of Westminster *Will Book Abst*; vols 2: Reg "Thirlby" 1540-1548 & 3: Reg "Wymesley" 1548-1556 (*relates to the Consistory Court of London (qv) after 1550*) [Mf 773]

WESTON *see St Mary Extra*

WETWANG, THE COURT OF THE PREBEND OF
Superior Courts: York (Chancery); York (Dean & Chapter); *see also Fridaythorpe*

1658-1709 York Registry; Cal of Wills & Admons - Separate Peculiars & Dean & Chapter's General Peculiars: *Wetwang*; York Registry; Names of Peculiars wherein separate lists are kept of the wills etc proved therein *including Wetwang* [*both* Mf 879]

WEYMOUTH, THE COURT OF THE MAYOR OF THE BOROUGH OF
1596 Cal of Wills & Admons relating to Dorset in the Courts of Sarum; *from Borough of Weymouth recs* (BRS vol 53) [BRS]

WHITCHURCH, THE TESTAMENTARY JURISDICTION OF THE PARISH OF
Superior Court: Winchester (Archdeaconry)

1605-1841 Cal of Hants Wills proved in the Prerogative & Peculiar Courts of Winchester with other Prob Docs: *Whitchurch including Freefolk - Separate Peculiar Wills* [HA/G 62]

WHITCOMBE *see Milton Abbas*

WHITE LACKINGTON, THE COURT OF THE PREBEND OF
Superior Court: Wells (Episcopal Consistory)

1665-1837 Wells Wills; vol 13: Indexes to Wells Registry Cals - Peculiar Courts: *White Lackington Wills & Admons* (Mfc) [Apply to Staff]

WHITTINGTON and BASWICH, THE COURT OF THE PREBEND OF
Superior Court: Lichfield (Dean & Chapter)

1529-1652 Cal of Wills & Admons registered in the various Peculiar Courts now preserved at the Lichfield Registry 1529-1652 (BRS vol 7) [BRS]

1674-1858 Cal of Wills & Admons of Peculiar Jurisdictions in the Diocese of Lichfield; vols 1 & 2 *including*: Prebendal Court of Whittington & Baswich 1674-1858 [Mf 801]

WIGTOWN, THE COMMISSARIOT OF
Superior Court: Court of Session; *see also Edinburgh (Commissariot)*

1700-1800 Commissariot Rec of Wigtown; Testmts 1700-1800 (*index to Warrants, Edicts & Processes as the Reg has not survived*) (Scottish Rec Soc vol 23) [SC/PER]

1801-1823 *Wigtown Regs of Testmts In* "Index to Regs of Testmts for various Commissariots 1801-1823" [Mf 2910]

WILSFORD and WOODFORD, THE COURT OF THE PREBEND OF
Superior Court: Sarum (Dean)

1615-1798 Peculiar & Prebendal Courts of the Diocese of Sarum - Indexes to Wills & Admons 1462-1810: *Prebendal Court of Wilsford & Woodford (with invents)* [Mf 836]

1800-1854 Wilts Wills Beneficiaries Index 1800-1858: Name Abst; vol 4: Bishopstone 1800-1848, Wilsford & Woodford 1800-1854, Chute & Chisenbury 1800-1855, Coombe & Harnham 1800-1856 (Peculiar Court docs 398-507) [WL/G 67]

1800-1858 Sarum Courts, Deanery & Archdeaconry of Wiltshire; vol "A": Index for Wills & *Admons* 1800-1858 with names beginning A-B only [Mf 838]

WILTON, BISHOP *see Bishop Wilton*

WILTSHIRE, THE COURT OF THE ARCHDEACON OF
Superior Court: Sarum (Consistory)
1557-1799   *Index to* Wills, Admons, Bonds & Invents 1557-1799 [WL/G 55]
1800-1858   Sarum Courts, Deanery & Archdeaconry of Wiltshire; vol "A": Index for Wills & *Admons* 1800-1858 with names beginning A-B only [Mf 838]

WIMBORNE MINSTER, THE COURT OF THE PECULIAR JURISDICTION OF
Superior Court: Dorset (Archdeaconry)*; see also Canterbury (PCC)*
1560-1637   Cals of Wills & Admons relating to Dorset in the Courts of Sarum; *from Wimborne Minster muniments* (BRS vol 53) [BRS]
1565-1857   Cals of Wills & Admons relating to the County of Dorset preserved in the Probate Registry at Blandford & among the Ecclesiastical Recs of Wimborne Minster to 1857 (*including the Peculiar Court of Wimborne Minster 1565-1700 & 1815-1857*) (*Fry MSS*) [Apply to Staff]
1588-1719   Cals of Dorset Wills, Admons, etc in the Probate Registry at Blandford; pt 1: Cal of Invents in the Peculiar Court of *Wimborne Minster* (BRS vol 53) [BRS]
1590-1823   Cals of Wills & Admons relating to the County of Dorset, proved in the Consistory Court (Dorset Div) of the late Diocese of Bristol 1681-1792, in the Archdeaconry Court of Dorset 1568-1792 & in the several peculiars 1660-1799 - *including* wills & admons of the Peculiar of Wimborne Minster previous to 1792 (*wills 1590-1823 & admons 1666-1814*) (BRS vol 22) [BRS]
1603-1857   Peculiar Court of Wimborne Minster - Index to Admons 1675-1857; Index to Wills 1603-1857; Copies of Original Wills: Bundles "A" & "B": 1603-1857 [Mf 732]

WINCHESTER, THE CONSISTORY COURT OF THE BISHOP OF
including the Registry of the Bishop of Winchester
Superior Court: Canterbury (PCC)*; for Hants,*

see also Winchester (Archdeaconry)
1398-1560   Unclassified Wills *in Winchester*, List of Loose Wills 1398, 1469, 1502-1560 but not indexed in either Consistory or Archdeaconry Court Indexes [HA/G 57]
1448-1515   *Index to* Some Winchester Wills (Genealogists' Mag vol 12) [PER/GEN]
1502-1602   Index of Wills *of testators from Surrey* proved in the Consistory Court of Winchester 1502-1602 [Apply to Staff]
1502-1640   Wills, Admons & Invents with the Winchester Diocesan Recs - *indexes to Registered Wills in the Consistory Court 1502, 1541, 1557, 1617-1620 & 1623-1640*; Diocese of Winchester; Index to Registered Copies of Wills in the charge of the Diocesan Registrar (*1502, 1541, 1557 & 1617-1640*) [HA/G 40 & 67]
1502-1652   Index of Wills proved in the Consistory Court of Winchester 1502-1652 [HA/G 64]; Winchester Probate Registry - Consistory Court *Index of* Wills of Testators in Surrey; pts 1 & 2: 1502-1652 [Apply to Staff]
1531-1700   Testmtry Cases *In* Diocese of Winchester; Consistory Court Cause Papers before 1700; vols 1: Lists & Abst & 2: Indexes of Names & Places [HA/G 12-13]
1540-1572   Wills, Admons & Invents with the Winchester Diocesan Recs; *index to Diocesan Court Book 26* [HA/G 40]
1540-1820   Diocese of Winchester; Wills, Invents & Admons remaining in the charge of the Diocesan Registrar: *Lists of Wills from Cause Papers 1552-1820 & of Commissions for the Grant of Admons 1705-1797; index of Invents 1540-1799*; Wills, Admons & Invents with the Winchester Diocesan Recs - *Invents List 1540-1799* [HA/G 68 & 40]
1552-1857   Wills, Admons & Invents with the Winchester Diocesan Recs - *indexes to Original Wills or copies in the Diocesan Regs 1552-1823 & 1857* [HA/G 40]
1576-1601   *Extr from* Testmtry Cases *In*

Winchester Consistory Court
Depositions 1561-1602 [HA/G
22]

1587-1635 Diocese of Winchester; Some
Prob & Admons granted in the
Diocese of Winchester 1587-
1635 with an appx of various
memoranda in the recs; vols 1:
Abst & Memoranda *from the Act
Books* & 2: Indexes [HA/G 69-70]

1605-1725 Index to a Parcel of Invents &
Admons at the Diocesan
Muniment Room, Winchester
1605-1725 [Apply to Staff]

1660-1749 Index of Wills proved in the
Consistory Court of Winchester
1660-1749 [HA/G 65]

1664-1797 Wills, Admons & Invents with the
Winchester Diocesan Recs -
*index to Admons in the Diocesan
Regs 1664-1797 with
Commissions for Taking Oath
1672-1739* [HA/G 40]

1700-1849 *Cal of* Winchester Guardnshps
after 1700 from Diocesan Recs
(*1700-1811 & 1849*) (reprinted
from the Genealogists' Mag with
a consolidated index) [HA/G 32]
(*also in* Genealogists' Mag vols
14 & 15) [PER/GEN]

1700-1858 Testmtry Cases *In* Diocese of
Winchester; Consistory Court
Cause Papers from 1700; vols 1:
Lists & Abst & 2: Indexes of
Names & Places [HA/G 14-15]

1750-1857 Index of Wills proved in the
Consistory Court of Winchester
1750-1857 [HA/G 66]

1795 Wills proved in the Registry of the
Bishop of Winchester during the
vacancy of the Archdeaconry
from 19th Jan-7th Jul 1795 [HA/G
57]

**WINCHESTER, THE REGISTRY OF THE
BISHOP OF** *see Winchester (Consistory)*

**WINCHESTER, THE COURT OF THE
ARCHDEACON OF**
*also called the Court of the Commissary of the
Bishop of Winchester for the Parts of the
County of Southampton*
Superior Court: Winchester (Consistory)
1398-1560 Unclassified Wills *in Winchester*;
List of Loose Wills 1398, 1469,
1502-1560 but not indexed in
either Consistory or
Archdeaconry Court Indexes

[HA/G 57]

1502-1653 Cal of Wills proved in the
Archdeaconry Court of
Winchester 1502-1653 (*in 3 pts*)
[HA/G 56]

1557-1626 Wills, Admons & Invents with the
Winchester Diocesan Recs -
*indexes to Registered Wills in the
Archdeaconry Court 1557 &
1617-1626*; Diocese of
Winchester; Index to Registered
Copies of Wills in the charge of
the Diocesan Registrar
(*Archdeacon's Court 1617-1623
& 1626*) [HA/G 40 & 67]

1561-1708 Cal of Admons from the
Archdeaconry Court of
Winchester 1561-1653 & 1660-
1708 including Testmtry Causes
1666-1678, 1700-1708 [HA/G 58]

1571-1858 Hants RO - Index to Hants Wills,
Admons & Invents 1571-1858:
Indexes by name, occupation &
place (Mfc) [Apply to Staff]

1660-1792 Cal of Wills proved in the
Archdeaconry Court of
Winchester 1660-1792 [HA/G 59]

1665-1694 Diocese of Winchester; Cal of
Admons 1665-1668 from an
Admon Act Book in the charge of
the Diocesan Registrar [Apply to
Staff]; Diocese of Winchester;
Admon Act Books 1669-1694
(Archdeaconry of Winchester) (in
the Diocesan Muniment Room
1669-1674 & 1677-1694) [HA/G
71]

1709-1741 Cal of Wills proved in the
Archdeaconry Court of
Winchester 1709-1741 [HA/G 60]

1741-1858 Cal of Wills (*1741-1752, 1760-
1764*) & Admons (*1741-1858*)
from the Archdeaconry Court of
Winchester 1741-1841 [HA/G 61]

1742-1858 Cal of Wills 1742-1858 proved in
the Archdeaconry Court at
Winchester with Wills proved in
the Registry of the Bishop of
Winchester during the vacancy of
the Archdeaconry from 19th Jan-
7th Jul 1795 [HA/G 57]

**WINCHESTER, THE COURT OF THE
PECULIAR JURISDICTION OF THE MASTER
OF THE HOSPITAL OF ST CROSS AT**
*sometimes called the "Hospital of St Faith or
St Cross"*
Superior Court: Winchester (Archdeaconry)

1614-1807 Cal of Hants Wills proved in the Prerogative & Peculiar Courts of Winchester with other Prob Docs: *St Faith or St Cross - Index of Peculiar Courts* [HA/G 62]

WINDSOR IN WANTAGE, THE COURT OF THE PECULIAR JURISDICTION OF THE DEAN and CANONS OF *see Wantage*

WINGHAM, THE PECULIAR JURISDICTION OF THE PROVOST OF THE COLLEGE AT *the College was dissolved in 1547: see Canterbury (Consistory) for later records*

WINTON *see Winchester*

WISBEACH, THE COURT OF THE MAYOR OF THE BOROUGH OF
1583-1793 List of Wills *In* "HMC Rep on the MSS of the Corp of Wisbeach" ("9th HMC Rep") [SP/HMC]

WISTOW, THE COURT OF THE PREBEND OF
Superior Courts: York (Chancery); York (Dean & Chapter)
1617-1707 York Registry; Cal of Wills & Admons - Separate Peculiars & Dean & Chapter's General Peculiars: *Wistow*; York Registry; Names of Peculiars wherein separate lists are kept of the wills etc proved therein *including Wistow* [*both* Mf 879]

WITHAM FRIARY, THE COURT OF THE PECULIAR JURISDICTION IN THE MANOR OF
Superior Court: Wells (Episcopal Consistory)
1669-1821 Wells Wills; vol 13: Indexes to Wells Registry Cals - Peculiar Courts: *Witham Friary Wills, Admons, Invents & Tuit Bonds* (Mfc) [Apply to Staff]

WITHERNWICK *see Holme Archiepiscopi*

WITHINGTON, THE COURT OF THE PECULIAR JURISDICTION OF
Superior Court: Gloucester (Consistory)
1622-1776 *Index to* Withington Wills & Invents 1622-1776 *In* "Wills & Admons proved in Glos Peculiar Courts" (Gloucester City Libs Loc Hist Pamphlet no 2) [GL/G 31 or GL Tracts]
1624-1776 Withington Peculiar - *Cal of*

Invents, Wills & Admons) (Trans Bristol & Glos Rec Soc vol 40) [GL/PER]; Wills proved & Admons granted in the Court of the Peculiar & Exempt Jurisdiction of Withington (offprint from the Trans Bristol & Glos Rec Soc vol 40) [GL Tracts]

WIVELISCOMBE, THE COURT OF THE PREBEND OF
Superior Court: Wells (Episcopal Consistory)
1656-1857 Wells Wills; vol 13: Indexes to Wells Registry Cals - Peculiar Courts: *Wiveliscombe & Fitzhead Wills, Admons & Tuit Bonds 1656-1857 & Admon Bonds, etc 1662-1719 (in 2 pts)* (Mfc) [Apply to Staff]

WOLVERHAMPTON, THE COURT OF THE ROYAL PECULIAR JURISDICTION OF
Superior Court: Delegates (High Court); *see also Lichfield (Consistory)*
1529-1652 Cal of Wills & Admons registered in the various Peculiar Courts now preserved at the Lichfield Registry 1529-1652 (BRS vol 7) [BRS]
1618-1847 Cal of Wills & Admons of Peculiar Jurisdictions in the Diocese of Lichfield; *vols 1 & 2 including*: Royal Peculiar Court of Wolverhampton 1618-1847 [Mf 801]

WOMBRIDGE, THE COURT OF THE PECULIAR JURISDICTION IN THE MANOR OF
formerly the Peculiar Jurisdiction of Wombridge Abbey
Superior Court: Lichfield (Consistory)
1787-1854 Cal of Salop Wills & Admons *(with invents)* deposited in Shrewsbury District Probate Registry *including*: Manor of Wombridge (supps to Trans Salop Archl & Nat Hist Soc 4th ser vols 12 *now 45* & 46) [Mf 800 or SH/PER]

WONSTON, THE TESTAMENTARY JURISDICTION OF THE PARISH OF
Superior Court: Winchester (Archdeaconry)
1541-1674 Cal of Hants Wills proved in the Prerogative & Peculiar Courts of Winchester with other Prob Docs: *Wonston including Sutton*

Scotney - *Index of "B" Wills 1541-1597, Enrolled Peculiar Wills 1624-1674 & Separate Peculiar Wills 1581-1674* [HA/G 62]

WOODBURY, THE COURT OF THE PECULIAR JURISDICTION OF THE CUSTOS and COLLEGE OF VICARS CHORAL OF EXETER IN
Superior Court: Exeter (Dean & Chapter)
1529-1812 Index to copies of Lost Prob Recs of the Diocese of Exeter in the Library of the Society of Genealogists, London & other sources outside Devon, up to 1812 (*wills, admons, invents, etc*) [DE/G 25]
1633-1858 Peculiar Court of the Custos & College of Vicars Choral, Woodbury 1633-1858 (*cal of Wills & Admons*) with *ca*l of Wills proved & Admons granted in the Peculiar Jurisdiction of the Dean of Exeter within the Close of Exeter & the parish of Braunton, Devon 1632-1857 [DE/G 72]

WOODFORD *see Wilsford*

WOODHAY and ASHMANSWORTH, THE TESTAMENTARY JURISDICTION OF THE PARISH OF
Superior Court: Winchester (Archdeaconry)
1587-1840 Cal of Hants Wills proved in the Prerogative & Peculiar Courts of Winchester with other Prob Docs: *E Woodhay including Ashmansworth - Enrolled Peculiar Wills 1622-1628, Index of "B" Wills 1587 & Separate Peculiar Wills 1587-1840* [HA/G 62]

WOOLLAND *see Milton Abbas*

WOOKEY, THE COURT OF THE PECULIAR JURISDICTION OF THE SUB DEAN OF WELLS IN
Superior Court: Wells (Episcopal Consistory)
1627-1857 Wells Wills; vol 13: Indexes to Wells Registry Cals - Peculiar Courts: *Wookey Wills, Admons, etc* (Mfc) [Apply to Staff]

WOOTTON, NORTH *see Pilton*

WORCESTER, THE CONSISTORY COURT OF THE BISHOP OF

Superior Court: Canterbury (PCC)
1277-1523 List of Wills registered in the Episcopal Regs of the See of Worcester (Misc Gen et Her 5th ser vol 4) [PER/MIS]
1375-1395 *Index of* Wills *In* "Cal of the Reg of Henry Wakefield, Bishop of Worcester 1375-1395" (Worcs Hist Soc new ser vol 7) [WO/PER]
1451-1642 Cal of Wills & Admons registered in the Consistory court of the Bishop of Worcester 1451-1642 (BRS & Worcs Hist Soc JP); pt 1: Transcripts 1451-1642 (*8 vols of Wills, Invents, Admons, Bonds, etc 1451-1495, 1509-1553, 1545-1621, 1623, 1633 & 1642*); pt 2: Original Wills 1493-1560; pt 3: Original Wills 1560-1581 [WO/G 43]
1451-1652 Cal of Wills, Admons, Marriage Licences & Sequestrations in the Consistory Court of the Bishop of Worcester, now deposited in the Probate Registry at Worcester; vols 1: 1451-1600 & 2: 1601-1652 (*with invents*) (BRS vols 31 & 39) [*both* BRS];
1509-1553 Worcester Bishop's Registry - Testamenta Vetusta Vigorniensia (*Will Book with some invents*); vols 2: 1509-1527, 4: 1543-1553 & 5: 1545-1553 [Mf 840]
1530-1668 Worcester Bishop's Registry - List of Prob Invents 1530-1668 (*A-M only*) [WO/G 38]
1536-1716 Worcester Admon Bonds & other Testmtry Papers formerly in the Edgar Tower, Worcester; pts 1: Cal of Admon Bonds (*1536-1700*), 2: Index of Worcester Invents (*1548-1716*), 3: Index of Testmtry Papers (*16-18th C, BIR-Z only*) & 4: Consistory Court Papers (*1593-1696*) [WO/G 39]
1545-1584 Index to Worcester Wills; vols 1: 1545-1550 & 2: 1554-1584 (*Phillips MSS*) [WO/G 37]
1554-1642 Worcester Bishop's Registry - Testamenta Vetusta Vigorniensia (*Will Book with some invents*); vols 6 pt 1: 1554-1561, 6 pt 2: 1561-1584 & 7: 1585-1642 [Mf 841]
1661-1858 Index to Worcs Wills (*wills & admons in the Diocesan Act Books*); vols 1: 1661-1668; 2:

1668-1676; 3: 1676-1685; 4: 1685-1691, 5: 1691-1699 & 6: 1699-1711; 7: 1711-1723 & 8: 1723-1730; 9: 1730-1742 & 10: 1742-1756; 11: 1756-1767 & 12: 1767-1784; 13: 1784-1799 & 14: 1799-1808; 15: 1809-1822 & 16: 1823-1836; 17: 1836-1847; 18: 1847-1856 & 19: 1857-1858 [Mf 842-852]

WORCESTER, THE ARCHDEACONRY OF
not a probate jurisdiction: see Worcester (Consistory)

WORCESTER, THE COURT OF THE DEAN and CHAPTER OF
Superior Court: Worcester (Consistory)
1331-1400 Some Early Wills at Worcester (*abst of wills in Worcester Cathedral Lib amongst the Dean & Chapter's Archives*) (Misc Gen et Her 5th ser vol 4) [PER/MIS]
1528-1539 Worcester Bishop's Registry; vol 1: Dean & Chapter's Will Book [Mf 840]

WORCESTER, THE TESTAMENTARY JURISDICTION OF THE PARISH OF ST SWITHIN IN
Superior Court: Worcester (Consistory)
1429-1495 Early Wills in Private Possession (*St Swithin's, Worcester*) (Misc Gen et Her 5th ser vol 4) [PER/MIS]

WORCESTER, THE DISTRICT PROBATE REGISTRY IN
Superior Registry: London (Principal Probate Registry)
1858-1928 Index to Regs of Wills proved in Worcester District Probate Registry 1858-1928; vols 1 & 2 [WO/G 42]

WRITHLINGTON *see Fordington*

WRITTLE WITH ROXWELL, THE COURT OF THE PECULIAR JURISDICTION OF THE WARDEN, FELLOWS and SCHOLARS OF NEW COLLEGE AT OXFORD IN
see also London (Commissary - Essex & Herts); Oxford (University)
1607-1858 Wills at Chelmsford *including the Peculiar Court of Writtle with Roxwell from 1607*; Index to Wills now preserved in the Essex RO at Chelmsford; vols 1: 1400-

1619, 2: 1620-1720 & 3: 1721-1858 (BRS vols 78, 79 & 84) [*all* BRS]
1618-1851 *Abst of* Wills, Admons, Bonds & Invents in the Peculiar of Writtle with Roxwell, County Essex [ES/G 65]
1635-1749 *Abst of Writtle & Roxwell* Farm & Cottage Invents of Mid-Essex 1635-1749 (Essex RO Pub no 8) (2nd ed) [ES/G 18]

YATTON, THE COURT OF THE PREBEND OF
Superior Court: Wells (Episcopal Consistory)
1660-1857 Wells Wills; vol 13: Indexes to Wells Registry Cals - Peculiar Courts: *Yatton Wills, Admons, Invents & Tuit Bonds 1662-1857 & Admon Bonds, etc 1660-1733* (in 2 pts) (Mfc) [Apply to Staff]

YETMINSTER and GRIMSTON, THE COURT OF THE PREBEND OF
Superior Court: Sarum (Dean)
1568-1757 *Abst of* Prob Invents (*1576-1757*) & Manorial Excepts (*ie enrolled extr 1568-1732*) of Chetnole, Leigh & Yetminster [DO/L 19]
1654-1799 Peculiar & Prebendal Courts of the Diocese of Sarum - Indexes to Wills & Admons 1462-1810: *Prebendal Court of Yetminster & Grimston (with invents)* [Mf 836]; Cal of Wills & Admons relating to Dorset in the Courts of Sarum & elsewhere (*including Yetminster with Chetnole, Grimston & Leigh*) (BRS vol 53) [BRS]
1800-1858 Sarum Courts, Deanery & Archdeaconry of Wiltshire; vol "A": Index for Wills & *Admons* 1800-1858 with names beginning A-B only [Mf 838]

**YORK, THE PREROGATIVE COURT OF THE
ARCHBISHOP OF ("the PCY")**
*this Court was created in c1502; prior to that
date the Archiepiscopal Registers or the
Exchequer Court (with whom PCY probate
records were generally combined) contain
provincial probates; the Dean of York
exercised some provincial probate jurisdiction
too; collections relating to locations, counties
or countries or for particular groups are shown
under the appropriate place or group*
Superior Courts: Canterbury (PCC),
Delegates (High Court), York (Dean & Chapter
*- during vacancies etc); see also York
(Chancery); York (Exchequer)*

PCY Administrations
16 C-1858 Wills & Admons etc: listings
taken from cals of the old
Diocese of York & the Diocese of
Lincoln (with certain additions
from Durham) (*index BUR-WRI*)
(Fam Hist vols 2 & 3) [PER/FAM]
1502-1686 Admons in the York Registry
(*including Prerogative Court
cals*); vols 1: 1502-1514, 2: 1514-
1553, 3: 1553-1568, 4: 1568-
1585, 5: 1585-1594, 6: 1594-
1602, 7: 1603-1611, 8: 1612-
1619, 9: 1620-1627, 10: 1627-
1652, 11: 1660-1665, 12**: 1666-
1672, 13: 1673-1680, 14: 1681-
1686 (appx to Yorks Archl Soc
rec ser vols 6, 11, 14, 19, 22, 24,
26, 28, 32, 35, 49, 60**, 68 &
appx 1 to 89) [*all* YK/PER *except*
**vol 60: Apply to Staff]
1679-1689 Act Books of the PCY (*cal of wills
& admons Mar 1679-Jun 1689*)
(Northern Genealogist vols 2-4)
[PER/NOR]
1688-1731 Cal of Prob Recs taken from the
Act Books of the PCY 1688-1731
[Mf 928]
1731-1799 York District Probate Registry
Cals of Wills & Admons
(*including the PCY*); vols 2: 1731-
1737 & 3: 1737-1741; 4: 1741-
1745, 5: 1745-1757 & 6: 1757-
1770; 7: 1771-1777, 8: 1777-
1785, 9: 1785-1793 & 10: 1793-
1799 [Mf 854-856]
1800-1842 Index to Wills, Admons, etc at the
PCY 1800-1842 (*A-G*) [Apply to
Staff]
1800-1858 York District Probate Registry
Cals of Wills & Admons
(*including the PCY*); vols 11:

1800-1803, 12: 1804-1809,13:
1809-1814 & 14: 1814-1819; 15:
1819-1823, 16: 1823-1826 & 17:
1827-1830; 18: 1830-1834, 19:
1834-1837, 20: 1837-1840 & 21:
1840-1842; 22: 1842-1845, 23:
1845-1847, 24: 1847-1849 & 25:
1849-1851; 26: 1851-1853, 27:
1853-1855, 28: 1855-1857 & 29:
1857-1858 [Mf 857-861]

PCY Wills
1316-1551 Testamenta Eboracensia or *Abst
of* Wills registered at York,
illustrative of the Hist, Manners,
Language, Statistics, etc of the
Province of York from the year
1300 onwards; vols 1: 1316-
1429, 2: 1429-1467, 3: 1395-
1491, 4: 1420-1509, 5: 1509-
1531 & 6: 1516-1551 (Surtees
Soc vols 4, 30, 45, 53, 79 & 106)
[*all* DU/PER]
1389-1684 Wills in the York Registry
(*including Prerogative Court cals
of Registered Wills*); vols 1:
1389-1514, 2: 1514-1553, 3:
1554-1568, 4: 1568-1585, 5:
1585-1594, 6: 1594-1602, 7:
1603-1611, 8: 1612-1619, 9:
1620-1627, 10: 1627-1636, 11:
1636-1652, 12: 1660-1665 also
unregistered Wills & Prob acts
1633-1634 & the "re infecta"
Wills & the Wills in Bundles "A" &
"B", 13**: 1666-1672, 14: 1673-
1680 & 15: 1681-1684 (Yorks
Archl Soc rec ser vols 6, 11, 14,
19, 22, 24, 26, 28, 32, 35, 4, 49,
60**, 68 & 89) [*all* YK/PER
except **vol 60: Apply to Staff]
Note: *see York (Dean & Chapter)
for vacancy probates 1683 &
1686-1688*
1389-1884 Wills & Admons etc: listings
taken from cals of the old
Diocese of York & the Diocese of
Lincoln (with certain additions
from Durham) (*index BUR-WRI*)
(Fam Hist vols 2 & 3) [PER/FAM]
1679-1689 Act Books of the PCY (*cal of wills
& admons Mar 1679-Jun 1689*)
(Northern Genealogist vols 2-4)
[PER/NOR]
1688-1731 Cal of Prob Recs taken from the
Act Books of the PCY 1688-1731
[Mf 928]
1688-1732 York District Probate Registry
(*including the PCY*) - Script

Indexes to Wills; vols 61: 1688-1690, 62: 1698-1699, 63: 1705-1706, 64: 1707-1708, 65: 1708-1709, 66: 1709-1710, 67: 1710-1711, 68: 1712-1713 & 69: 1713-1714; 69: 1713-1714, 70: 1714-1715, 71: 1716-1717, 72: 1717-1718, 73: 1718-1719, 74: 1719-1720, 75: 1720-1721, 76: 1721-1723, 77: 1723-1724, 78: 1724-1725, 79: 1725-1728, 80: 1728-1729, 81: 1730-1731 & 82: 1731-1732 [Mf 853-854]

1688-1741 Wills in the York Registry (*including the PCY*); vol 16: "re infecta" Wills 1688-1741 (appx 2 to Yorks Archl Soc rec ser vol 89) [YK/PER]

1731-1799 York District Probate Registry Cals of Wills & Admons (*including the PCY*); vols 2: 1731-1737 & 3: 1737-1741; 4: 1741-1745, 5: 1745-1757 & 6: 1757-1770; 7: 1771-1777, 8: 1777-1785, 9: 1785-1793 & 10: 1793-1799 [Mf 854-856]

1800-1842 Index to Wills, Admons, etc at the PCY 1800-1842 (*A-G*) [Apply to Staff]

1800-1858 York District Probate Registry Cals of Wills & Admons (*including the PCY*); vols 11: 1800-1803, 12: 1804-1809, 13: 1809-1814 & 14: 1814-1819; 15: 1819-1823, 16: 1823-1826 & 17: 1827-1830; 18: 1830-1834, 19: 1834-1837, 20: 1837-1840 & 21: 1840-1842; 22: 1842-1845, 23: 1845-1847, 24: 1847-1849 & 25: 1849-1851; 26: 1851-1853, 27: 1853-1855, 28: 1855-1857 & 29: 1857-1858 [Mf 857-861]

Other Papers in the PCY

1337-1399 Cal of Testmtry Cases *In* "Ecclesiastical Cause Papers at York: The PCY 1301-1399" (Borthwick Texts & Cals no 14) [YK/PER]

1397 Cal of the Reg of Robert Waldby, Archbishop of York 1397 (*with wills*) (Borthwick Texts & Cals no 2) [YK/PER]

1398-1405 Cal of Wills & Admons *In* "Reg of Richard Scrope, Archbishop of York 1398-1405" (Borthwick Texts & Cals no 11) [YK/PER]

15-16 C Index of Wills; an arbitrary coll of 15th & 16th C wills (*Soper*)

[WILLS/GEN]

1547-1857 Cal of Testmtry Cases *In* "Ecclesiastical Cause Papers at York: Files Transmitted *to PCY* on appeal 1500-1883" (Borthwick Texts & Cals no 9) [YK/PER]

YORK, THE CONSISTORY COURT OF THE ARCHBISHOP OF
this court exercised no probate jurisdiction in the Diocese of York, such powers being held by York (Chancery), York (Exchequer) & the peculiars

YORK, THE CHANCERY COURT OF THE ARCHBISHOP OF
this court exercised probate jurisdiction during visitations, over cases relating to clergy in the Diocese of York & on appeals from inferior courts **Superior Courts:** York (PCC); York (Dean & Chapter - *during vacancies*); *see also* York (Exchequer)

1316-1551 Testamenta Eboracensia or *Abst of* Wills registered at York, illustrative of the Hist, Manners, Language, Statistics, etc of the Province of York from the year 1300 onwards; *see* York (PCY - Wills) for details

1316-1822 Index of the Wills & Admons entered into the Regs of the Archbishops at York, being Consistory Wills 1316-1822 known as The Archbishops' Wills (Yorks Archl Soc rec ser vol 93) [YK/PER]

1427-1658 Index to the Original Docs of the Consistory Court of York 1427-1658 & also of the Prob & Admon Acts in the Court of the Dean of York 1604-1722 (Yorks Archl Soc rec ser vol 73) [YK/PER]

1660-1714 Index to York Consistory Wills & Admons; vol 31A: Index Testamentorum et Administratiorum Clericorum [Mf 877]

1713-1745 Index to York Consistory Wills & Admons - vol 34; pts 1: 1713-1724, 2: 1731-1737, 3: 1737-1741 & 4: 1741-1745 [Mf 877]

1808-1858 List of Wills proved in the Consistory Court during Archbishop Vernon's time & during Archbishop Musgrave's time to 1858 [Mf 877 *at the back of vol 34 pt 1*]

1825-1857 Chancery Court Prob Index

1825-1857 (*wills & admons*)
(Borthwick Inst Bull vol 1)
[YK/PER]

YORK, THE EXCHEQUER COURT OF THE ARCHBISHOP OF

this court exercised probate jurisdiction over the Diocese of York for the laity & unbeneficed clergy
Superior Courts: York (PCY); York (Dean & Chapter - *during vacancies): see also York (Chancery)*

1316-1551   Testamenta Eboracensia or *Abst of* Wills registered at York, illustrative of the Hist, Manners, Language, Statistics, etc of the Province of York from the year 1300 onwards; *see York (PCY - Wills) for details*

1389-1684   Wills in the York Registry (*including Exchequer Court cals of Registered Wills); see York (PCY - Wills) for details*

1389-1884   Wills & Admons etc: listings taken from cals of the old Diocese of York & the Diocese of Lincoln (with certain additions from Durham) (*index BUR-WRI*) (Fam Hist vols 2 & 3) [PER/FAM]

1427-1658   Index to the Original Docs of the Consistory Court of York 1427-1658 (*including the Exchequer Court*) & also of the Prob & Admon Acts in the Court of the Dean of York 1604-1722 (Yorks Archl Soc rec ser vol 73) [YK/PER]

1502-1686   *Admons* in the York Registry (*including Exchequer Court cals); see York (PCY - Administrations) for details*

1683-1688   Wills & *Admons* in the York Registry (*including Exchequer Court cals of Registered Wills*) - vol 15: *"Vacancies" of Jun-Aug 1683 & of Apr 1686-Dec 1688* (Yorks Archl Soc rec ser vol 89) [YK/PER]

1688-1732   York District Probate Registry (*including the Exchequer Court*) - Script Indexes to Wills; *see York (PCY - Wills) for details*

1688-1741   Wills in the York Registry (*including the Exchequer Court); see York (PCY - Wills) for details*

1731-1858   York District Probate Registry Cals of Wills & Admons (*including the Exchequer Court*);

see York (PCY - Wills & Administrations) for details

YORK OR THE WEST RIDING OF YORKSHIRE, THE ARCHDEACONRY OF

not a probate jurisdiction: see York (Chancery); York (Exchequer); see also Mexbrough

YORK, THE COURT OF THE PECULIAR JURISDICTIONS OF THE DEAN OF

including the Courts of the Peculiar Jurisdiction of the Dean of York in Pocklington, of the Prebend of Givendale (except 1661-1669) & of the Prebend of Barnby from 1736
Superior Courts: York (Chancery); York (Dean & Chapter)

1604-1722   Index to the Original Docs of the Consistory Court of York 1427-1658 & also of the Prob & Admon Acts in the Court of the Dean of York 1604-1722 (Yorks Archl Soc rec ser vol 73) [YK/PER]

YORK, THE COURT OF THE DEAN and CHAPTER OF

ie the Court of the Dean & Chapter of the Cathedral & Metropolitical Church of St Peter at York; this court also exercised prerogative jurisdiction during vacancies in the primacy; this Court's registers include the records of the Courts of the Peculiar Jurisdictions of the Chancellor, Precentor & Succentor Canonicorum of York Cathedral & of the Sub Dean of York
Superior Court: York (Chancery)

1316-1551   Testamenta Eboracensia or *Abst of* Wills registered at York, illustrative of the Hist, Manners, Language, Statistics, etc of the Province of York from the year 1300 onwards;; *see York (PCY - Wills) for details*

1321-1724   Wills, *Admons,* etc from the Dean & Chapter Court at York 1321-1636 (*index*) with an Index of Original Wills 1524-1724 (Yorks Archl Soc rec ser vol 38) [YK/PER]

1336-1429   Index of Wills, Admon & Prob acts in the York Registry ... *including* Wills in the Chapter Act Books of the Peculiar of the Dean & Chapter of York (*1352-1429*) & Wills in the Registrum Antiquum de Testamentis (*1336-1343*) (Yorks Archl Soc rec ser vol 60) [Apply to Staff]

1369-1835 Cal of Testmtry Cases *In*
"Ecclesiastical Cause Papers at
York: Dean & Chapter's Court
1350-1843" (Borthwick Texts &
Cals no 6) [YK/PER]

1438-1728 York Registry; Cal of Wills &
Admons - Separate Peculiars &
Dean & Chapter's General
Peculiars (*in 2 pts*) [Mf 879]

1650-1858 Court of the Dean & Chapter of
York; vol 1: Cal of Wills 1650-
1756; Cal of Wills & Admons
1757-1858 [Mf 875]

1683-1688 Court of the Dean & Chapter of
York; Vacancy Act Books 1683,
1686-1688 [Mf 875]; Wills in the
York Registry (*including
Prerogative Court cals*) - Vacancy
Reg & Vacancy Act Book *of the
Dean Chapter's Court for the
"Vacancies" of Jun-Aug 1683 &
of Apr 1686-Dec 1688* (appx 3 to
Yorks Archl Soc rec ser vol 89)
[YK/PER]; Index to Vacancy
Original Docs May 1686-Jun
1688 (appx 4 to Yorks Archl Soc
rec ser vol 89) [YK/PER]

1807-1808 Court of the Dean & Chapter of
York - Vacancy Wills & *Admons*
1807-1808 [Mf 875]

YORK, THE DISTRICT PROBATE REGISTRY IN
Superior Registry: London (Principal Probate
Registry)

1858-1884 Wills & Admons etc: listings
taken from cals of the old
Diocese of York & the Diocese of
Lincoln (with certain additions

from Durham) (*index BUR-WRI*)
(Fam Hist vols 2 & 3) [PER/FAM]

YORK, THE COURT OF THE PECULIAR JURISDICTION OF THE GUARDIAN OF THE SPRITUALITIES OF THE HOSPITAL OF ST LEONARD IN
Superior Court: York (Dean & Chapter)

1410-1533 Index of Wills, Admon & Prob
acts in the York Registry ...
including Wills in the Peculiar of
St Leonard's Hospital, York
(Yorks Archl Soc rec ser vol 60)
[Apply to Staff]

YORK IN THE PREBEND OF PRESTON IN HOLDERNESS, THE COURT OF THE PECULIAR JURISDICTION OF THE SUB DEAN OF *see Preston in Holderness*

YORK, THE COURT OF THE PECULIAR JURISDICTION OF THE TREASURER OF THE CATHEDRAL CHURCH AT
*Court dissolved to the Peculiar Jurisdictions
(qv) of Acomb; Alne & Tollerton; Bishop
Walton*

YORKSHIRE, THE ARCHDEACONRY OF THE EAST RIDING OF
*not a probate jurisdiction: see York
(Chancery); York (Exchequer); see also
Mappleton*

YORKSHIRE, THE ARCHDEACONRY OF YORK OR THE WEST RIDING OF
*not a probate jurisdiction: see York
(Chancery); York (Exchequer); see also
Mexbrough*